Isaac Maths S

Using Essential GCSE Mathematics

S.A. Waugh & J.N. Waugh

Periphyseos Press
Cambridge

Cavendish Laboratory
J. J. Thomson Avenue, Cambridge CB3 0HE, UK

Published in the United Kingdom by Periphyseos Press, Cambridge
www.periphyseos.org.uk

Using Essential GCSE Mathematics

First published & First reprint 2022
Second reprint 2023, Third reprint 2024

Printed and bound in the UK by Short Run Press Limited, Exeter.

Typeset in LaTeX

ISBN 978-0-9572873-9-6 Paperback

Use this collection of worksheets in parallel with the electronic version at https://isaacphysics.org/books/maths_book_gcse. Marking of answers and compilation of results is free on Isaac Physics. Register as a student or as a teacher to gain full functionality and support.

About this book

This book is designed to provide practice for GCSE-level mathematics. It can be used by those taking GCSE mathematics courses, and also by students in other subjects who need to learn or brush up on their knowledge of particular topics. The goals of the book are to help students master the skills they learn at GCSE level, and act as a resource for students who need to use these skills in their courses at A-level.

The book covers all major areas of mathematics in the various GCSE-level courses that are available. Where you see the § symbol, this indicates material that would usually be taught only in a Higher level (grades 4-9) GCSE course. However, don't let this put you off! The intent of the book is to help you learn mathematics, so if you would like to read the text or try the questions in a section that is outside the confines of your course then we would strongly encourage you to challenge yourself and have a go!

The focus of this book is on helping students master the skills they learn at GCSE. Being a short book, it is not intended as a complete stand-alone resource for learning GCSE mathematics from scratch. Likewise, you can use it as part of general maths revision for GCSE exams, but it is not intended to be a complete revision guide.

Teachers are encouraged to use whichever sections of the book would be helpful for their classes.

JNW & SAW
Aylesbury, 2021

Acknowledgements

The authors would like to thank all of the team at Isaac Physics at the University of Cambridge for the opportunity to engage with them to write and produce this book, and for their help during the project. In particular we are grateful to Dr Anton Machacek for his continued encouragement and hours of tea-time discussions over Zoom, and Dr Lee Phillips, Sam Lambrick and their colleagues Ashnoy Nazareth, Miguel Nocum and Jia Hao Guo for typesetting the book and preparing the content for the Isaac Physics website. We would also like to thank Dr Lisa Jardine-Wright and Prof Mark Warner for their encouragement that this book would be useful for developing maths skills for STEM and other subjects, Laura Moat for creating the cover design, and David Taylor for his efforts on our behalf.

JNW & SAW
Aylesbury, 2021

Using Isaac Physics with this book

An online version of this book is implemented on the Isaac Physics website at `https://isaacphysics.org/books/maths_book_gcse`. In line with other subjects on the website, students may enter their answers to the questions in the book for immediate marking and feedback, and teachers are able to create bespoke worksheets using their own selections of questions from the book for use in class or as homework.

Contents

Solving Maths Problems

1 Solving Maths Problems

In each chapter of this book there are questions to help you practise your mathematics skills. While the style of question varies, there are a number of general problem-solving strategies that apply to all topics.

- Whenever possible, draw a labelled diagram showing all the information in the question.
- Try to take the information you are given in words, and write it in algebra.
- When a question includes a graph, read the labels on the axes to find the quantities that are plotted and their units.
- Write down all your working as you go along. This can be time-consuming, but is worth it as it will help you get correct answers.
- If you get stuck, read the question again to check what the question is asking for and whether there is any information you have missed.
- Make sure you give your answers in the form the question requires. Use a suitable number of significant figures and state the units.

When tackling a multi-step problem, a useful approach is to start by writing out in words a quick plan for finding a solution. This doesn't have to be a long paragraph - bullet points will do. Don't worry about whether you know how to carry out every part of the plan. Just get the plan down on paper.

Next, break your plan down into a series of individual steps and work out how to do each one. List the quantities you wish to calculate, and write down the formulae you intend to use. If you find there is a step you don't know how to do, try looking up the topic where that step is covered elsewhere in the book (or in your class notes). Consider if you have done something similar before which is appropriate to use as an analogy.

Finally, carry out your plan.

To see this in action, Example 1 shows a rather complicated-looking problem. Do not worry if you do not know how to solve the problem yourself at the moment. The techniques that you need are covered later in the book.

Focus instead on the approach that is taken - drawing a diagram, writing a plan, and then carrying out the plan.

Example 1 – A winch and a small pulley are used to lower a heavy box . The arrangement is shown in the diagram. If the height of the box is 50 cm, what is the minimum length of rope needed to lower the box to the ground?

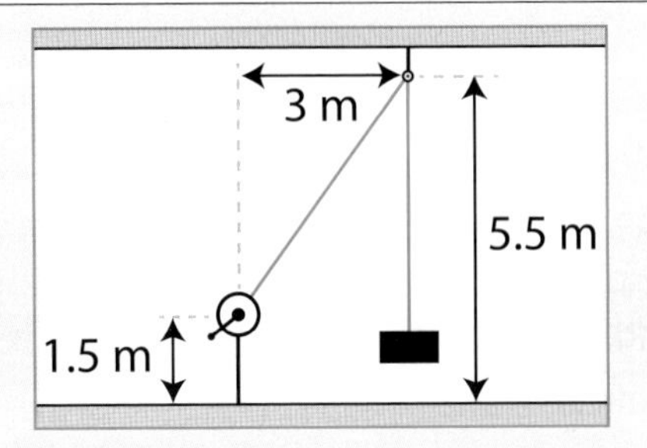

The rope goes from the winch to the pulley and down to the box. The rope has to be long enough for the box to reach the ground. The diagram shows the box in the air, so the first task is to draw a new diagram.

We keep the diagram simple, label lengths that we know, and use our experience with this type of problem to mark on extra lines and right-angles that might be useful. The height of the box is converted into metres.

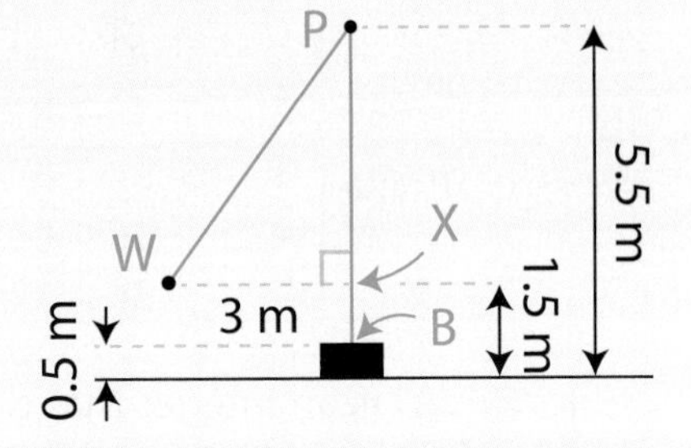

Next, plan how to solve the problem. We need to find the length of the rope. The rope has two sections: WP and PB. We will find the length of each section separately, then add them together.

$$\text{Minimum length of rope needed} = WP + PB$$

To find WP: WXP is a right-angled triangle, so we can use Pythagoras' Theorem: $WP^2 = WX^2 + XP^2$. From the diagram, $WX = 3$ m and $XP = 5.5 - 1.5 = 4$ m.

$$\therefore WP^2 = 3^2 + 4^2 = 25 \qquad \Rightarrow WP = 5\text{ m}$$

PB is equal to the height of the pulley above the ground minus the height of the box. So, $PB = 5.5 - 0.5 = 5.0$ m.

Therefore,

$$\text{Minimum length of rope needed} = 5.0 + 5.0 = 10.0\text{ m}$$

Skills

2 Factors

An integer is a whole number, for example 12.

A sum is the result of adding numbers together. A difference is the result of subtracting one number from another. A product is the result of multiplying numbers together. A quotient is the result of dividing one number by another.

If a number is multiplied by itself, a power (index) records how many times that number is used. For example, $2 \times 2 \times 2 = 2^3$.

The first 5 powers of the integers 2 to 5 are listed in the table below.

$a^{(1)}$	a^2	a^3	a^4	a^5
2	4	8	16	32
3	9	27	81	243
4	16	64	256	1 024
5	25	125	625	3 125

A factor (divisor) is an integer that divides into a number exactly. For example, 2 is a factor of 6 because $6 \div 2 = 3$, and 3 is a whole number.

A prime number is an integer which has only two factors: 1 and itself. An example is 13, which only has factors 1 and 13. 1 is not considered to be a prime number.

A prime factor is a factor that is also a prime number. For example, 13 is a prime factor of 26.

A factor tree can be used both to find the prime factors of a number and to write the number as a product of prime factors. Writing a number in terms of its prime factors is called factor decomposition.

Example 1 – Write 420 as a product of prime factors.

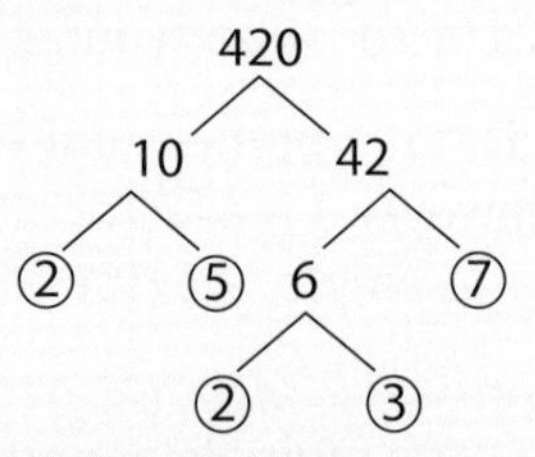

At each branching of the tree, take out another factor. In the first branching, 10 is a factor of 420. $420 \div 10$ is 42.

If a factor is a prime factor, circle it. Keep going until every branch ends in prime factors.

Written as a product of prime factors, $420 = 2 \times 2 \times 3 \times 5 \times 7$.

2.1 You are given a set of integers: $\{-5, -2, -1, 3, 4, 7\}$. Write down two numbers which give:

(a) A sum of 3. (b) A difference of 6. (c) A product of 2.

2.2 Beginning with 2, Adam starts making a list of prime numbers in order of increasing size. He doesn't skip any numbers.

(a) What is the sum of the first 9 numbers on the list?

(b) What is the 10th number on the list?

2.3 Write each number as a product of prime factors:

(a) 66 (b) 210 (c) 182

2.4 You are given the following set of positive integers: $\{1, 3, 4, 5, 6, 9, 12, 13\}$. For this set, find:

(a) The sum of the square numbers.

(b) The sum of the prime numbers.

(c) The sum of the numbers which are multiples of 2.

2.5 Write down or find:

(a) The two prime numbers separated by 1.

(b) The smallest pair of prime numbers that differ by 6.

(c) Three pairs of prime numbers that each have a sum of 30.

(d) The product of the numbers in the answer to (a), added to the sum of all eight numbers in the answers to (b) and (c).

A product of prime factors can be written using index notation. For example, $6300 = 2 \times 2 \times 3 \times 3 \times 5 \times 5 \times 7 = 2^2 \times 3^2 \times 5^2 \times 7$.

The highest common factor (HCF) of two numbers is the largest number that is a factor of both numbers. For example, the HCF of 28 and 42 is 14.

1 is not a prime number, so is not listed in a prime factor decomposition. However, 1 is a factor of every integer and can be a highest common factor. For example, the HCF of 3 and 5 is 1.

The lowest common multiple (LCM) of two numbers is the smallest number that is a multiple of both numbers. For example, the LCM of 8 and 12 is 24.

Example 2 shows how to use factor decomposition to find an HCF or LCM.

Example 2 – What are the HCF and LCM of 84 and 140?

$$84 = 2 \times 2 \times 3 \times 7 \qquad 140 = 2 \times 2 \times 5 \times 7$$

(i) The factors that are common to 84 and 140 are 2, 2 and 7. Therefore the HCF is $2 \times 2 \times 7 = 28$.

(ii) The LCM contains all the prime factors that make up the two numbers. The LCM is $2 \times 2 \times 3 \times 5 \times 7 = 420$.

2.6 By listing the multiples of each number, find the lowest common multiples of

(a) 3 and 15 (b) 8 and 10 (c) 18 and 24

2.7 By writing each number in terms of prime factors, find the HCF and LCM of

(a) 6 and 40 (b) 15 and 70 (c) 24 and 25

2.8 (a) Write 44 100 as a product of prime factors.

(b) Use your answer to part (a) to find the square root of 44, 100.

2.9 Find the prime factors of the following numbers, writing your answers in the form $a^p \times b^q \times c^r$, where a, b and c are prime numbers.

(a) 28 (b) 90 (c) 96

2.10 (a) A number is written as $2^2 \times 3 \times 7$. What is the number?

(b) A number is written as $2 \times 3^3 \times 5^2 \times 7$. What is the number?

(c) You are told that 5 460 is a factor of 3 248 700. Using factor decomposition, find the value of $3\,248\,700 \div 5\,460$.

3 BIDMAS / BODMAS and Substituting Values Into Formulae

The acronym BIDMAS or BODMAS is used as a way to help remember the order in which in which operations are done in a mathematical calculation. By following BIDMAS rules, all users of mathematics do the same operations in the same order, and so always arrive at the same answers when evaluating expressions or formulae.

- B Brackets (do calculations inside brackets first)
- I/O Indices or Order (calculate powers next)
- DM Division and Multiplication
- AS Addition and Subtraction

Division and multiplication are done together, working through a calculation from left to right. The same is true for addition and subtraction.

Example 1 – Evaluate $3 - \frac{(9-5)^2}{2}$.

First evaluate the brackets, then evaluate the indices:

$$3 - \frac{(9-5)^2}{2} = 3 - \frac{4^2}{2} = 3 - \frac{16}{2}$$

Next, do the division. Then, finally, the subtraction.

$$3 - \frac{(9-5)^2}{2} = 3 - 8 = -5$$

When dealing with fractions, treat the numbers above the dividing line and the numbers below the dividing line as though they were in separate brackets. Evaluate them before performing the division.

Roots (square roots, cube roots etc.) are calculated along with I/O because taking a root is the inverse operation to raising to a power. Calculate everything included under a root sign as if it was in a bracket before taking the root.

Example 2 – Evaluate $2\sqrt{\frac{70-30}{5\times2}} + 1$.

First, evaluate the top and bottom of the fraction as though they were in separate brackets. Then do the division under the square root sign.

$$2\sqrt{\frac{70-30}{5\times 2}}+1=2\sqrt{\frac{40}{10}}+1=2\sqrt{4}+1$$

Next, take the square root. Then do the multiplication, followed by the addition.

$$\Rightarrow 2\sqrt{\frac{70-30}{5\times 2}}+1=2\times\sqrt{4}+1=2\times 2+1=4+1=5$$

3.1 Evaluate the following using BIDMAS rules:
(a) $3-5$ (b) $8\div 16+5$ (c) $1+6\div 2$

3.2 Insert brackets in these calculations so that they are correct:
(a) $2\times 9+4=26$ (c) $5\times 5+2\times 2>60$
(b) $6-6\times 7+11=11$ (d) $6\times 8+3\times 7=174$

3.3 Insert $>$, $=$ or $<$ to make the following statements correct:
(a) $5^2\ ?\ 2^2$ (b) $(2+1)^3\ ?\ 4^2$ (c) $\sqrt{36}\ ?\ \sqrt{25}+\sqrt{81}$

3.4 Evaluate the following using BIDMAS rules:
(a) $1+8\div 3$ (b) $\frac{1\times 7}{4-2}$ (c) $1\frac{1}{2}-\frac{7}{42\div 3}$

3.5 Insert brackets in these calculations so that they are correct:
(a) $1+7+1\div 18=\frac{1}{2}$ (c) $\frac{-5}{16-6\times 5-1}=\frac{1}{3}$
(b) $4+5\div 2+2=\frac{13}{2}$ (d) $\sqrt{3^2+1\times 2-4}=\sqrt[3]{64}$

Substituting values into a formula means putting numerical values (including minus signs) in place of algebraic variables and using the BIDMAS rules to calculate a value.

Example 3 – Substitute $q=7$, $r=2$ and $s=8$ into the formula $p=\sqrt{q^2+2rs}$ to find the value of p.

Insert the values into the appropriate places in the formula, then perform the calculation in BIDMAS order.

$$p=\sqrt{7^2+2\times 2\times 8}=\sqrt{49+2\times 2\times 8}=\sqrt{49+32}=\sqrt{81}=9$$

3.6 Given $a = -4$, $b = -6$ and $c = 2$, find the value of $3(c-b) - \frac{a}{2}$.

3.7 If $a = 2$, $b = -3$ and $c = 5$, find the value of p when

(a) $p = 2a + 5$ (b) $p = 3b + 2c$ (c) $p = 4ac - 6b$

3.8 $x = 3$, $y = -5$ and $z = 2$. Find the following:

(a) $(x-y)^2$ (b) $y + z(x+z)^2$ (c) $yz + \frac{xz}{y}$

3.9 Find the values of p, q and r if $s = 6$, $t = 3$ and $u = -8$.

(a) $p = \frac{1}{2}u - st$ (b) $3q = ut + s$ (c) $2r = \frac{2t-u}{7} + 4$

3.10 Evaluate

(a) $2 + (3^2 - 5)^2$ (b) $5 + \sqrt{7^2 - 13}$ (c) $1 + \frac{4}{3} + \frac{1+4}{3}$

The following questions use formulae from real-world applications.

3.11 Interest calculations:

$$A = C\left(1 + \frac{I}{100}\right)^n$$

A is the amount of money in an account after n years if an amount of capital C is invested with a compound interest rate of $I\%$. Calculate the value of A to the nearest penny if:

(a) $C = £100$, $I = 4$ and $n = 2$

(b) $C = £750$, $I = 3.2$ and $n = 6$

(c) £100 is invested at a rate of 12% for 4 years.

3.12 Gas laws in physics:

$$V = V_0\left(1 + \frac{T}{273}\right)$$

V_0 is the volume of a gas at a temperature of 0°C. V is the volume the same amount of gas would occupy at a temperature T°C if the gas has the same pressure.

(a) Find V if $V_0 = 22.4\ \text{m}^3$ and $T = 273$°C.

(b) Find V if $V_0 = 0.14\ \text{m}^3$ and $T = 136.5$°C.

4 Fractions

The number on the top of a fraction is the numerator and the number on the bottom is the denominator. The line between the numerator and the denominator is equivalent to "divided by", i.e. $\frac{3}{4}$ is equivalent to $3 \div 4$.

Dividing by 0 is not possible, and all divisions by zero, including fractions with 0 in the denominator, are undefined and cannot be worked out.

A numerical fraction with the same number in both the numerator and denominator has a value of 1 because anything divided by itself is 1.

$$\frac{3}{3} = \frac{1}{1} = 1$$

In proper fractions such as $\frac{3}{4}$, the numerator is smaller than the denominator, while in improper fractions the numerator is larger than the denominator. Mixed fractions have both an integer and a fraction part.

Example 1 – Write (i) $5\frac{1}{4}$ as an improper fraction (ii) $\frac{9}{4}$ as a mixed number.

(i) In words, $5\frac{1}{4}$ is "five and a quarter". 1 is the same as four quarters, so 5 is the same as twenty quarters. Therefore,

$$5\frac{1}{4} = 5 + \frac{1}{4} = \frac{20}{4} + \frac{1}{4} = \frac{21}{4}$$

(ii) First, rewrite the numerator as a multiple of the denominator plus a remainder: $9 = 2 \times 4 + 1$

Then, $\frac{9}{4} = \frac{2\times4+1}{4} = \frac{2\times4}{4} + \frac{1}{4}$, so $\frac{9}{4} = 2 + \frac{1}{4} = 2\frac{1}{4}$

When multiplying or dividing fractions, always start by converting any mixed numbers to improper fractions. To do the division or multiplication it can be helpful to think of the second fraction as a pair of scale factors.

Example 2 – Calculate (i) $\frac{3}{7} \times \frac{2}{5}$ (ii) $\frac{3}{7} \div \frac{2}{5}$.

(i) In words, $\frac{2}{5}$ is "two divided by five". So, starting with $\frac{3}{7}$, scale up by 2 ($\times 2$) and down by 5 ($\div 5$).

$$\frac{3}{7} \times \frac{2}{5} = \frac{3 \times 2}{7 \times 5} = \frac{6}{35}$$

(ii) Multiply and divide are inverse operations. So if multiply scales $\frac{3}{7}$ up by 2 and down by 5, then divide scales $\frac{3}{7}$ down by 2 and up by 5. This is equivalent to multiplying by $\frac{5}{2}$.

$$\frac{3}{7} \div \frac{2}{5} = \frac{3}{7} \times \frac{5}{2} = \frac{3 \times 5}{7 \times 2} = \frac{15}{14}$$

If the numerator and denominator of a fraction have the same factor, this factor can be cancelled to leave a simpler equivalent fraction. There are several ways this can be written:

$$\frac{6}{8} = \frac{3 \times 2}{4 \times 2} = \frac{3}{4} \times \frac{2}{2} = \frac{3}{4} \times 1 = \frac{3}{4} \quad \text{or} \quad \frac{6}{8} = \frac{3 \times \cancel{2}}{4 \times \cancel{2}} = \frac{3}{4}$$

Note: Cancelling down is only possible when every term in both the numerator and denominator has the same factor.

Creating an equivalent fraction with a denominator that is a multiple of the starting denominator is the opposite of cancelling down. For example, to find a fraction equivalent to $\frac{1}{6}$ with a denominator of 18, start by noting that $18 = 6 \times 3$. Write $\frac{1}{6}$ as $\frac{1}{6} \times 1$, then rewrite the 1 as $\frac{3}{3}$:

$$\frac{1}{6} = \frac{1}{6} \times 1 = \frac{1}{6} \times \frac{3}{3} = \frac{1 \times 3}{6 \times 3} = \frac{3}{18}$$

To add or subtract fractions, first re-write them as equivalent fractions with a common denominator. Next, add or subtract the numerators and simplify the result.

Example 3 – Calculate (i) $\frac{2}{3} + \frac{3}{4}$ (ii) $\frac{2}{3} - \frac{3}{4}$.

The lowest common multiple (LCM) of the denominators of $\frac{2}{3}$ and $\frac{3}{4}$ is 12. Rewriting both fractions as equivalent fractions with a denominator of 12,

$$\frac{2}{3} = \frac{2 \times 4}{3 \times 4} = \frac{8}{12} \qquad \frac{3}{4} = \frac{3 \times 3}{4 \times 3} = \frac{9}{12}$$

(i) $\frac{2}{3} + \frac{3}{4} = \frac{8}{12} + \frac{9}{12} = \frac{17}{12} = 1\frac{5}{12}$.

(ii) $\frac{2}{3} - \frac{3}{4} = \frac{8}{12} - \frac{9}{12} = \frac{-1}{12} = -\frac{1}{12}$.

4.1 Convert the following into mixed fractions:

(a) $\frac{29}{3}$ (b) $\frac{17}{13}$ (c) $-\frac{105}{4}$

4.2 Convert the following into improper fractions:

(a) $3\frac{1}{5}$ (b) $9\frac{2}{7}$ (c) $-4\frac{24}{25}$

4.3 Write as proper fractions in their simplest form:

(a) $\frac{16}{18}$ (b) $\frac{56}{74}$ (c) $-\frac{96}{120}$

4.4 Multiply the following fractions:

(a) $\frac{6}{7} \times \frac{2}{3}$ (b) $1\frac{1}{3} \times \frac{3}{8}$ (c) $2\frac{1}{6} \times 2\frac{5}{26}$

4.5 Divide the following fractions:

(a) $\frac{2}{3} \div \frac{8}{9}$ (b) $1\frac{5}{6} \div \frac{5}{12}$ (c) $5\frac{1}{7} \div 4\frac{1}{8}$

4.6 Add the following fractions:

(a) $\frac{1}{3} + \frac{1}{9}$ (b) $\frac{2}{3} + \frac{3}{4}$ (c) $\frac{11}{12} + \frac{1}{18} + 1\frac{1}{3}$

4.7 Subtract the following fractions:

(a) $\frac{5}{12} - \frac{1}{4}$ (b) $\frac{6}{7} - \frac{1}{6}$ (c) $2\frac{2}{3} - 1\frac{7}{11}$

4.8 Cancel these fractions down to their simplest form:

(a) $\frac{3}{14} \times \frac{49}{8} \times \frac{5}{21}$ (b) $\frac{5}{9} \times \frac{22}{15} \div \frac{11}{27}$ (c) $-\frac{3}{5} \div -\frac{3}{5}$

4.9 Rank the following fractions by size, starting with the smallest.

$$\frac{19}{24} \quad \frac{7}{12} \quad \frac{2}{3} \quad \frac{3}{4}$$

4.10 Calculate the following:

(a) $1\frac{1}{8} - 2\frac{5}{6} + 3\frac{1}{4}$ (b) $5\frac{1}{2} \div 1\frac{4}{11} \times 7\frac{1}{5}$

4.11 A baker works 6 days a week. Every day she uses $\frac{3}{5}$ of a sack of bread flour for regular loaves of bread. On Saturday she bakes special loaves in addition, and this needs an extra $\frac{4}{5}$ of a sack of flour.

(a) What is the total amount of flour used each week, expressed as a mixed fraction?

(b) If there is 20 kg of flour in a sack, how many kilograms of flour does the baker use each week?

4.12 A large group of friends ordered some pizzas to share. 1 person ate half a pizza, 3 people ate $\frac{3}{5}$ of a pizza each, and 7 people ate $\frac{2}{3}$ of a pizza each. What is the minimum number of pizzas the friends ordered?

4.13 Two children are given pocket money for helping with the gardening. Child 1 receives $\frac{2}{5}^{\text{ths}}$ of the money and immediately spends $\frac{3}{4}$ of his share on a magazine.

(a) What fraction of the original amount was spent on the magazine?

(b) If the total amount of money that was split between the children was £12.50, what was the price of the magazine?

4.14 A man is putting up some metal supports for a fence. A support is 4 ft in length and $\frac{3}{16}^{\text{ths}}$ of this is driven into the ground. At the top of the support the man screws in a decorative knob which is $3\frac{1}{2}$ inches tall. How high above ground level is the top of the knob?

4.15 A carpenter is making decorative panels. She cuts a panel out of a piece of wood and measures its length. The panel is $\frac{24}{50}$ m long, which is $\frac{8}{9}^{\text{ths}}$ of the length of the original piece of wood. How long was the original piece?

5 Decimals and Rational and Irrational Numbers

Decimals, based on powers of 10, show whole numbers to the left of the point and fractions of numbers to the right. Each step to the left increases the power of 10 by one. Each step to the right divides by 10.

Example 1 – Write two thousand and three hundredths in figures.

1000s	100s	10s	1s	•	$\frac{1}{10}$ths	$\frac{1}{100}$ths
2	0	0	0	•	0	3

2000.03

To convert a fraction into a decimal, use long division.

Example 2 – Convert $\frac{7}{8}$ to a decimal.

$\frac{7}{8}$ is equivalent to "7 divided by 8". The calculation is shown on the right.

$$\therefore \frac{7}{8} = 0.875$$

```
   0.875
8)7.000
 -6.4      ←8×8=64
  0.60
 -0.56     ←8×7=56
  0.040
 -0.040    ←8×5=40
  0.000
```

Decimal numbers are either terminating or non-terminating. A terminating decimal, such as 26.18304, has a finite number of non-zero values after the decimal point, while a non-terminating decimal goes on forever.

Rational numbers are numbers that can be written as a fraction with integers in both the numerator and denominator. Terminating decimals are always rational. Example 3 shows how to convert a terminating decimal into an equivalent fraction.

Example 3 – Convert the number 3.04 into a fraction. Write your answer as a fraction in its simplest form.

3.04 is the same as $3 + 0.04$. The number 0.04 has two places after the decimal point. Therefore, 0.04 is equivalent to $4 \div 100$.

$$\therefore 3.04 = 3 + \frac{4}{100} = 3 + \frac{1}{25} = 3\frac{1}{25}$$

Recurring decimals have a pattern of digits after the decimal point that repeats forever. They can also always be written as fractions. For example, $0.33333... = \frac{1}{3}$.

The repeating part of a recurring decimal can be indicated using dots. Dots are placed over the first and last digits of the repeating unit. For example, $14.769769769... = 14.\dot{7}6\dot{9}$. If the repeating unit contains only one number, the dot is placed over a single digit. For example $0.66666... = 0.\dot{6}$.

Irrational numbers are numbers that cannot be written as fractions. The square roots of prime numbers are all irrational numbers, as is π. Integer multiples of irrational numbers, such as 2π, are always irrational.

In this exercise answer the questions without using a calculator.

5.1 Write as decimals:

(a) Sixty-two point four. (b) $5\frac{33}{100}$

(c) Five hundred and six and four thousandths.

5.2 Convert these fractions to decimals.

(a) $\frac{3}{4}$ (b) $\frac{34}{50}$ (c) $\frac{5}{2}$ (d) $\frac{27}{6}$

5.3 Convert the following decimals to fractions.

(a) 0.30 (b) 0.75 (c) 0.18

5.4 Convert the following decimals to mixed fractions.

(a) 1.16 (b) 2.07 (c) 5.72

5.5 Convert these fractions to recurring decimals.

(a) $\frac{2}{9}$ (b) $\frac{16}{11}$ (c) $\frac{3}{7}$

5.6 Here is a list of numbers: $-1, 7, \sqrt{2}, 3, \frac{5}{2}, \pi$.

(a) Identify the two irrational numbers in the list.

(b) Find the product of the remaining numbers, giving your answer as a decimal.

5.7 Using $\frac{1}{9} = 0.\dot{1}$, deduce the recurring decimals for

(a) $\frac{2}{9}$ (b) $\frac{7}{9}$ (c) $\frac{1}{3}$ (d) $\frac{1}{18}$

5.8 Expressed in their simplest form, which of the following are irrational?

$$\frac{22}{7} \quad \frac{\pi}{\pi} \quad \sqrt{2} \times \sqrt{2} \quad 6\pi \quad \sqrt{25}$$

§ A method for turning a recurring decimal into an equivalent fraction is shown in example 4.

Example 4 – Convert the number $14.\dot{7}6\dot{9}$ into a fraction.

Let $x = 14.769769769...$

The repeating unit is three digits long. Therefore, multiply x by 10 three times; this is equivalent to multiplying by $10^3 = 1000$.

$$1000x = 1000 \times 14.769769769...$$
$$\Rightarrow 1000x = 14769.769769769...$$

Subtract x from both sides to eliminate the digits after the decimal point.

$$1000x - x = 14769.769769769... - 14.769769769...$$
$$\Rightarrow 999x = 14769 - 14 = 14755$$

Divide both sides by 999.

$$x = \tfrac{14755}{999} \quad \therefore 14.\dot{7}6\dot{9} = \tfrac{14755}{999} = 14\tfrac{769}{999}$$

In this exercise answer the questions without using a calculator.

5.9 Convert these recurring decimals to fractions.

(a) $0.\dot{4}\dot{5}$ (b) $0.\dot{1}463\dot{4}$ (c) $3.\dot{2}$

5.10 Convert these fractions to recurring decimals.

(a) $\frac{17}{9}$ (b) $\frac{5}{66}$ (c) $-\frac{5}{13}$

5.11 Use the information below to write each fraction as a decimal.

$$\frac{1}{11} = 0.\dot{0}\dot{9} \quad \frac{1}{7} = 0.\dot{1}4285\dot{7} \quad \frac{1}{13} = 0.\dot{0}7692\dot{3}$$

(a) $\frac{1}{33}$ (b) $-\frac{2}{33}$ (c) $\frac{1}{21}$

Write these decimals as fractions.

(d) $-0.\dot{9}\dot{0}$ (e) $0.\dot{4}2857\dot{1}$ (f) $0.\dot{3}0769\dot{2}$

6 Percentages

Fractions, percentages and decimals are closely related. Percentage means "out of one hundred", so 20% is the fraction $\frac{20}{100}$, which can be cancelled down to $\frac{1}{5}$. $\frac{1}{5}$ can be written as the decimal 0.2.

Example 1 – Express 38% as (i) a fraction (ii) a decimal.

(i) $38\% = \frac{38}{100} = \frac{19}{50}$ (ii) $38\% = \frac{38}{100} = 38 \div 100 = 0.38$

Example 2 – Express the following as percentages: (i) $\frac{17}{20}$ (ii) 0.348.

(i) $\frac{20}{20}$ would be 100%, so $\frac{17}{20} = \frac{17}{20} \times 100\% = 85\%$

(ii) The number of digits 0.348 has after the decimal point is 3.

$$\therefore 0.348 = \frac{348}{1000} \qquad \frac{348}{1000} \times 100\% = \left(\frac{348}{10}\right)\% = 34.8\%$$

To calculate percentage changes, you must decide if you are starting with 100% of a quantity, or if you are given a different percentage and must calculate 100%.

Example 3 – There is a 25%-off sale. What is the sale price of a coat which was originally priced at £120?

In this example you are starting with 100%. If 25% is taken off, you will pay 75% of the starting cost, or $\frac{75}{100}$ of £120. $\frac{75}{100}$ is a scale factor, so multiply.

$$\frac{75}{100} \times £120 = £90$$

Example 4 – In the same 25%-off sale, there is a pair of shoes priced at £48. What was the original price?

This time you know what 75% of the original price is. Scale down to find 1%, then scale up to find 100%.

$$75\% \xrightarrow{\div 75} 1\% \xrightarrow{\times 100} 100$$

So the multiplier is $\frac{100}{75}$, or $\frac{4}{3}$. The original price was $\frac{4}{3} \times £48 = £64$.

6.1 Write these percentages as fractions.

(a) 30% (b) 5% (c) 0.5%

6.2 Write these percentages as decimals.

(a) 25% (b) 0.7% (c) 0.003%

6.3 Write these decimals as percentages.

(a) 0.10 (b) 0.01 (c) 0.005 (d) 2.00

6.4 Write these fractions as percentages.

(a) $\frac{3}{4}$ (b) $\frac{5}{8}$ (c) $\frac{7}{350}$

6.5 Which is larger in each case?

(a) 21.5% or $\frac{9}{20}$ (b) $\frac{7}{6}$ or 1.16 (c) 112% or $\frac{20}{18}$

6.6 Rank the following in order of size, starting with the smallest.

62% $\frac{5}{8}$ 0.629

6.7 Evaluate the following:

(a) 20% of £16 (b) 65% of 400 g (c) 160% of $240

6.8 Calculate

(a) 27% of £24 000 (b) 15% of 75 (c) 7.5% of 6 kg

6.9 Write the first quantity as a percentage of the second.

(a) 3 minutes out of 2 hours

(b) £1.40 out of £40.00

(c) 366 g out of 3 kg

6.10 A family needs to buy a new washing machine and have it delivered.

Company A sells a machine at 15% off an original purchase price of £275, and charges £25 for delivery.

Company B sells the same machine. Their usual price is £300, but the machine is on sale at 20% off. Delivery is free.

From which company would it be cheaper to buy the machine?

6.11 Rohit saves 5% when purchasing a coat originally costing $£100$, and 8% on a sofa which originally costs $£200$. What is his overall saving as a percentage of the total original price of these goods?

6.12 Rank the following in order of size, starting with the largest.

$$\frac{17}{20} \qquad 87\% \qquad \frac{7}{8} \qquad 0.889 \qquad \frac{349}{400}$$

6.13 A new process reduces the time to manufacture a product by 25%. If it takes 2 hours 21 minutes to make the product using the new process, how long did it take to make the item with the old process?

In a simple interest scheme, the interest added to an account each year is calculated as a percentage of the original amount deposited. The same amount of interest is added each year.

Example 5 - $£250$ is invested in a simple interest scheme at an interest rate of 4% per year. Calculate the total amount of money at the end of 5 years.

The amount of interest paid after each year is 4% of the starting $£250$. This is

$$4\% \times £250 = \frac{4}{100} \times £250 = \frac{4 \times £250}{100} = \frac{£1000}{100} = £10$$

After 5 years the amount of interest paid is $5 \times £10 = £50$.
The total amount of money in the account is therefore

$$£250 + £50 = £300$$

In a compound interest scheme, the interest added to an account each year is calculated as a percentage of the amount in the account during that year. Assuming that no money is taken out, the amount of interest added increases from year to year.

If the interest rate is $I\%$ per year, then after one year the amount in an account is $(100 + I)\%$ of the original amount. This is equivalent to multiplying the starting amount by the fraction $\frac{100+I}{100}$.

Example 6 – £250 is invested in a compound interest scheme at an interest rate of 4% per year. Calculate the total amount of money at the end of 5 years to the nearest penny.

For an interest rate of 4%, the multiplier is $\frac{100+I}{100} = \frac{104}{100} = 1.04$.

To find the amount after 5 years, apply the multiplier 5 times. To the nearest penny the amount in the account is $£250 \times 1.04^5 = £304.16$.

6.14 Calculate, to the nearest penny, the amount that will be in an account if

(a) £1 000 is invested for one year in a simple interest scheme with a 5% interest rate.

(b) £1 500 is invested for two years in a simple interest scheme with a 3% interest rate.

(c) £4 000 is invested for one year in a compound interest scheme with a 4% interest rate.

(d) £4 500 is invested for three years in compound interest scheme with a 2.5% interest rate.

6.15 For each of the percentages below, calculate the amount in an account after 10 years if £3 000 is invested in a scheme with (i) simple interest (ii) compound interest. Give your answers to the nearest penny.

(a) 0.1% (b) 1% (c) 3% (d) 6%

6.16 Dan uses a balance to find the mass of some objects. The machine has an offset error, so it registers a mass of 9.0 g even when there is no mass on it.
Find the percentage error in his measurements when he weighs objects which have a true mass of

(a) 90 g (b) 720 g (c) 36.0 g

6.17 A carpenter is cutting a long, thin plank of wood into shorter lengths using a band saw. The saw blade is 2 mm wide, so each cut wastes 2 mm of wood as sawdust.

(a) How many 10 cm lengths can they cut from a plank with a total length of 2 m?

(b) What percentage of the original plank will not be used to make 10 cm lengths?

(c) What percentage of the plank will be turned into sawdust?

6.18 The average attendance at a sporting fixture went up by 40% every year. In year 2 the attendance was 35 000. Find the attendance
(a) in year 3 (b) in year 1

6.19 Uranium has many isotopes. 99.274% of natural uranium is the isotope U_{238}. 720 out of 100 000 atoms of natural uranium are the isotope U_{235}. What percentage of natural uranium is accounted for by the other isotopes?

6.20 For the formula $P = IV$, what is the percentage change in P if the current I increases by 3.0% and the voltage V falls by 10.0% at the same time?

7 Ratio

A ratio compares the sizes of two or more quantities with each other.
A proportion is the amount of one quantity as a fraction of the total amount.

Example 1 – In a playground there are 10 boys, 12 girls and 8 adults.

(i) What is the ratio of girls to boys in its simplest form?
The ratio of girls to boys is $12 : 10$. This cancels down to $6 : 5$.

(ii) What proportion of the people in the playground are adults?
The total number of people in the playground is $10 + 12 + 8 = 30$. The proportion of of the people that are adults is $\frac{8}{30} = \frac{4}{15}$.

Example 2 shows how to share out an amount according to a given ratio.

Example 2 – Two friends, Peter and Alice, share out 220 flower bulbs in the ratio $2 : 3$. Work out how many bulbs they each receive.

Think of the ratio as dividing the bulbs into portions. If Peter receives 2 portions, and Alice 3 portions, there are $2 + 3 = 5$ portions overall.

The size of one portion is therefore $220 \div 5 = 44$ bulbs. Peter receives $2 \times 44 = 88$ bulbs, and Alice receives $3 \times 44 = 132$ bulbs.

7.1 Calculate the ratio of what each person has, giving your answer as the simplest possible ratio of whole numbers in the form A : B.

(a) A has 10 potatoes, B has 20 potatoes.

(b) A has 80 kg of coal, B has 60 kg of coal.

(c) A is paid £12.60 per hour, B is paid £14.40 per hour.

(d) A has 51 models, B has 68 models.

7.2 £120 is divided between two people, A and B. Calculate how much each person would get if the ratio of what they receive (£A : £B) is

(a) $1 : 1$ (b) $2 : 1$ (c) $3 : 2$ (d) $1.5 : 1$ (e) $11 : 13$

7.3 (a) A fizzy orange drink is made by mixing 1 part orange juice with 3 parts lemonade. What proportion of the drink is lemonade?

(b) The table shows how many grams of each ingredient are needed in two cherry cake recipes. Which contains the higher proportion of cherries?

	Flour	Sugar	Butter	Cherries	Milk
Recipe 1	200	100	100	50	50
Recipe 2	160	80	70	40	30

7.4 When it is painted onto new plaster, a certain type of emulsion paint has to be watered down in a ratio:

Volume of paint : Volume of water $10 : 1$

Work out in litres how much water is needed for the following volumes of undiluted paint:

(a) 1 litre (b) 10 litres (c) 3.5 litres

(d) After one job, 4.4 litres of watered-down paint was left over. How much undiluted paint was wasted?

7.5 Blocks of printer paper are to be ordered for two offices as the stock has run out. Office 1 has 6 desks, and office 2 has 8 desks.

(a) What is the ratio of the number of desks in the two offices in its simplest form? Give your answer in the form Office 1 : Office 2.

(b) Each desk needs to be supplied with two blocks of paper. Blocks of paper come in multiples of 5. How many blocks of paper will be ordered?

(c) After putting 2 blocks of paper onto each desk, the left over paper is put into the store room. What fraction of the paper that is ordered ends up in the storeroom?

7.6 450 sweets are divided between three people, A, B and C. Calculate how many each person would get if the ratio of what they receive (A : B : C) is

(a) $1 : 1 : 1$ (b) $3 : 1 : 1$ (c) $2 : 5 : 2$ (d) $22 : 0 : 23$ (e) $1 : 3 : 14$

Given the ratio between two quantities, and the value of one of them, it is possible to find the value of the other by scaling up or down. This is the basis of all conversion calculations such as converting units or currencies.

Example 3 – A man exchanges £120 for \$150 at a currency exchange.

(i) What is the exchange rate for turning £1.00 into dollars?

Fact: £120 = \$150

Scale factors:

£		\$
120.00	:	150.00
÷120 ↓		↓ ÷120
1.00	:	1.25

Answer: £1.00 = \$1.25

(ii) To the nearest penny, how many pounds would be equivalent to \$278.00?

Fact: £1.00 = \$1.25

Scale factors: £ → \$ ×1.25; \$ → £ ÷1.25

Answer: \$278 = £(278 ÷ 1.25) = £222.40

7.7 A currency converter shows that the ratio of £1 in the UK to the Japanese Yen on one particular day is £1 : ¥150.

(a) Convert £33 to Yen.

(b) Converting ¥2355 will give how many Pounds?

7.8 On a certain day the exchange rate between euros and pounds is €1.10 : £0.95. Giving your answers to the nearest penny or €0.01,

(a) Convert €12.60 to pounds.

(b) Convert £278.00 to euros.

7.9 A recipe for cheese biscuits requires 150 g of flour, 75 g of butter, and 50 g of grated cheese.

(a) Write the quantities as a ratio in its simplest form.

(b) How many 12.5 g biscuits will this recipe make?

(c) What fraction of each biscuit is flour? What fraction of each biscuit is butter? What fraction of each biscuit is cheese?

7.10 Two children are picking strawberries. In the time that child A picks 200 g, child B picks 300 g.

(a) Express this as a ratio A : B in the form $1 : n$.

(b) If child A picks x g, how many grams are picked by child B?

(c) If child A picks 1.2 kg, what does child B pick?

(d) If child B picks a total of 2.25 kg, what does child A pick?

7.11 The resolution of a digital display is limited by the number of pixels. Assuming that pixels are square, find in its simplest form the ratio (screen width) : (screen height) for the following screens.

(a) A full HD screen has 1 920 pixels in the horizontal direction and 1 080 pixels in the vertical direction.

(b) A 4k screen has 3 840 pixels in the horizontal direction and 2 160 pixels in the vertical direction.

7.12 A mortar used for binding bricks together in a wall uses 4 parts sand to 1 part cement, as well as water and a liquid plasticiser. For the two solid ingredients:

(a) Write down the ratio of cement to sand.

(b) Give the quantities of cement and sand as (i) fractions and (ii) percentages of the overall amount of solid ingredients.

Concrete used in load-bearing situations contains an aggregate (such as gravel) as a solid ingredient in addition to sand and cement. A typical mix for concrete would be 2 parts sand, to 4 parts gravel, to 1 part cement.

(c) Write down the ratio cement : sand : gravel.

(d) What fraction of the solid ingredients is cement?

(e) Find, to 2 sf, the difference between the percentage of cement in the concrete mix, and the percentage of cement in the mortar mix.

8 Rounding, Limits of Accuracy and Bounds

When the answer to a calculation is a decimal with a lot of digits, a decision has to be made about the accuracy to which the answer is stated, i.e. how many figures to write down.

Truncation, which is sometimes used by digital instruments such as calculators, is where all the decimal places after a cut-off point are simply discarded. For example, if 1.418263748 is truncated after the fourth decimal place, the digits $63748...$ are discarded to leave 1.4182.

Rounding is where a figure is approximated by the nearest value with the desired accuracy. Rounding may be to a set number of significant figures (sf) or decimal places (dp). The key principle is to look at one more digit than the desired accuracy requires. If the value of this digit is 5 or more, then when the number is rounded the final digit is rounded up by 1.

Example 1 - Round 2.5647 to (i) 3 significant figures (ii) 1 decimal place.

(i) The third significant figure is the 6. 2.5647 is between 2.56 and 2.57.

The fourth significant figure is a 4. It is not necessary to round up the third significant figure, because 2.5647 is closer to 2.56 than to 2.57.

$$\therefore 2.5647 = 2.56 \text{ to } 3 \text{ sf.}$$

(ii) The first decimal place is the 5. 2.5647 is between 2.5 and 2.6.

The second decimal place is a 6. It is necessary to round up the first decimal place, because 2.5647 is closer to 2.6 than to 2.5.

$$\therefore 2.5647 = 2.6 \text{ to } 1 \text{ dp.}$$

When rounding decimals where all the digits before the decimal point are zero, the first significant figure is the first non-zero digit after the decimal point.

Example 2 - Round 0.009984 to 3 significant figures.

The first significant figure is the first 9. The fourth significant figure is a 4, so it will not be necessary to round up. $0.009989 = 0.00999$ to 3 sf.

When calculating a value from an expression or formula, it is important to round only the final answer. Rounding too early leads to a loss of accuracy, because subsequent steps in the calculation are using approximated values. Always state the number of significant figures to which you give an answer.

In real-world applications the precision of measurements is limited. The final answer to a calculation cannot be given to more significant figures than the values from which it is calculated. In general it is appropriate to find the value which is stated to the smallest number of significant figures, and give your answer to the same number of significant figures.

Example 3 - Use the formula $V = IR$ to find the value of V when $I = 0.5943$ A and $R = 1.2\,\Omega$.

Using the formula gives $V = 0.5943 \times 1.2 = 0.71316$ V. The value for I is given to 4 sf, and the value of R is given to 2 sf. The answer should therefore be stated to 2 sf.

$$V = 0.71\,\Omega \text{ to 2 sf}$$

8.1 Round the following to the stated accuracy:

(a) 81.63 to 2 sf (b) 0.0027356 to 3 sf (c) 0.49999 to 3 sf

8.2 Round the following to the stated accuracy:

(a) 6432 to 2 sf (b) 58.743 to 3 sf (c) 1.84338 to 2 sf

8.3 Round the following to the stated accuracy:

(a) 10.6845 (2 dp) (b) 10.6845 (1 dp) (c) 0.0347859 (2 dp)

8.4 Round the following to the stated accuracy:

(a) 0.0347859 (3 dp) (b) 0.00382 (2 dp) (c) -1.57864 (3 dp)

8.5 Find:

(a) 155.68 to the nearest integer

(b) -227.1848 to the nearest 10

(c) $43\,608$ to the nearest $1\,000$

(d) 0.0054545 to the nearest 1000th

8.6 Here is a list of values

$$\tfrac{3}{4} \quad \sqrt{3} \quad \tfrac{5}{8} \quad 6 \quad 2\pi$$

(a) Which of these values cannot be written as terminating decimals?

(b) Which values would need to be rounded if you were asked to write each value as a decimal number correct to 2 significant figures?

(c) How many values would need to be rounded if you were asked to write each value as a decimal number correct to 3 significant figures?

8.7 Two students try the following question: "Calculate the volume of a sphere of diameter 2.30 cm using the formula $V = \frac{4}{3}\pi r^3$. Give your answer correct to 2 significant figures."

(a) Student A sees that this is a 2 significant figures question and rounds the value of the radius before using the formula. He then also rounds the answer he gets from the formula. What value does he get for the volume?

(b) Student B uses all the figures for the radius, and only rounds the final answer. What value do they get for the volume?

(c) Which student calculates the volume correctly?

(d) What is the percentage error of the answer of the student who calculates incorrectly?

Stating a quantity to a set number of significant figures or decimal places means that the quantity lies within a range of values which would all round to the same answer. This range is called an error interval and can be expressed as an inequality between upper and lower bounds (limits).

In Example 4 the lower bound is 2.475 mm, and the upper bound is 2.485 mm. The inequality signs for the two bounds are different; p can be equal to the lower bound, but cannot be equal to the upper bound.

Example 4 - The length of an object, l, is 2.48 mm to 3 significant figures. Write down the error interval for l as an inequality.

When rounding to 2 significant figures, a value of l below 2.475 mm would round down to 2.47 mm, and a value of 2.485 mm would round up to 2.49 m.

Therefore, 2.475 mm $\leqslant p <$ 2.485 mm.

§ When dealing with a quantity that has to be an integer, there are two ways of writing the upper limit of the inequality.

Example 5 - The number of people in a stadium, p, is 85 000, to 2 significant figures. What are the minimum and maximum values of p? Write down the range of values for p as an inequality.

The minimum value of p is 84 500. If there were any fewer people, p would round down to 84 000 when rounding to 2 significant figures.

The maximum value of p is 85 499. If there were any more people, p would round up to 86 000 when rounding to 2 significant figures.

When expressed as an inequality, $84\,500 \leqslant p \leqslant 85\,499$.

The alternative inequality is $84\,500 \leqslant p < 85\,500$.

8.8 Write error intervals for the following rounded values.

(a) $l = 12$ m to 2 sf
(b) $v = 31.4$ m/s to 3 sf
(c) $V = 4.78$ litres to 2 dp
(d) $f = 6.178$ Hz to 3 dp
(e) $n = 60$ to 1 sf
(f) $m = 22.3$ g to 1 dp

8.9 (a) Give the maximum and minimum numbers of people that these rounded values could represent:

(i) 420 to 2 sf (ii) 2 200 to 2 sf

(b) State, as an inequality, the number of people in a crowd with a size of 29 500 to 3 sf.

8.10 Find the upper and lower bounds of the following quantities:

(a) 120 km to 2 sf (b) 2.0 minutes to 1 dp (c) 51.2 g to 3 sf

§ When more than one variable is used in a calculation, upper and lower bounds for the final answer are found by considering the upper and lower bounds of the individual variables from which the answer is calculated.

Example 6 - To one decimal place, $a = 11.1$ and $b = 14.5$. Find
(i) Find the upper bound of $a + b$. (ii) The lower bound of $a - b$.

The error intervals for a and b are $11.05 \leqslant a < 11.15$ and $14.45 \leqslant b < 14.55$.

(i) The upper bound of $a + b$ is found by adding the upper bounds of a and b. The upper bound of $a + b$ is $11.15 + 14.55 = 26.7$.

(ii) The lower bound of $a - b$ is found by subtracting the upper bound of b from the lower bound of a. The lower bound of $a - b$ is $11.05 - 14.55 = -4.5$.

8.11 To two significant figures, $a = 150$ and $b = 720$. Find:
(a) The upper bound of $a + b$.
(b) The lower bound of $a + b$.
(c) The upper bound of $a - b$.
(d) The lower bound of $a - b$.

8.12 To one decimal place, $a = 5.3$ and $b = 2.9$. Find, giving your answer to 3 sf:
(a) The upper bound of $a \times b$.
(b) The lower bound of $a \div b$.

8.13 A cuboid has sides of length 1.58 m, 2.39 m and 6.44 m. Giving your answers to 4 significant figures, what are
(a) its maximum volume?
(b) its minimum surface area?

8.14 Find the upper and lower bounds of G, where $G = 2p + q$ and p and q have the values $p = 1.6$ cm (1 dp) and $q = 7.4$ cm (1 dp).

9 Approximation

To estimate the answer to a calculation, proceed through the calculation in BIDMAS order, at each stage using numbers that are close to the true values but easier to work with. When estimating the signs $\approx$ or $\simeq$ are used, which mean "approximately equal to."

> Example 1 – Estimate the value of the calculation $\frac{102\times 13.5}{8.2+1.6}$.
>
> Replace 102 by 100, 13.5 by 14, 8.2 by 8 and 1.6 by 2.
>
> $$\frac{102 \times 13.5}{8.2+1.6} \approx \frac{100 \times 14}{8+2}\frac{100 \times 14}{10} = \frac{100}{10} \times 14 = 10 \times 14 = 140$$

When doing a difficult calculation, it is a good idea to use estimation to find a rough value for the answer to compare with your accurate solution. This will help you spot mistakes, such as mis-placed decimal points. This is particularly important if you are doing calculations on a calculator.

9.1 Estimate

(a) $\frac{3}{5}$ of 24 (b) $\frac{5}{8}$ of 38 (c) 53% of £25.50

9.2 Estimate the values of the following:

(a) $10(4.3+7.1)$ (b) $\frac{2.1\times 5.1}{12.3}$ (c) $\frac{\sqrt{4.1^2+3.1^2}}{2.1}$

9.3 Estimate the values of the following:

(a) $\frac{8.9\times 6.1}{5.1\div 2.2}$ (b) $\frac{7.28+5.01}{9.23-5.09}$ (c) 75% of £179

9.4 By estimating an answer, work out which value is correct for each of the following calculations:

(a) 62×51 (i) 2902 (ii) 3162 (iii) 3692

(b) $1+1.21 \div 5.1$ (i) 1.01 (ii) 1.24 (iii) 1.502

(c) $\frac{62\,500-1700}{3.1}$ (i) 1846 (ii) 9723 (iii) 19 613

(d) $32+(\frac{202}{51})^3$ (i) 94.1 (ii) 150.7 (iii) 278.1

9.5 Estimate the following:

(a) The time needed to put 12 screws into a piece of wood if each screw takes an average of 5.2 seconds. Give your answer in seconds.

(b) The mass in grams of one tin of beans if a 4-pack has a mass of 1.63 kg.

(c) The distance travelled in 22 minutes at 50 miles per hour.

9.6 Suzie is buying food for a barbecue. She needs 60 rolls and 60 sausages. Rolls come in packs of 6, each pack costing 82 p. Sausages come in packs of 8, costing £2.95.

(a) Estimate how much Suzie will have to spend.

(b) How many £10 notes should Suzie withdraw at a cashpoint to cover the cost?

9.7 Estimate the income of a theatre that sells the following tickets for one of its performances:

Price per seat / £	Number sold
15.50	41
27.50	122
58.00	285
72.00	53

9.8 A quantity surveyor estimates the cost of materials for a building project. 102 houses are to be built. There will be a few Large properties. The rest will be a mixture of Medium and Small properties. There will be more of the Medium size than the Small size.

(a) Which of these options best fits this description?

(i) 25 Large houses, 45 Medium and 32 Small
(ii) 6 Large houses, 48 Medium and 48 Small
(iii) 5 Large houses, 57 Medium and 50 Small

(b) If the cost of materials is £110 000 for a Large house, £73 000 for a Medium house and £58 000 for a Small house, estimate the total cost of materials for building all the houses.

10 Standard Form

Standard form is useful for writing very large or small numbers compactly. To write a number in standard form, express it as $a \times 10^b$, where $1 \leqslant a < 10$ and b is an integer.

Example 1 - Write (i) 253.84 (ii) -0.003578 in standard form.

(i) $253.84 = 2.5384 \times 10^2$ (ii) $-0.003578 = -3.578 \times 10^{-3}$

2 1
253.84

1 2 3
-0.003578

Numbers such as 31×10^3 and 0.87×10^{-3} contain powers of 10 but are not in standard form because 31 and 0.87 are not in the range $1 \leqslant a < 10$. To write them in standard form, first write 31 and 0.87 in standard form. Then combine the powers of 10 by adding them together.

Example 2 - Write (i) 31×10^3 (ii) 0.87×10^{-3} in standard form.

(i) In standard form 31 is 3.1×10^1.

$$\therefore 31 \times 10^3 = 3.1 \times 10^1 \times 10^3 = 3.1 \times 10^4$$

(ii) In standard form 0.87 is 8.7×10^{-1}.

$$\therefore 0.87 \times 10^{-3} = 8.7 \times 10^{-1} \times 10^{-3} = 8.7 \times 10^{-4}$$

Answer the following questions without using a calculator.

10.1 Put the following numbers into standard form:
(a) 11.7 (b) 0.5 (c) 123 (d) 0.0021

10.2 Put the following numbers into standard form:
(a) 1 103 457 (b) 0.000456 (c) 7310.08 (d) 0.00000315

10.3 Write these values as ordinary numbers:
(a) 2.6×10^4 (b) 4.9×10^{-2} (c) 5.17×10^3 (d) 8.8×10^{-6}

10.4 Put the following numbers into standard form:
(a) 47×10^2 (b) 12.34×10^6 (c) 0.56×10^{-5} (d) 101×10^{-3}

10.5 Write the following quantities in units of metres in standard form:
(a) 900 km (b) 0.01 mm (c) 20×10^{-5} m (d) 1 μm

When adding or subtracting numbers in standard form, start by re-writing the numbers in terms of the same power of ten. Next, do the addition or subtraction. Finally, re-write the numbers in standard form if necessary.

Example 3 - Evaluate, giving your answers in standard form:
(i) $3.2 \times 10^3 + 2.9 \times 10^4$ (ii) $1.1 \times 10^{-2} - 9.8 \times 10^{-3}$

(i) 2.9×10^4 is the same as 29×10^3.

$\therefore 3.2 \times 10^3 + 2.9 \times 10^4 = 3.2 \times 10^3 + 29 \times 10^3 = 32.2 \times 10^3$

In standard form, 32.2×10^3 is 3.22×10^4.

(ii) 1.1×10^{-2} is the same as 11×10^{-3}.

$\therefore 1.1 \times 10^{-2} - 9.8 \times 10^{-3} = 11 \times 10^{-3} - 9.8 \times 10^{-3} = 1.2 \times 10^{-3}$

1.2×10^{-3} is already written in standard form.

When multiplying numbers in standard form, multiply the numbers in front of the powers of 10, and combine the powers of the powers of 10 by adding the powers. Likewise, when dividing numbers in standard form, divide the numbers in front of the powers of 10, and subtract the powers of 10. Finally, check that the answer is in standard form.

Example 4 - Evaluate, giving your answers in standard form:
(i) $(7.5 \times 10^2) \times (2.0 \times 10^3)$ (ii) $(8.2 \times 10^4) \div (2.0 \times 10^2)$

(i)
$$\begin{aligned}(7.5 \times 10^2) \times (2.0 \times 10^3) &= (7.5 \times 2.0) \times (10^2 \times 10^3)\\ &= 15 \times 10^5 = 1.5 \times 10^6\end{aligned}$$

(ii)
$$\begin{aligned}(8.2 \times 10^4) \div (2.0 \times 10^2) &= (8.2 \div 2.0) \times (10^4 \div 10^2)\\ &= 4.1 \times 10^2\end{aligned}$$

Evaluate the following without using a calculator, giving your answers in standard form:

10.6 (a) $7.3 \times 10^2 + 4.8 \times 10^3$ (c) $4.2 \times 10^{-2} - 1.1 \times 10^{-3}$
(b) $9.7 \times 10^4 + 9.7 \times 10^3$ (d) $5.27 \times 10^5 - 2.8 \times 10^4$

10.7 (a) $(5 \times 10^2) \times (6 \times 10^3)$ (c) $(6.2 \times 10^2) \div (3.1 \times 10^3)$
(b) $(1.8 \times 10^6) \times (3 \times 10^3)$ (d) $(5.4 \times 10^4) \div (2 \times 10^{-2})$

10.8 (a) $1.6 \times 10^3 + 4.0 \times 10^4$ (c) $(2.5 \times 10^2) \times (5.0 \times 10^6)$
(b) $2.6 \times 10^{-4} - 1.7 \times 10^{-5}$ (d) $(4.2 \times 10^3) \div (1.4 \times 10^{-2})$

10.9 Evaluate the following with a calculator. Give your answers in standard form, using 3 sf where rounding is necessary.
(a) $2500 + 4.0 \times 10^3$ (c) $(2.81 \times 10^3) \div 9.81$
(b) $3.3 \times (5.0 \times 10^6)$ (d) $\sqrt{\frac{8.0\times10^6}{4.1}}$

10.10 Evaluate the following without using a calculator, giving your answers in standard form:
(a) $3.3 \times 10^{-4} + 1.9 \times 10^{-2}$ (c) $(2.6 \times 10^{-2}) \times (4.3 \times 10^{-7})$
(b) $2.9 \times 10^{-6} - 5.7 \times 10^{-5}$ (d) $(8.0 \times 10^{-3}) \div (6.4 \times 10^{-9})$

10.11 A ream of paper contains 500 sheets. Fabi measured the height of a ream of A4 printer paper stacked vertically to be 4.9 cm.
(a) In millimetres, what is the thickness of one sheet of paper?
(b) Write the value from part (a) in metres in standard form.

10.12 The number of seconds in a year is approximately $\pi \times 10^7$. Using this approximation, find the number of seconds in 250 years, giving your answer in standard form to 2 sf.

10.13 Avogadro's number, 6.02×10^{23}, is the number of molecules in 1 mole of a substance. How many molecules are in 0.05 moles? Give your answer in standard form.

10.14 (a) Write $(\frac{1}{2} \times 10^9) \times (5 \times 10^8)$ in standard form.
(b) You are told that 6×10^8 is the same as $(3 \times 10^n) \times (2 \times 10^5)$. What is the value of n?

10.15 Round the following to the nearest power of 10. State the power.
(a) $0.6 \times 10^7 \times 4.5 \times 10^8$ (b) $(2 \times 10^6) \div (4.5 \times 10^{-3})$

10.16 On the atomic scale energies are measured in a unit called the electron-Volt (eV). $1\text{ eV} = 1.602 \times 10^{-19}$ J. The energy levels of the electron in a Hydrogen atom are given by the formula below, where n is an integer. Find the energies E_1, E_2, E_3 and E_4 in Joules. Give your answers in standard form to 2 sf.

$$E_n = -\frac{13.6}{n^2}\text{ eV}$$

11 Units

The table below shows a list of common unit prefixes.

n	μ	m	c	d	-	k	M	G
nano	micro	milli	centi	deci	-	kilo	mega	giga
$\times 10^{-9}$	$\times 10^{-6}$	$\times 10^{-3}$	$\times 10^{-2}$	$\times 10^{-1}$	-	$\times 10^{+3}$	$\times 10^{+6}$	$\times 10^{+9}$

For example, 1 cm $= 1 \times 10^{-2}$ m. This is equivalent to 1 cm $= 1 \times \frac{1}{100}$ m.

When converting from one set of units to another, write down a fact for each quantity you need to convert, turn that into a scale factor, and then apply this factor. For example, the fact 1 cm $= 1 \times \frac{1}{100}$ m tells us that to convert a quantity in centimetres to a quantity in metres, divide by 100. To go the other way, from a quantity in metres to a quantity in centimetres, multiply by 100. The scale factor is 100.

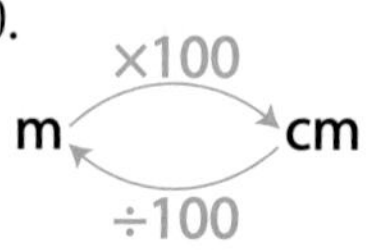

m → cm: $\times 100$; cm → m: $\div 100$

Example 1 – Convert 3 cm into metres.

Fact: 1 m = 100 cm Scale factor: m → cm: $\times 100$; cm → m: $\div 100$

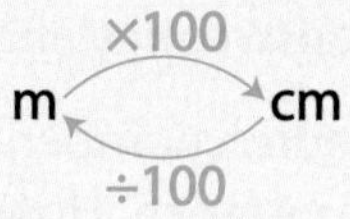

Answer: 3 cm $= 3 \div 100$ m $= 0.03$ m $= 3.0 \times 10^{-2}$ m

Sometimes you may need more than one scale factor. This often happens with time problems.

Example 2 – Change 2.5 hours into seconds.

Fact: 1 hour = 60 minutes 1 minute = 60 s

Scale factors: hours → min: $\times 60$; min → hours: $\div 60$; min → s: $\times 60$; s → min: $\div 60$

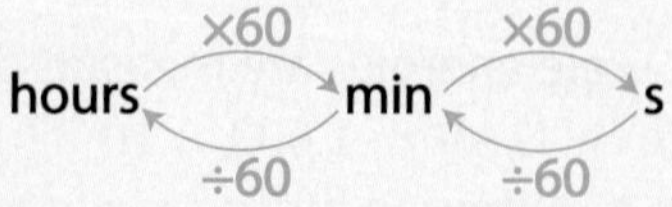

Answer: 2.5 hours $= 2.5 \times 60 \times 60$ s $= 9000$ s

You may have a fact in which neither quantity is exactly 1 unit. In this case, scale down the fact to make one quantity exactly 1 unit in size, and then proceed as in the previous examples.

Example 3 – Some old scales read 8.0 lb (pounds) when a cat is put on them. What is this in kilograms? 14.00 lb (one stone) is 6.3503 kg.

Fact: $14.0\ \text{lb} = 6.3503\ \text{kg}$

Divide by 14.00 to find how to convert 1.000 lb into kilograms.

Read off the scale factor.

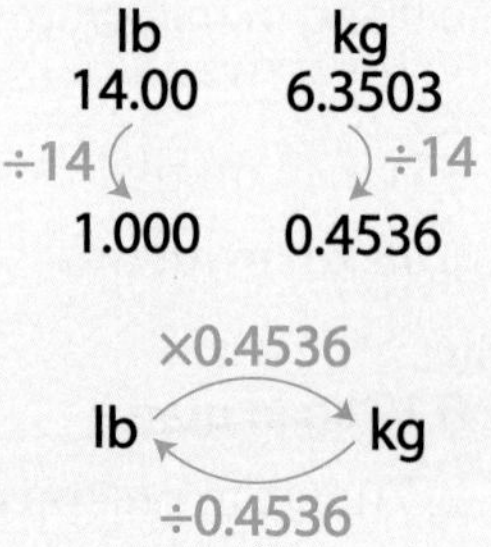

lb	kg
14.00	6.3503
÷14	÷14
1.000	0.4536

lb → kg: ×0.4536; kg → lb: ÷0.4536

Answer: $8.0\ \text{lb} = (8.0 \times 0.4536)\ \text{kg} = 3.7\ \text{kg}$ to 2 sf

When dealing with units which involve powers other than one, or when handling compound units, convert each power of each unit in turn.

Example 4 – Convert 3 m^3 to cm^3.

Fact: $1\ \text{m} = 100\ \text{cm}$

$\therefore 1\ \text{m}^3 = (100\ \text{cm})^3 = (100)^3\ \text{cm}^3$

$\Rightarrow 1\ \text{m}^3 = 100 \times 100 \times 100\ \text{cm}^3$

$\Rightarrow 1\ \text{m}^3 = 10^6\ \text{cm}^3$

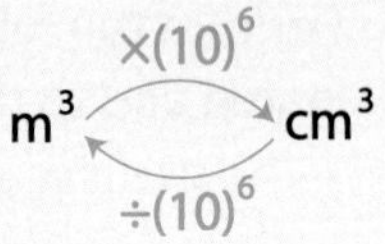

m^3 → cm^3: $\times(10)^6$; cm^3 → m^3: $\div(10)^6$

Answer: $3\ \text{m}^3 = 3 \times 10^6\ \text{cm}^3$

Example 5 – Convert a density of 3 kg/m^3 to g/cm^3.

Fact: $1\ \text{kg} = 1000\ \text{g}$ $\quad 1\ \text{m} = 100\ \text{cm}$

Scale factors: kg → g: ×1000; g → kg: ÷1000 $\quad$ m^3 → cm^3: $\times(10)^6$; cm^3 → m^3: $\div(10)^6$

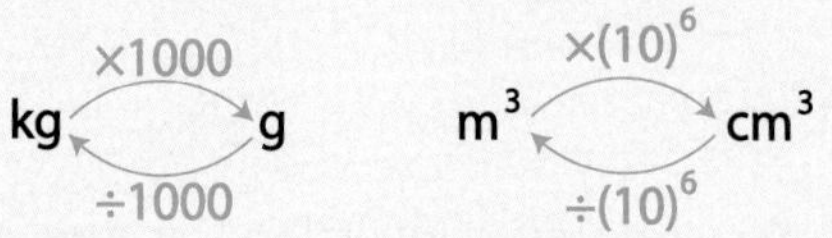

Answer: $3\ \text{kg/m}^3 = 3\ \frac{kg}{m^3} = 3 \times \frac{1000}{10^6}\ \frac{g}{cm^3} = 3 \times \frac{10^3}{10^6}\ \frac{g}{cm^3}$

$\therefore 3\ \text{kg/m}^3 = 3 \times 10^{-3}\ \text{g/cm}^3$

Note: You may see units with a denominator part written in an alternative form with a negative index. For example, the units of speed, m/s, may also be written m s^{-1}, and the units of density, kg/m^3, may also be written kg m^{-3}.

11.1 Write:
(a) 2 300 g in kilograms
(b) 0.002 g in milligrams
(c) 0.6 kg in grams
(d) 150 mg in grams

11.2 Write:
(a) 15 cm in metres
(b) 3.48 km in metres
(c) 67.2 km in centimetres
(d) 0.1 cm in kilometres

11.3 Write:
(a) 0.15 kg in grams
(b) 2.5 hours in seconds
(c) 365 days in seconds

11.4 Write:
(a) 3.31 mm in metres
(b) 15.2 μm in metres
(c) 60 km in millimetres
(d) 0.12 cm in nanometres

11.5 Perform the following unit conversions:
(a) 30 km/s to m/s (b) 16 N/m^2 to kN/m^2 (c) 15 000 Hz to MHz

11.6 Perform the following calculations, giving your answer in the units stated and to the given accuracy:
(a) 3.875×0.985 V, to 3 sf, in units of V.
(b) 51.85 cm $\times$ 98.75 cm, to 3 sf, in units of cm^2.
(c) 106.75 m^3 $\div$ 43.1, to 2 sf, in units of m^3.

11.7 Concentrations are often written as values in moles per litre. An example is 4 moles/litre. 1 litre $=$ 1 dm^3, and 1 dm $=$ 10 cm. Convert 4 moles/litre into units of
(a) moles/m^3.
(b) moles/cm^3.

11.8 Perform the following unit conversions. In this question you will need to know that 1 mile $=$ 1 609.34 metres, "mph" stands for miles per hour, "kph" for kilometres per hour, and "m/s" for metres per second. Give your answers to 2 significant figures.
(a) 15 kph to m/s
(b) 33 m/s to kph
(c) 16 mph to m/s
(d) 64 kph to mph

11.9 A student claims that 15 cm is exactly the same as 6 inches. A conversion calculator states that 50 cm = 1.64042 feet. What is the percentage error in the student's claim? Give your answer to 2 significant figures.

11.10 Perform the following calculations, giving your answer in the units stated and to the given accuracy:

(a) $0.02511\text{ cm} \times 78.34\text{ cm}$, to 3 sf, in units of m^2.

(b) $91.25 \times 0.00006751\text{ V}$, to 2 sf, in units of mV.

(c) Find, to 2 significant figures, the distance in metres covered by a car which travels for 45 minutes at 15 km per hour.

11.11 Put ticks in the table to show whether these expressions represent lengths, areas, volumes, or none of these. You are told that r and l have units of metres.

Expression	Length	Area	Volume	None of these
$\frac{4}{3}\pi r^3$				
$\pi r l$				
$\pi(r+l)$				
πr^2				
$r+l$				

11.12 Put ticks in the table to show whether these expressions represent lengths, areas, volumes, or none of these. You are told that π, p, q and s are unitless constants, and k, l and m have units of metres.

Expression	Length	Area	Volume	None of these
πm^2				
$plmk$				
$\frac{qm^2}{k}$				
$\frac{s\pi l}{mk}$				
$\frac{pqs}{2}$				

Algebra

12 Writing and Using Algebra

Algebra has its own terminology:

$4\pi x^2$	A term is made up of constants (such as 4 and π) and variables (such as x). Together the leading constants are known as the coefficient (here 4π). Like terms contain the same variables, to the same powers. They differ only in the values of their coefficients.
$4\pi x^2 - 3x$	An expression is made up of terms linked by operators ($+, -, \times, \div$).
$x - 5 = 4\pi x^2 - 3x$	An equation links two expressions with an equals sign.

If an equation is true for all possible values of the variable it is called an identity, and the $\equiv$ sign may be used. One side of an identity is effectively just a re-arrangement of the other. For example, $(2x + 3) - 4 \equiv 2x - 1$.

$7x^2 - 3x + 2$ and $5x^3 + 2x$ are polynomials. Polynomials have terms which contain only constants and positive, whole number powers of variables, linked together by addition or subtraction.

- If the highest power of the variable is 1, the polynomial is linear. For example, $2x - 5$ and $y + 3$.
- If the highest power of the variable is 2, the polynomial is quadratic. For example, $7x^2 + 4x - 2$ and $y^2 - 9$.
- If the highest power of the variable is 3, the polynomial is cubic. For example, $9x^3 + 2x^2 - 7x$ and $y^3 - 4$.

Writing algebra involves replacing words with variables, constants and operators. Brackets are often needed to ensure that applying the rules of BIDMAS when doing calculations will give correct answers.

Example 1 - Write the following as an equation:
"To find Q, add 6 to p, then divide by 5."

First add 6 to p: $p+6$ Next divide everything by 5: $\frac{p+6}{5}$

This is equal to Q: $Q=\frac{p+6}{5}$

12.1 (a) Write the following as an equation: "To find y, multiply x by four then subtract three."

(b) When $x=5$ what is y?

12.2 (a) Write the following statement as an algebraic equation: "y is found by adding eight to six x."

(b) Find y if $x=10$.

(c) Find y if $x=-5$.

12.3 A child says "Two p and three q make z."

(a) Write this statement as an equation.

(b) Find z if $p=9$ and $q=-7$.

12.4 The costs of pieces of fruit are: apple 30 p, pear 35 p, banana 28 p and orange 25 p.

(a) Write an equation to find the total cost, C p, of d apples, e pears, f bananas and g oranges.

(b) What is the change from £10.00 if $d=4$, $e=4$, $f=7$ and $g=6$?

12.5 A gardener walks up and down his garden sowing seeds. The garden has length L, and he makes twelve trips down the garden and back. In total he walks 336 m.

(a) Write an equation for this information.

(b) What is the length of the garden, L?

Superscripts and subscripts perform different roles. A superscript, such as the 2 in x^2, is used to indicate that a number or variable is raised to a power. Subscripts are used purely as labels. For example, the initial speed of a vehicle might be written as v_0, v_S or even v_{Start}. Numbers in subscripts are part of the label, and do not indicate that a mathematical operation is taking place.

Example 2 - the velocity of a car at time t is given by

$$v_t = v_0 + at$$

where v_0 is the initial velocity of the car and a is the acceleration. Find the value of v_t when $v_0 = 5$ m/s, $a = 2$ m/s^2 and $t = 8$ s.

$$v_t = 5 + 2 \times 8 = 5 + 16 = 21 \text{ m/s}$$

12.6 Using the equation $v_t = v_0 + at$, find v_t if

(a) $v_0 = 0$ m/s, $a = 3$ m/s^2 and $t = 10$ s.

(b) $v_0 = 50$ mm/s, $a = 2$ mm/s^2 and $t = 4$ s.

(c) $v_0 = 0.7$ km/s, $a = -0.04$ km/s^2 and $t = 10$ s.

12.7 (a) If R is the number of rabbits now, and R_0 is the number of rabbits originally, write an equation for the statement "The number of rabbits now is twice the starting number of rabbits, minus 10 which have been sold."

(b) Find R if $R_0 = 210$.

Greek letters are commonly used in algebra in mathematics and the sciences. They can be manipulated in exactly the same way as Roman letters such as x and y. The table below shows those that are used most often and their names. On the left are lower case letters, and on the right are a smaller number of upper case letters.

	Name		Name		Name		Name
α	alpha	θ	theta	ρ	rho	Δ	delta
β	beta	λ	lambda	σ	sigma	Λ	lambda
γ	gamma	μ	mu	ϕ	phi	Σ	sigma
δ	delta	ν	nu	ω	omega	Φ	phi
ϵ, ε	epsilon	π	pi			Ω	omega

Example 3 - The resistance of a piece of wire, R, is equal to the resistivity of the wire ρ multiplied by the length of the wire l and divided by the wire's cross-sectional area A.

Multiply the wire's resistivity by its length. $\rho \times l$

Next divide by the cross-sectional area. $\frac{\rho \times l}{A}$

This is equal to the wire's resistance. $R = \frac{\rho \times l}{A}$

12.8 Λ is equal to ϕ minus ω.

(a) Write an equation for Λ.

(b) Find Λ for $\phi = 45°$ and $\omega = 15°$.

12.9 (a) Write this information as an equation: "To find γ start with 24 and subtract 4 times α, then divide the answer by 3."

(b) Find γ when $\alpha = 3$.

Simplifying "tidies up" algebra into a neater form. Simplifying includes collecting like terms together; using the rules of indices to combine different powers of a variable; and cancelling a common factor in the numerator and denominator of a fraction.

Example 4 - Simplify $\frac{1}{2} \times 4x^2 + 2p + 3\frac{p^2}{p}$.

The first term can be simplified by multiplying the $\frac{1}{2}$ and the 4 together. The third term can be simplified by cancelling a factor of p in the top and bottom of the fraction. Finally, combine like p terms.

$$\frac{1}{2} \times 4x^2 + 2p + 3\frac{p^2}{p} = 2x^2 + 2p + 3p = 2x^2 + 5p$$

In general it is good practice to simplify algebra whenever possible, even if not explicitly asked to do so.

12.10 Simplify:

(a) $3\alpha + 2\alpha$

(b) $5\lambda - \pi - 2\pi - \lambda$

(c) $M = M_0 + 3m + 5m - 6m + 4m$

12.11 Simplify:

(a) $3p - 6s + 2t - p + s$ (c) $fg + gf + 2hj + jh$

(b) $\frac{3}{4}vw + \frac{1}{4}vw$

12.12 Simplify:

(a) $2p \times 3q^2r + 4r \times 2pq^2$ (b) $\frac{1}{2} \times 2x^9 \div x^7 - 2x + x^2 + 20x$

12.13 A bar-tender is counting cans for stock-taking. He has x 4-packs, y 12-packs and z single cans.

(a) Write this information as an equation to find the total number of cans T.

(b) What is T if $x = 11, y = 10$ and $z = 7$?

12.14 A postman delivers mail to four houses. House 1 receives $3s$ letters and t parcels. House 2 receives $7s$ letters. House 3 receives $5s$ letters and $2t$ parcels. House 4 receives t parcels.

(a) Write an equation for the total number of items the four houses receive, N. Simplify your answer as far as possible.

(b) Assuming that the cost to send a letter is 80 pence and the cost to send a parcel is £5.50, write an equation for C, the total cost in pounds to send all the items that were delivered.

12.15 A quantity called the discriminant is used in the calculation of solutions of quadratic equations.

(a) Using δ for the discriminant, write the following as an equation: "The discriminant is found by subtracting four times a times c from the square of b."

(b) Find δ if $b = 16, a = 1$ and $c = 4$.

(c) Find δ if $b = 100, a = 3$ and $c = 7$.

12.16 Write the following statements in algebra.

(a) α is twice β. (b) α cubed is the same as γ squared.

$\beta = 2$ and γ is a positive integer.

(c) Find the value of γ.

13 Indices and Taking Roots

The table below illustrates the meaning of positive and negative indices (powers).

a^{-3}	a^{-2}	a^{-1}	a^0	a^{+1}	a^{+2}	a^{+3}
$\frac{1}{a\times a\times a}$	$\frac{1}{a\times a}$	$\frac{1}{a}$	1	a	$a\times a$	$a\times a\times a$

- Increasing the power of a by 1 is equivalent to multiplying by a, and decreasing the power of a by 1 is equivalent to dividing by a.
- Anything raised to the power 0 has the value 1, i.e. $a^0 = 1$. The exception is 0^0, the value of which is undefined.
- Negative indices indicate reciprocals. A number can be written in the numerator with a negative power or in the denominator with a positive power. For example, $3^{-2} = \frac{1}{3^2}$.

The rules for indices show how to combine powers of a single number:

- When multiplying powers, indices add:

$$2^3 \times 2^5 = 2^{3+5} = 2^8 \qquad a^m \times a^n = a^{m+n}$$

- When dividing powers, indices subtract:

$$3^4 \div 3^3 = 3^{4-3} = 3^1 \qquad a^m \div a^n = a^{m-n}$$

- When raising a power to a power ("power on power"), indices multiply:

$$(2^3)^4 = 2^{3\times 4} = 2^{12} \qquad (a^m)^n = a^{m\times n}$$

13.1 (a) Express the following in index form with a single power:
(i) $2^2 \times 2^3$ (ii) $3^9 \div 3^7$ (iii) $5^{-2} \times 5^4$

(b) Evaluate the following, writing your answers without indices:
(i) $2^2 \times 2^3$ (ii) $3^9 \div 3^7$ (iii) $5^{-2} \times 5^4$

Simplify the following, giving your answers in index form:

13.2 (a) $2^4 \times 2^{-6}$ (b) $3^3 \div 3^4$ (c) $5^{-3} \times 5$

13.3 (a) $10^{-1} \times 10^{-1}$ (b) $10^{-1} \div 10^1$ (c) $3^{-1} \times 9$

13.4 (a) $a^2 \times a^3$ (b) $a^7 \div a^8$ (c) $\frac{a^1}{a^5}$

13.5 (a) $a^2 \times a^{-5}$ (b) $(a^3)^2 \div a$ (c) $3(a^2)^2 \div 6a$

13.6 (a) $3^0 \div 3$ (b) $10^2 \times 10^3 \times 10^{-1}$ (c) $2^2 \times 2^{-1} \times 2^4$

13.7 (a) $(10^2)^2$ (b) $(10^2)^3$ (c) $(10^{-2})^3$ (d) $\frac{10^3}{10^6}$ (e) $\frac{10^3}{(10^2)^3}$

13.8 (a) $a^6 \times a^{-4} \times a^3$ (b) $a^2 \times a^3 \div a$ (c) $\frac{3(a^4)^2}{a}$ (d) $((a^2)^2)^3$

13.9 A quantity p is found by multiplying the value of x^2 by the value of x^3 and then dividing by 2.

(a) Write this information algebraically, and simplify as far as possible.

(b) Evaluate p when $x = 3$.

13.10 (a) A quantity F is found by calculating a squared, multiplying by b cubed, and finally dividing by c. Write this formula algebraically using indices.

(b) You are told additionally that $c = a$. Rewrite your formula in terms of a and b only, simplifying the indices as far as possible.

(c) Find F for $a = 7$ and $b = 2$.

Taking a root is the inverse operation to raising a number to a power. Squaring a positive or negative number always produces a positive result. Hence, taking the square root of a positive number can produce two answers. Since the squares of both positive and negative numbers are positive, there are no real numbers which square to give a negative number.

The number included in a root sign indicates the type of root. $\sqrt[2]{}$ is a square root, $\sqrt[3]{}$ is a cube root, and so on. A $\sqrt{}$ symbol without a number is always assumed to be a square root. By convention, the $\sqrt{}$ sign indicates that you are to find the positive value of the square root.

$$3^3 = 9, \quad \sqrt[2]{9} = 3 \qquad 4^3 = 64, \quad \sqrt[3]{64} = 4$$

There are instances where both the positive and negative solutions to a square root are required, such as solving quadratic equations. In these cases, you can indicate the need to find both solutions by putting the $\pm$ symbol in front of the square root. For example, $\pm\sqrt{9}$ has solutions $+3$ and -3.

13.11 Write down the values of

(a) $\sqrt{25}$ (b) $\sqrt{49}$ (c) $\sqrt{8^2+17}$

13.12 Calculate the following, simplifying as far as possible.

(a) $\sqrt[2]{4}+\sqrt[2]{16}$ (b) $\sqrt[3]{27}+\sqrt[3]{8}$ (c) $\sqrt[2]{9+16}$

13.13 Find

(a) $\sqrt{5^2}$ (b) $\sqrt{4^3}$ (c) $\sqrt{9^2+12^2}$

13.14 Write down the values of

(a) $\sqrt{4}$ (b) $(\sqrt{11})^2$ (c) $9-(\sqrt{3})^2$

13.15 Calculate the following, simplifying as far as possible.

(a) $\sqrt[2]{9}+\sqrt[2]{64}$ (b) $\sqrt[3]{27}-\sqrt[2]{16}$ (c) $\sqrt{4}\times\sqrt{9}$

13.16 Calculate the following, simplifying as far as possible.

(a) $-\sqrt[2]{9}+\sqrt[4]{81}$ (b) $2\sqrt[2]{4}+5\sqrt[3]{8}$ (c) $1-7\sqrt[3]{8}+\sqrt[2]{81}$

13.17 Calculate the following, simplifying as far as possible.

(a) $\frac{\sqrt[2]{16}}{2\sqrt[2]{4}}-\frac{\sqrt[3]{27}}{\sqrt[3]{8}}$ (b) $\frac{\sqrt[2]{16}-\sqrt[3]{27}}{2\sqrt[2]{4}-\sqrt[3]{8}}$ (c) $2\sqrt{9}-4\sqrt[5]{243}$

13.18 Write down the values of

(a) $\sqrt[3]{64}$ (b) $\sqrt[3]{-64}$ (c) $\sqrt[3]{8}$ (d) $\sqrt[3]{-27}$

§ Raising a number to the power n, then taking the nth root, gives back the original number. From the "power on power" rule, we know that raising a number to the power n, then raising the result to the power $\frac{1}{n}$, also has this property.

$$\sqrt[n]{a^n}=a \qquad (a^n)^{\frac{1}{n}}=a^{n\times\frac{1}{n}}=a^1=a$$

This result suggests that taking an nth root is equivalent to raising a number to the power $\frac{1}{n}$, and this is indeed the case. Fractional indices are used for roots, and the general rule is:

$$\sqrt[n]{m}=a^{\frac{m}{n}}$$

e.g. $\sqrt{9}=9^{\frac{1}{2}}$ $\qquad \sqrt[3]{8}=8^{\frac{1}{3}}$ $\qquad \sqrt[3]{8^2}=(8^2)^{\frac{1}{3}}=a^{\frac{2}{3}}$

13.19 Evaluate:

(a) $27^{\frac{1}{3}}$ (b) $32^{\frac{1}{5}}$ (c) $\sqrt[2]{4^3}$

13.20 Write the following in the form $\sqrt[n]{a^m}$.

(a) $p^{\frac{5}{7}}$ (b) $q^{\frac{3}{4}}$ (c) $r^{\frac{5}{3}}$

13.21 Write the following with fractional indices.

(a) $\sqrt[3]{a^4}$ (b) $\sqrt[7]{b^9}$ (c) $(\sqrt[5]{z})^2$

13.22 Evaluate:

(a) $9^{\frac{3}{2}}$ (b) $16^{\frac{5}{4}}$ (c) $(-8)^{\frac{2}{3}}$

13.23 Simplify the following to a single power of a in the numerator:

(a) $\frac{a^3}{(a^1)^7}$ (b) $\frac{(a^7)^2}{a^{-1}}$ (c) $(a^7)^{\frac{1}{2}}$ (d) $\sqrt[4]{\frac{a^7 \times a^4}{a^6}}$

14 Expanding

Expanding is the process of multiplying out one or more brackets. Example 1 shows how to expand a single bracket with a term in front of it.

> Example 1 - Expand the expression $3x(5x-1)$.
>
> Multiply the $3x$ by the two terms in the bracket, and add the results together.
>
> $$3x \times 5x = 15x^2 \qquad 3x \times -1 = -3x$$
>
> $$\therefore 3x(5x-1) = 15x^2 - 3x$$

Expand and simplify:

14.1 (a) $3(y+2)$ (b) $p(3-r)$ (c) $2(x+3-y)$

14.2 (a) $4(r+1)+3$ (b) $2(1+s)+6(s-1)$ (c) $z(z-1)+2z-1$

14.3 (a) $-2(3+x)$ (b) $-x(x-1)$ (c) $2xy(x-2)$

14.4 (a) $2x(x+7)$ (b) $a(1+a)+a^2+3$ (c) $\frac{1}{2}y(2y+4)$

14.5 (a) $3(2m-1)+2(m+3)-5(3+m)$

(b) $3p(4+2r)-3r(2p-5)$

Expanding a pair of brackets means multiplying the whole of the second bracket by each of the terms in the first bracket taken one after the other (including any minus signs).

$$(x-5)(2x-3) \qquad (x-5)(2x-3)$$

$$(x-5)(2x-3) = x(2x-3) \; -5(2x-3)$$

$$(x-5)(2x-3) = 2x^2 - 3x \; -10x + 15 = 2x^2 - 13x + 15$$

You may have seen the expansion of a pair of binomial brackets (brackets which contain exactly two terms) summarised by the acronym FOIL:

Firsts Outers

$$(x-5)(2x-3)$$

Inners Lasts

Example 2 - Expand and simplify the expression $(x+2)(x-3)$.

To multiply out the brackets, go through the FOIL acronym in order, multiplying pairs of terms together, and at the end add up the result.

$(\times \quad x)$	Firsts:	$x \times x = x^2$	Outers:	$x \times -3 = -3x$
$(\times +2)$	Inners:	$+2 \times x = +2x$	Lasts:	$2 \times -3 = -6$

$$\therefore (x+2)(x-3) = x^2 - 3x + 2x - 6 = x^2 - x - 6$$

Example 3 - Expand and simplify $(x-12)^2$.

Squaring a bracket means multiplying it by itself, so $(x-12)^2$ can be rewritten as two brackets:

$$(x-12)^2 = (x-12)(x-12)$$

This can be multiplied out in the same way as Example 2, to give:

$$(x-12)^2 = x^2 - 24x + 144$$

Expand and simplify the following:

14.6 (a) $3t(t-5)+2(t-5)$ (b) $(a+2)(a+3)$ (c) $(a-2)(a-7)$

14.7 (a) $(m+5)(m-2)$ (b) $(n-7)(n+3)$ (c) $(p-4)(p-9)$

14.8 (a) $(x+4)^2$ (b) $(n-2)^2$ (c) $(2p-5)^2$

14.9 (a) $(x+2)(x+0)$ (b) $(x-13)(x+13)$ (c) $(a+b)(a-b)$

14.10 (a) $(h+3)(h-3)$ (b) $(2x-1)(x+3)$ (c) $(3x+2)(5x-1)$

14.11 (a) $(2x+0)(5-3x)$ (c) $(\frac{1}{2}s+1)(\frac{1}{2}s-1)$
(b) $(pq+p^2)(pq+q^2)$ (d) $(2^n+2)(2^n-2)$

§ The same principle that lies behind the FOIL acronym also applies when multiplying out brackets containing more than two terms. First, multiply every term in the first bracket by every term in the second bracket separately, including the signs. Then collect like terms together and simplify the result.

Example 4 - Expand and simplify the expression $(x^2+x-5)(x-3)$.

To multiply out the brackets, multiply terms together separately, and then add up the results.

$(\times \quad x)$	$x^2 \times x = x^3$	$x \times x = x^2$	$-5 \times x = -5x$
$(\times -3)$	$x^2 \times -3 = -3x^2$	$x \times -3 = -3x$	$-5 \times -3 = 15$

$$(x^2+x-5)(x-3) = x^3+x^2-5x-3x^2-3x+15$$
$$(x^2+x-5)(x-3) = x^3-2x^2-8x+15$$

When it is necessary to expand more than two brackets, tackle the problem in stages. Multiply out and simplify one pair of brackets at a time.

Example 5 - Expand and simplify the expression $(2x-1)(x+2)(x-1)$.

Start by expanding and simplifying the $(x+2)$ and $(x-1)$ brackets.

$$(2x-1)(x+2)(x-1) = (2x-1)(x^2-x+2x-2)$$
$$(2x-1)(x+2)(x-1) = (2x-1)(x^2+x-2)$$

Now multiply out the $(2x-1)$ and (x^2+x-2) brackets.

$$(2x-1)(x+2)(x-1) = 2x^3+2x^2-4x-x^2-x+2$$
$$(2x-1)(x+2)(x-1) = 2x^3+x^2-5x+2$$

Expand and simplify the following:

14.12 (a) $(x+1)(x+2)(x+3)$ (c) $(x-3)(x-7)^2$
(b) $(x-5)(2x-a+4)$ (d) $(\frac{1}{x}+5)(3x^2-9)$

14.13 (a) $(2x-1)(x+2)(\frac{1}{2}-x)$ (c) $(\frac{1}{4}x+x^2)(4x+\frac{1}{x^2})$
(b) $5(2x+7)(3x-\frac{1}{2})(x+1)$ (d) $2(2x+1)(3x-7)^2$

14.14 (a) $(\sin x+7)(\cos x+\sin x)$
(b) $(\sin x-\cos x)(\sin x+\cos x)$

15 Factorising I: Common Factors

Factorising is the opposite of expanding brackets.

To factorise an expression such as $4ax + 2a$, start by identifying the factors that are common to every term. Take these factors outside a bracket, and leave everything else inside the bracket. Remember that 1 is a factor of any term, so if all the other factors are removed you are left with a 1. This is shown in Example 1(ii).

Example 1 – Factorise (i) $28bq - 21b$ (ii) $4ax + 2a$.

(i) 7 and b are factors of both terms. The common factor to take out is therefore $7b$. Hence, $28bq - 21b$ factorises to

$$28bq - 21b = 7 \times 4 \times b \times q - 7 \times 3 \times b = 7b(4q - 3)$$

(ii) 2 and a are factors of both terms. The common factor to take out is therefore $2a$. Hence, $4ax + 6a$ factorises to

$$4ax + 2a = 2a \times 2x + 2a \times 1 = 2a(2x + 1)$$

In some problems, it is necessary to expand brackets and collect terms before factorising:

Example 2 – Factorise $3(2 - x) + 5x + 4$.

First expand the bracket: $3(2 - x) + 5x + 4 = 6 - 3x + 5x + 4$

Next collect like terms: $3(2 - x) + 5x + 4 = 2x + 10$

Then take out common factors: $3(2 - x) + 5x + 4 = 2(x + 5)$

When factorising expressions which contain π, treat π in the same way as algebraic quantities like x or a.

Example 3 – Factorise $28\pi^2x^2 + 12\pi x$.

4, π and x are factors of both terms. The common factor to take out is therefore $4\pi x$. Hence, $28\pi^2x^2 + 12\pi x$ factorises to

$$28\pi^2x^2 + 12\pi x = 4\pi x \times 7\pi x + 4\pi x \times 3 = 4\pi x(7\pi x + 3)$$

Factorise and simplify the following as fully as possible.

15.1 (a) $6x-3$ (b) $2x^2+3x$ (c) $2(x+1)+3(x+1)$

15.2 (a) $5a-10b$ (b) $2x^2-4x$ (c) $3p+6pq$

15.3 (a) $4a+6b$ (b) $3a^3+6ab$ (c) $10ab^2c^2+15a^2bc$

15.4 (a) $2a^3b+4cd-10e$ (c) $6ST-3S^2+21ST$
(b) $pqr-2qr+3pr$

15.5 (a) $2ab^2+4ab$ (c) $5pqr^2+10r\times\frac{pqr}{2}+2pr$
(b) $6(2x+1)-3(x-1)+6$

15.6 Simplify as fully as possible, then factorise:
(a) $2(x+y)+3(x-y)+6y$ (b) $\frac{8-4x-4(x-2)}{2}$

15.7 Simplify then factorise:
(a) $\frac{\pi r^2}{r}+2\pi ra$ (b) $\frac{\lambda}{\theta}(\alpha\theta^2+\beta\theta^3)$

15.8 Simplify the following, factorising if possible:
(a) $3x^2\times 2a\times ax^3$ (c) $3c\times(\frac{1}{2}x)^2\times 8c^2x+4c^3$
(b) $7p\times\frac{1}{2}x^2\div\frac{p}{4}-7x$

15.9 (a) Evaluate $-n^4-n^3$ for $n=-2$.

(b) Factorise $-n^4-n^3$ as fully as possible.

(c) Use your answer to part (b) to evaluate the expression $-n^4-n^3$ for $n=5$.

15.10 Factorise as fully as possible:

(a) $x\times 5^2+x\times y\times 10^2$

(b) $2x\cos\theta-2x$

(c) $\pi(2r)^2h-\frac{4}{3}\pi r^2l$

16 Factorising II: Quadratic Expressions

A quadratic polynomial has the general form $ax^2 + bx + c$, where a, b and c are constants. Examples include:

$$x^2 + 2x + 1 \qquad -2p^2 + 3p \qquad 5y^2 - 1 \qquad \frac{3}{2}s^2 - \frac{1}{3}s + 17$$

To factorise a quadratic expression which has no constant term, such as $12x^2 + 9x$, start by identifying the common factor of both terms. This will include an x.

Example 1 – Factorise $12x^2 + 9x$.

The common factor of both terms is $3x$. $12x^2 + 9x$ factorises to

$$12x^2 + 9x = 3x \times 4x + 3x \times 3 = 3x(4x + 3)$$

Factorising a quadratic expression which includes a constant is the opposite of multiplying out a pair of brackets which each contain two terms (binomial brackets). Consider expanding the brackets $(x + 2)(x + 3)$:

$$(x + 2)(x + 3) = x^2 + 3x + 2x + 6 = x^2 + 5x + 6$$

- The coefficient of x in the answer is equal to the sum of the constants in the brackets, $(+5) = (+2) + (+3)$.
- The constant in the answer is equal to the product of the constants in the brackets, $(+6) = (+2) \times (+3)$.

These observations allow us to work backwards and turn a quadratic expression into a pair of brackets.

Example 2 – Factorise $x^2 - 4x - 12$.

We wish to turn this expression into a pair of brackets $(x + p)(x + q)$.

p and q multiply to give -12:
The magnitude (size) of this number tells us that the magnitudes of p and q are factors of 12. List the factors of 12 in ordered columns.

1	12
2	6
3	4

The sign of -12 is negative. In order for two numbers to multiply to give -12, one of them must be positive and one negative.

p and q add to give -4: This is a negative number, which tells us that the minus sign must go with the larger factor of 12. Put the "-" over the column of larger numbers in the factor table.	$+$	$-$
	1	12
	2	6
	3	4

Finally, find the row of the factor table which add up to give -4. This is the second row. This tells us that $p = 2$, and $q = -6$.

$$(+1) + (-12) = -11$$
$$(+2) + (-6) = -4$$
$$(+3) + (-4) = -1$$

The quadratic factorises as $x^2 - 4x - 12 = (x + 2)(x - 6)$

A quadratic expression such as $x^2 - 25$, where there is no linear term and the constant is subtracted, factorises to a pair of brackets $(x + p)(x - p)$. The reason for this is that terms in x automatically cancel when multiplying out brackets which differ only in central sign:

$$(x + p)(x - p) = x^2 - px + px - p^2 = x^2 - p^2$$

Due to the $x^2 - p^2$ here, expressions such as $x^2 - 25$ are said to have difference of two squares form.

Example 3 – Factorise $x^2 - 25$.

$$x^2 - 25 = x^2 - p^2 \quad \Rightarrow p^2 = 25 \quad \Rightarrow p = 5$$
$$\therefore x^2 - 25 = (x + 5)(x - 5)$$

Factorise the following expressions.

16.1 (a) $x^2 + x$ (b) $x^2 - 2x$ (c) $6x^2 - 21x$

16.2 (a) $3x^2 - 15x$ (b) $2x + 4x^2$ (c) $10x - 15x^2$

16.3 (a) $a^2 + 7a + 6$ (b) $a^2 + 3a - 40$ (c) $a^2 - 11a + 24$

16.4 (a) $c^2 + 9c + 20$ (b) $b^2 + 3b - 18$ (c) $c^2 + 15c + 36$

16.5 (a) $p^2 - 10p + 21$ (b) $r^2 + 2r - 48$ (c) $s^2 + 11s - 80$

16.6 (a) $p^2 - 4$ (b) $r^2 - 36$ (c) $2m^2 - 32$

16.7 (a) $x^2 - 9x - 22$ (b) $B^2 - 8B + 16$ (c) $25 - y^2$

16.8 (a) $x^2 + 2x + 1$ (b) $x^2 + 10x + 25$ (c) $x^2 - 18x + 81$

16.9 Without calculating either 23^2 or 17^2, find the value of $23^2 - 17^2$.

§ Factorising a quadratic expression with both constant and linear terms is more difficult when the co-efficient of x^2 is not equal to 1.

Example 4 – Factorise $6x^2 - 11x - 10$.

We wish to turn this expression into a pair of brackets $(rx + p)(sx + q)$.

First, consider the $6x^2$ term. The only contribution to this is $rx \times sx$. Therefore, $r \times s = 6$. Hence r and s are either 1 & 6, or 2 & 3.

Next, consider the constant -10. The only contribution to this is $p \times q$. Therefore, $p \times q = -10$. The "$-$" tells us p and q have opposite signs. p and q are -1 & 10, 1 & -10, -2 & 5 or 2 & -5.

Finally, consider the $-11x$ term. There are two contributions to this, $rx \times q$ and $p \times sx$. Therefore, $rq + sp = -11$. Combine pairings of r and s with pairings of p and q to find one which satisfies this equation. The combination $r = 2$ & $s = 3$, $p = -5$ & $q = 2$ works.

$$\therefore 6x^2 - 11x - 10 = (2x - 5)(3x + 2)$$

Finally, check the answer by multiplying out:

$$(2x - 5)(3x + 2) = 6x^2 + 4x - 15x - 10 = 6x^2 - 11x - 10 \quad \checkmark$$

Quadratic expressions in difference of two squares form can factorise to a pair of brackets where the constants in the brackets are surds.

Example 5 – Factorise $x^2 - 6$.

$$x^2 - 6 = x^2 - p^2 \qquad \Rightarrow p^2 = 6 \qquad \Rightarrow p = \sqrt{6}$$
$$\therefore x^2 - 6 = (x + \sqrt{6})(x - \sqrt{6})$$

Take out a common factor and then factorise fully.

16.10 (a) $3a^2 + 18a + 15$ (b) $2a^2 + 12a + 18$ (c) $2a^2 + 4a - 30$

Factorise the following expressions.

16.11 (a) $2a^2 + 5a - 12$ (b) $6a^2 - 19a + 10$ (c) $20a^2 + 6a - 8$

16.12 (a) $4p^2 - 9$ (b) $p^2 - 5$ (c) $16p^2 - 200$ (d) $7p^2 - 3$

16.13 (a) $\frac{x^2}{3} + \frac{2x}{3} + \frac{1}{3}$ (c) $3\pi x^2 + 14\pi x - 5\pi$

(b) $x^2 - \frac{1}{2}x - 3$ (d) $(\sin\theta)^2 - 4\sin\theta + 4$

17 Re-arranging and Changing the Subject

Changing the subject of an equation or formula means re-arranging until the variable chosen to be the subject is on its own. This gives an equation or formula that can be used to find the value of the subject.

The order of operations when rearranging is is equivalent to applying BIDMAS in reverse order: start with "undoing" addition and subtraction, and work through BIDMAS backwards, keeping brackets until last. Finally, simplify the result if possible.

Example 1 - Re-arrange the formula $v = u + at$ to make t the subject.

Calculating v from t involves multiplying t by a, then adding u. To make t the subject, these operations are undone in reverse order. First u is subtracted from both sides, then both sides are divided by a.

$$v = u + at$$

↓ Subtract u from both sides.

$$v - u = u + at - u$$

$$v - u = at$$

↓ Divide both sides by a.

$$\frac{v-u}{a} = \frac{at}{a}$$

$$\frac{v-u}{a} = t$$

$$\Rightarrow t = \frac{v-u}{a}$$

Finally, write the formula the other way round so that it is in the form $t = \dots$.

17.1 Rearrange $V = E - Ir$:

(a) To make E the subject. (b) To make I the subject.

17.2 (a) Rearrange $m = 3 + 2n$ to make n the subject.

(b) Expand and simplify $p = 4(2s - r) - 5r$.

(c) Rearrange your answer to part (b) to make s the subject.

17.3 (a) Rearrange $y = mx + c$ to make x the subject.

(b) Simplify the following: $Q = (5p + 2) - 2(p - 3) - 4$.

(c) Rearrange your answer to part (b) to make p the subject.

17.4 It is given that $y = 2x - 13$.

(a) Re-arrange this equation to make x the subject.

(b) If $x = 4$, find y.

(c) Find the value of x if $y = -43$.

17.5 For the formula $F = BIl$, F is measured in Newtons (N), B is measured in Teslas (T), I is measured in Amps (A) and l is measured in metres.

(a) Find F if $B = 0.19$ T, $I = 0.50$ A and $l = 1.2$ m.

(b) Find B if $F = 0.36$ N, $I = 3.0$ A and $l = 2.0$ m.

17.6 Re-arrange $F = \frac{GMm}{r^2}$ to give an expression for

(a) m (b) r

Problems which involve circles or spheres often produce formulae which include π. When re-arranging these formulae, π can be treated like any other algebraic letter.

Example 2 - Re-arrange the formula for the volume of a sphere, $V = \frac{4}{3}\pi r^3$ to make r the subject.

$$V = \frac{4}{3}\pi r^3$$

↓ Multiply both sides by 3.

$$3V = 4\pi r^3$$

↓ Divide both sides by 4.

$$\frac{3V}{4} = \pi r^3$$

↓ Divide both sides by π.

$$\frac{3V}{4\pi} = r^3$$

$$\therefore r^3 = \frac{3V}{4\pi} \quad \Rightarrow r = \sqrt[3]{\frac{3V}{4\pi}}$$

Exchange sides so r^3 is on the left, then take the cube root of both sides.

17.7 The surface area A of a sphere is given by $A = 4\pi r^2$, where r is the radius.

(a) Rearrange the formula to make r the subject.

(b) If $A = 4$ cm^2 find r to 2 decimal places, stating the units.

17.8 Re-arrange $s = ut + \frac{1}{2}at^2$ to give an expression for

(a) u (b) a

17.9 The cooking time for a type of pudding is "40 minutes per kilo and then 30 minutes extra." Let T be the cooking time in minutes.

(a) Write an equation for T in terms of the mass m in kilograms.

(b) If $m = 500$ g what is the cooking time?

(c) A pudding was cooked for 1 hour 20 minutes. What was its mass in kg?

17.10 "Fahrenheit" and "Centigrade" are two scales for measuring temperature.

(a) Using C and F for temperatures in Centigrade and Fahrenheit, write a conversion formula according to the following instructions: To find a Centigrade reading, take the measurement in Fahrenheit, subtract 32, and then take $\frac{5}{9}$ths of that value.

(b) Use your formula to convert a Fahrenheit reading of 98.4 to Centigrade, giving your answer to 3 sf.

(c) Re-arrange your formula to convert Centigrade readings into Fahrenheit.

(d) Convert 50.0 Centigrade into Fahrenheit.

When changing the subject of a formula, if the variable that is to become the new subject appears more than once, a factorisation step may be required.

Example 3 - Re-arrange $A = 3r + 2\pi r$ to make r the subject.

$$A = 3r + 2\pi r$$
$$A = r(3 + 2\pi)$$

r appears twice on the right hand side. In order to make r the subject, we need to factorise so that r only appears once.

$$\Rightarrow r = \frac{A}{3 + 2\pi}$$

Then, divide both sides by $(3 + 2\pi)$, and write the formula in the form $r = \ldots$.

17.11 It is given that $y = (x - 3)^3 + 4$.

(a) Re-arrange the original equation to make x the subject.

(b) Find the value(s) of x corresponding to a y-value of 31.

17.12 (a) Re-arrange the formula $P = \sigma A T^4$ to make T the subject.

(b) Temperature measured in Kelvin, T, is related to temperature measured in Centigrade, C, by the formula $T = C + 273$. A beaker of liquid is heated by 35 °C from 20 °C. What is the final temperature of the liquid in Kelvin?

17.13 This is a formula for calculating the area of a complicated shape:

$$A = \frac{5}{2}\pi r^2 + 2bh + \frac{3}{2}b(h+2)$$

(a) Find A when $r = 20$ cm, $b = 10$ cm and $h = 15$ cm.

(b) Find r in terms of π if $A = 60\ \text{cm}^2$, $b = 2$ cm and $h = 3$ cm.

17.14 The table below shows population density figures for the UK in 2019.

Nation / Country	Population (Millions)	Land Area (km^2)	Population Density (People / km^2)
The UK	67	244 000	A
England	56	B	432
Scotland	C	77 000	70
Wales	3.1	D	152
Northern Ireland	1.9	E	137

$$\text{Population density} = \frac{\text{Population}}{\text{Land Area}}$$

Use the formula and the information in the table to find the values of the five missing figures A to E. Give your answers to 2 sf.

17.15 Simplify and re-arrange the following to make the stated variable the subject.

(a) $c^2 = 4 - 2t; t$

(b) $6 - t^3 = 4p - 3; t$

(c) $3x + y = 6xy^2 - (2 + x); x$

(d) $4y = 3x^3 + y + 4; x$

18 Formula Triangles

Formula triangles can be used to save time re-arranging formulae which involve exactly three quantities in a relationship of the form $a = b \times c$. These formulae can always be rearranged algebraically using the method in the previous chapter. Here are some common formula triangles:

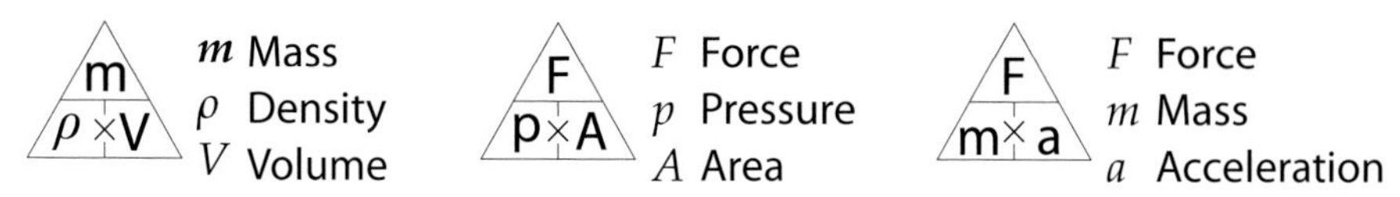

Note: Some books write formula triangles with a vertical line on the bottom instead of a multiplication symbol. The meaning is the same.

To find a formula from a formula triangle, cover up the quantity to be found. The pattern of the remaining letters shows how to calculate this quantity.

Example 1 - Use the formula triangle relating mass m, density ρ and volume V to write formulae for each of the three quantities in terms of the other two.

m
ρ × V

$$\rho = \frac{m}{V} \qquad m = \rho \times V \qquad V = \frac{m}{\rho}$$

When performing a calculation using a formula triangle, it is necessary to make sure that the units you are using are consistent.

Example 2 - Find the volume of a block of steel which has a mass of 0.156 kg and a density of 7.8 g/cm^3.

There is a mixture of units of mass in the question (g and kg). We will choose to do the calculation in grams. 0.156 kg = 156 g.

$$V = \frac{m}{\rho} = \frac{156}{7.8} = 20 \text{ cm}^3$$

18.1 Using the mass-density-volume triangle, or otherwise, find:

(a) ρ in g/cm^3 if $m = 200$ g and $V = 25$ cm^3.

(b) m in g if $\rho = 10$ g/cm^3 and $V = 10$ cm^3.

(c) V in cm^3 if $m = 0.54$ g and $\rho = 6$ g/cm^3.

18.2 Using the mass-density-volume triangle, or otherwise, find:

(a) The density in g/cm^3 if $m = 0.045$ kg and $V = 2.5$ cm^3.

(b) The volume in cm^3 if $m = 50$ g, $\rho = 4\,000$ kg/m^3.

(c) The mass in kg if $\rho = 7\,500$ kg/m^3 and $V = 1\,000$ cm^3.

18.3 Using a formula triangle, or otherwise, find:

(a) The pressure in N/m^2 exerted by a force of 16.2 N on an area of 1.50 m^2.

(b) The force in Newtons (N) required to maintain a pressure of 15.0 N/m^2 on an area of 0.150 m^2.

(c) The area in cm^2 of a surface which experiences a pressure of 11.3 N/cm^2 from a uniformly applied force of 4.52 kN.

It is also possible to write your own formula triangles.

18.4 Write the following formulae as formula triangles.

(a) $V = IR$ (b) $v = s/t$ (c) $\frac{P}{V} = I$

18.5 Which of these formulae can be written as a formula triangle? Write a formula triangle where it is possible.

(a) $v = u + at$ (b) $\frac{Q}{C} = V$ (c) $L = a - b$

(d) Magnification, $M = \frac{\text{Image size, } i}{\text{Object size, } o}$

18.6 The concentration of salt in water, C g/cm^3, is found by dividing the mass of salt in grams, m, by the volume of water in cm^3, V.

(a) Create a formula triangle for concentration, mass and volume.

(b) Write a formula for volume in terms of mass and concentration.

(c) Find the volume of a solution with concentration 0.0020 g/cm^3 if the total mass of salt dissolved is 2.4 g.

(d) Write a formula for m in terms of C and V.

(e) Find m if $V = 1$ litre and $C = 0.004$ g/cm^3.

19 Sequences

A sequence is an ordered list of values related by a rule. In sequence notation, $\mathsf{T}(1)$ is the value of the first term in the sequence, $\mathsf{T}(2)$ the value of the second term, and so on. Using n for the position of a term within a sequence, $\mathsf{T}(n)$ is the value of the nth term.

A term-to-term description of a sequence explains how to calculate the value of a term from the value of the previous term (or terms).

Example 1 – For the sequence $1, 4, 7, 10, 13, ...$, the term-to-term description is:

$$\mathsf{T}(1) = 1, \quad \mathsf{T}(n) = \mathsf{T}(n-1) + 3$$

The value of the first term is 1: $\mathsf{T}(1) = 1$.

The value of each term is greater than the previous term by $+3$.
$\mathsf{T}(2) = \mathsf{T}(1) + 3$, $\mathsf{T}(3) = \mathsf{T}(2) + 3$, and so on. The value of the nth term is 3 greater than the $(n-1)^{\text{th}}$ term: $\mathsf{T}(n) = \mathsf{T}(n-1) + 3$.

A position-to-term description of a sequence explains how to calculate the value of a term from its position in the list, n.

Example 2 – For the sequence $1, 4, 7, 10, 13, ...$, the position-to-term description is:

$$\mathsf{T}(n) = 3n - 2$$

The value of the first term is: $\mathsf{T}(1) = 3 \times 1 - 2 = 1$.
The value of the second term is: $\mathsf{T}(2) = 3 \times 2 - 2 = 4$. And so on.

There are a number of standard sequences to know. These include:

The squared numbers: $1, 4, 9, 16, 25, 36, 49, 64, 81...$
Each term is the square of its position in the sequence, $\mathsf{T}(n) = n^2$.

The cubed numbers: $1, 8, 27, 64, 125, 216, ...$
Each term is the cube of its position in the sequence, $\mathsf{T}(n) = n^3$.

The Fibonacci Sequence: $1, 1, 2, 3, 5, 8, 13, 21, 34, 55, ...$
Each term is the sum of the two previous terms,

$$\mathsf{T}(1) = 1, \ \mathsf{T}(2) = 1, \quad \mathsf{T}(n) = \mathsf{T}(n-1) + \mathsf{T}(n-2)$$

The triangular numbers: $1, 3, 6, 10, 15, 21, 28, \ldots$

To get from one term in the sequence to the next add n (the position of the new term) to the value of the previous term.

$$\mathrm{T}(1) = 1, \ \mathrm{T}(n) = \mathrm{T}(n-1) + n \qquad \mathrm{T}(n) = \frac{1}{2}n(n+1)$$

19.1 Find the missing terms in these sequences:

(a) $4, 6, 8, ?, 12, ?$ (b) $1, 4, ?, ?, 25, 36$ (c) $1, ?, 2, 3, 5, ?, 13$

19.2 Find the missing terms in these sequences:

(a) $1, 8, ?, 64, ?, 216$ (b) $4, 7, 10, 13, ?, ?, 22$ (c) $2, ?, 8, ?, 32, 64$

19.3 Find the first 5 terms of these sequences from the rules for the nth terms:

(a) $\mathrm{T}(n) = n$ (b) $\mathrm{T}(n) = 2n + 3$ (c) $\mathrm{T}(n) = 5 - 3n$

19.4 Find terms two to six of the sequences given by these term-to-term rules:

(a) $\mathrm{T}(1) = 6, \ \mathrm{T}(n) = \mathrm{T}(n-1) + 3$

(b) $\mathrm{T}(1) = 3, \ \mathrm{T}(n) = \mathrm{T}(n-1) - 2$

(c) $\mathrm{T}(1) = 2, \ \mathrm{T}(n) = 2\mathrm{T}(n-1)$

19.5 Generate the first four terms of the sequences described by the following rules for the nth term:

(a) $\mathrm{T}(n) = 2n^3$ (b) $\mathrm{T}(n) = (n+1)^2$ (c) $\mathrm{T}(n) = \frac{1}{2}n(n+1)$

In an arithmetic sequence (also called an arithmetic progression), to go from one term to the next the same numerical constant is added on each time. This constant is called the common difference.

Example 3 – The table shows the start of an arithmetic sequence. $\mathrm{T}(n)$ is the value of the term at position n in the sequence. Find an expression for the nth term, $\mathrm{T}(n)$.

n	1	2	3	4	5	6	7	8
$\mathrm{T}(n)$	3	5	7	9	11	13	15	17

Each term in the sequence is greater than the previous term by $+2$. Therefore make a table of multiples of 2.

n	1	2	3	4	5	6	7	8
$2n$	2	4	6	8	10	12	14	16

Now compare the multiples of 2 with the terms of $\mathsf{T}(n)$. Each term in $\mathsf{T}(n)$ is greater than the corresponding term in $2n$ by $+1$.

n	1	2	3	4	5	6	7	8
$2n$	2	4	6	8	10	12	14	16
$2n+1$	3	5	7	9	11	13	15	17

Therefore the nth term of $\mathsf{T}(n)$ is equal to $2n+1$, $\quad \mathsf{T}(n) = 2n+1$.

In a geometric sequence (also called a geometric progression), to go from one term to the next involves multiplication by the same numerical constant each time. This constant is called the common ratio.

Example 4 – A geometric sequence begins $5, 15, 45, 135, 405, \ldots$.
Find term-to-term and position-to-term expressions for the value of the nth term in the sequence.

(i) Each term in the sequence is equal to $3\times$ the previous term.
$\therefore \mathsf{T}(n) = 3 \times \mathsf{T}(n-1)$, with the first term $\mathsf{T}(1) = 5$.

(ii) The value of the first term is 5. To get to the nth term from the first term involves multiplication by 3, $(n-1)$ times.
$\therefore \mathsf{T}(n) = 5 \times 3^{n-1}$.

19.6 Find the missing terms in these sequences:
(a) $3, 7, 11, ?, ?, 23$ (b) $7, 5, 3, ?, -1, ?$ (c) $6, 2, -2, ?, -10, ?$

19.7 Find the missing terms in these sequences:
(a) $6, 12, 24, ?, 96, ?$ (b) $?, 6, 18, 54, ?$ (c) $\frac{1}{2}, ?, 2, ?, 8, 16$

19.8 For each sequence, find
(i) the term-to-term rule (ii) the position-to-term rule.
(a) $5, 7, 9, 11, 13$ (b) $9, 5, 1, -3, -7$

19.9 For each sequence, find
(i) the term-to-term rule (ii) the position-to-term rule.
(a) $1, 3, 9, 27, 81$ (b) $4, 8, 16, 32, 64$

19.10 For each sequence, find
(i) the next two terms in the sequence
(ii) the term-to-term rule
(iii) the position-to-term rule.
(a) $6, 12, 18, 24, 30$ (b) $-1, -4, -16, -64, -256$

§ The differences between the terms of a sequence are called first differences, and the differences between first differences are called second differences. In a quadratic sequence such as $7, 19, 39, 67, 103, \ldots$, the first differences follow an arithmetic progression and the second differences all have the same value.

A general formula for the nth term of a quadratic sequence is $\mathrm{T}(n) = an^2 + bn + c$, where a is equal to half the second difference value.

Example 5 – Find the nth term of the sequence $7, 19, 39, 67, 103, \ldots$.

Find the first and second differences:

n	1	2	3	4	5
$\mathrm{T}(n)$	7	19	39	67	103

+12 +20 +28 +36 First differences

+8 +8 +8 Second differences

The value of the second differences is $+8$. a in the formula for the nth term is equal to half of this value. $\therefore a = 4$, and $\mathrm{T}(n) = 4n^2 + bn + c$.

To find b and c, write the first two terms of the sequence in terms of b and c and solve these equations simultaneously.

$\mathrm{T}(1) = 4(1)^2 + b(1) + c = 7 \quad \Rightarrow 4 + b + c = 7 \quad \Rightarrow b + c = 3$

$\mathrm{T}(2) = 4(2)^2 + b(2) + c = 19 \quad \Rightarrow 16 + 2b + c = 19 \quad \Rightarrow 2b + c = 3$

Subtracting $b + c = 3$ from $2b + c = 3$ gives $b = 0$, and substituting this into $b + c = 3$ gives $c = 3$. Therefore, $\mathrm{T}(n) = 4n^2 + 3$.

19.11 Find the missing terms in these sequences:

(a) $\frac{1}{2}, \frac{1}{4}, \frac{1}{8}, ?, ?$ (b) $4, 6, 9, \frac{27}{2}, ?, ?$ (c) $\frac{27}{4}, ?, 3, 2, ?, \frac{8}{9}$

19.12 Find the missing terms in these sequences:

(a) $8, ?, 14, 17, ?$ (b) $\frac{1}{3}, -\frac{1}{6}, \frac{1}{12}, ?, \frac{1}{48}, ?$ (c) $\frac{1}{3}, -\frac{1}{9}, ?, ?, \frac{1}{243}, -\frac{1}{729}$

19.13 Find the missing terms in these sequences:

(a) $1, \sqrt{2}, ?, 2\sqrt{2}, 4, ?$ (c) $12, -4\sqrt{3}, ?, \frac{-4}{\sqrt{3}}, \frac{4}{3}, ?$

(b) $3, \frac{3}{\sqrt{2}}, ?, \frac{3}{2\sqrt{2}}, ?, \frac{3}{4\sqrt{2}}$

19.14 For each of these quadratic sequences, find -

(i) the next two terms in the sequence

(ii) the position-to-term rule.

(a) $3, 6, 11, 18, 27$ (b) $4, 21, 48, 85, 132$ (c) $66, 45, 28, 15, 6$

19.15 The diagram shows a spiral construction. Each triangle has two 45° angles. The areas of the triangles form the start of a sequence, and the area of the first triangle is $A_1 = \frac{1}{2}$.

(a) What are the values of the second and third terms in the sequence, A_2 and A_3?

(b) Write down a formula for the area A_n in terms of n.

(c) What is the total area of the first 8 terms in the sequence?

19.16 The diagram below shows the first four triangles in a sequence. A_n is the area of the nth triangle in the sequence.

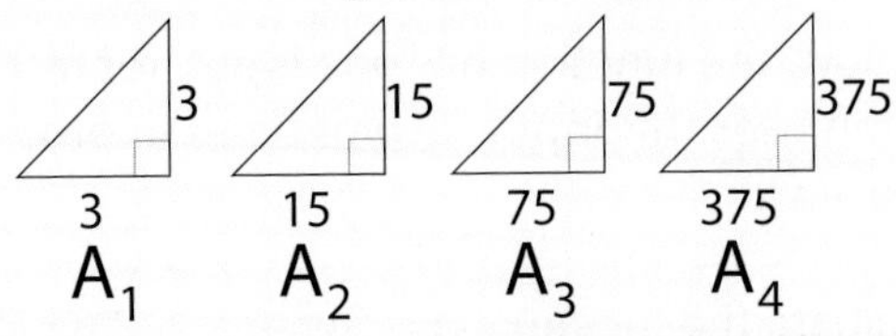

(a) Find the areas of the first four triangles in the sequence.

(b) Find a formula for the area of the nth term in the sequence.

20 Functions

A function is a set of instructions for turning one number (the input) into another (the output). Functions have only one possible output for each input. Functions can be illustrated using number (function) machines.

Example 1 – The diagram below shows a number machine which turns an input x into an output y. The input is first multiplied by 2, then 5 is subtracted.

$x \rightarrow$ [×2] $\rightarrow$ [-5] $\rightarrow y$

(i) Find the output when the input is 6
The output is $(6 \times 2) - 5 = 12 - 5 = 7.$

(ii) Find an equation for y in terms of x.
The output of the function is $y = 2x - 5.$

There are several ways to write a function, each of which means something slightly different:

$x \longrightarrow 2x + 4$	• When the input is x, the output is $2x + 4.$
$y = 2x + 4$	• When the input is x, the output is $2x + 4.$ y is equal to the output.
$f(x) = 2x + 4$	• When the input is x, the output of the function named "f" is $2x + 4.$

The trigonometric function $\sin(\theta)$ is an example of a function written in $f(x)$ form. $\sin$ is the function name, and θ is the value of the input.

In the example below, the function has one input, represented by the variable x. The function uses this input several times in producing the output (the terms $3x^2$ and $-x$).

Example 2 – Evaluate the function $y = 3x^2 - x - 3$ when $x = 2.$

$$y = 3(2)^2 - 2 - 3 = 3 \times 4 - 2 - 3 = 12 - 2 - 3 = 7$$

Example 3 – For $s = 5$, evaluate (i) $s \longrightarrow 3 - s^2$ and (ii) $g(s) = \frac{20}{5+s}$.

(i) When $s = 5$, the value of the function is $3 - (5)^2 = 3 - 25 = -22$.

(ii) $g(5) = \frac{20}{5+5} = \frac{20}{10} = 2$

20.1 Find the value of the function $y = x + 3$ when:
(a) $x = 2$ (b) $x = -3$ (c) $x = \frac{1}{3}$

20.2 (a) Draw a number machine to illustrate the function $y = 3x - 4$.
Find the value of the function $y = 3x - 4$ when:
(b) $x = 5$ (c) $x = 1$ (d) $x = -5$

20.3 (a) Construct a number machine to calculate y given that $y = 5(2x + 3) + 1$.
Find the values of this function when:
(b) $x = 3$ (c) $x = 0$ (d) $x = -1$

20.4 Evaluate the function $y = \frac{1}{4}x^2 + \frac{1}{4}$ for
(a) $x = 1$ (b) $x = 2$ (c) $x = -2$

20.5 Evaluate $s \longrightarrow \frac{1}{s} + s$ for
(a) $s = 1$ (b) $s = 5$ (c) $s = 2$

20.6 Evaluate $t \longrightarrow \frac{t^2}{1+t^2}$ for:
(a) $t = 1$ (b) $t = 0$ (c) $t = -2$

20.7 Find the values of these functions when $x = 2$.
(a) $f(x) = 5x + 1$ (c) $h(x) = x^3 + x^2 + x + 1$
(b) $g(x) = x^2 - 3x + 7$

20.8 Evaluate $Q(R) = \frac{4}{R^2} - \frac{1}{R} + 2$ for:
(a) $R = 2$ (b) $R = 4$ (c) $R = \frac{1}{2}$

20.9 Find the values of $u(t) = 3 \sin t$ for:
(a) $t = 90°$ (b) $t = 180°$ (c) $t = 30°$

20.10 Find the values of x such that $x \longrightarrow 2x + 6$ has a value of
(a) 10 (b) -10

20.11 Find the values of y, such that $y \longrightarrow \frac{y}{2} + \frac{3}{2}$ has a value of
(a) 2 (b) 6

20.12 Find the values of r, such that $V(r) = \frac{18}{r}$ has a value of
(a) 6 (b) $\frac{1}{2}$

20.13 $x \rightarrow$ [+2] $\rightarrow$ [×2] $\rightarrow$ [-3] $\rightarrow y$

(a) Use the number machine to find y when (i) $x = 2$ (ii) $x = -4$.
(b) Find the value of x that produces a y value of 25.

§ An inverse function is essentially using a function machine running in reverse. The inverse operations are carried out, in the reverse order.

Example 4 – For the function machine below, write an equation to represent (i) the function (ii) the inverse function.

$x \rightarrow$ [×3] $\rightarrow$ [+2] $\rightarrow$ [÷5] $\rightarrow y$

The diagram tells us that in this problem the input to the machine is called x, and the output is called y.

x ×3 → +2 → ÷5 → y

(i) The input is on the left. The (forwards) function works from left to right. First the input is multiplied by 3, then 2 is added, then the result is divided by 5. This gives $y = \frac{3x+2}{5}$.

y ← ÷3 ← -2 ← ×5 x

(ii) In the inverse function the input x is put into the machine from the right hand side. The machine is run in reverse from right to left. First the input is multiplied by 5, then 2 is subtracted, then the result is divided by 3. This gives for the output $y = \frac{5x-2}{3}$.

When a function is written in $f(x)$ form, the inverse is indicated by a superscript $^{-1}$ between the name of the function and the bracket containing the variable. For example, the inverse of $\sin(x)$ is written $\sin^{-1}(x)$.

A composite function is where the output of one function is used as the input to a second function.

Example 5 – The diagram shows a composite function where the output of function A is used as the input of function B.

$$x \rightarrow \underbrace{\boxed{+4}}_{A} \rightarrow (x+4) \rightarrow \underbrace{\boxed{\div 3} \rightarrow \boxed{+5}}_{B} \rightarrow \frac{(x+4)}{3}+5$$

Brackets are used here to indicate that the whole of $(x+4)$ is used as the input to function B. The output of function B could be tidied up at the end to give $\frac{(x+4)}{3}+5=\frac{1}{3}x+\frac{4}{3}+5=\frac{1}{3}x+6\frac{1}{3}$.

A composite function made up of a function and its inverse has the property that the output is always equal to the input. The operations in the inverse function effectively "undo" the operations in the original function.

20.14 $x \rightarrow \boxed{+1} \rightarrow \boxed{\times 4} \rightarrow \boxed{-5} \rightarrow y$

(a) Write an equation for the function represented by this number machine.

(b) Write an equation for the inverse function.

(c) Evaluate the inverse function to find y when $x=11$.

20.15 $x \rightarrow \boxed{-1} \rightarrow \boxed{\times 7} \rightarrow \boxed{+3} \rightarrow y$

(a) For this number machine, write an equation for the function. Simplify your equation as far as possible.

(b) Using the number machine, find an equation for the inverse function. Simplify this equation as far as possible.

(c) For the inverse function, what value of x gives a y value of 24?

20.16 The composite function $h(x)$ uses the output of function A as the input to function B. Find an expression for $h(x)$ when

(a) Function A is "divide the input by four"; function B is "add 2 to the input, then multiply by 5".

(b) Function A is "multiply by 2, then subtract 3"; function B is "divide by 5, then subtract 1".

(c) Function A is "multiply by 2, then subtract 3"; function B is "add 3, then divide by 2".

21 § Surds and Rationalising a Denominator

Square numbers such as 4, 16 and 25 have integer square roots. The square roots of the other positive integers are irrational.

Surds are expressions that include an instruction to take a root which has an irrational answer. Examples are $\sqrt{2}$, $5\sqrt{3}$ and $\sqrt[3]{11}$. Keeping $\sqrt{}$ signs in an answer keeps the answer exact.

Square roots can be simplified when the number under the root sign has a factor which is a square number.

Example 1 – Simplify $\sqrt{18}$.

$$\sqrt{18} = \sqrt{9 \times 2} = \sqrt{3^2 \times 2} = \sqrt{3^2} \times \sqrt{2} = 3\sqrt{2}$$

When two surds are multiplied together, the numbers in front of the square root signs multiply, and the numbers under the square root signs multiply.

Example 2 – Simplify $2\sqrt{3} \times 5\sqrt{7}$.

$$2\sqrt{3} \times 5\sqrt{7} = 10\sqrt{21}$$

When two surds are divided, the numbers in front of the square root signs are divided, and the numbers under the square root signs are divided.

Example 3 – Simplify $5\sqrt{3} \div 10\sqrt{7}$.

There are two equivalent ways of writing this,

$$5\sqrt{3} \div 10\sqrt{7} = \frac{5}{10}\sqrt{\frac{3}{7}} = \frac{1}{2}\sqrt{\frac{3}{7}} \quad \text{or} \quad 5\sqrt{3} \div 10\sqrt{7} = \frac{5\sqrt{3}}{10\sqrt{7}} = \frac{1}{2}\sqrt{\frac{3}{7}}$$

Addition and subtraction of surds is only possible when the number under the square root is the same. An initial simplification step may be needed.

Example 4 – Calculate $5\sqrt{32} + 8\sqrt{2}$

$$5\sqrt{32} = 5\sqrt{16 \times 2} = 5\sqrt{16}\sqrt{2} = 5 \times 4\sqrt{2} = 20\sqrt{2}$$

$$\therefore 5\sqrt{32} + 8\sqrt{2} = 20\sqrt{2} + 8\sqrt{2} = 28\sqrt{2}$$

These rules apply in a similar way when combining cube roots. When multiplying or dividing roots of a different type, such as a square root and a cube root, the numbers in front of the roots can be combined but the roots cannot. For example, $2\sqrt[3]{7} \times 5\sqrt[4]{6}$ cannot be simplified further than $10\sqrt[3]{7}\sqrt[4]{6}$.

Simplify as far as possible.

21.1 (a) $\sqrt{2} \times \sqrt{2}$ (b) $(2\sqrt{3})^2$ (c) $5\sqrt{5} \times 2\sqrt{2}$

21.2 (a) $\frac{\sqrt{5}}{\sqrt{20}}$ (b) $\frac{7\sqrt{7}}{\sqrt{56}}$ (c) $\frac{-2\sqrt{11}}{\sqrt{44}}$

21.3 (a) $\sqrt{6} \times \sqrt{12}$ (b) $\sqrt{2} \times \sqrt{6} \times \sqrt{15}$ (c) $\frac{\sqrt{51}\sqrt{34}}{\sqrt{6}}$

21.4 (a) $\sqrt{\frac{27}{4}}$ (b) $\sqrt{\frac{7}{36}}$ (c) $3\sqrt{\frac{54}{243}}$

21.5 (a) $\sqrt{8} \times \sqrt{20}$ (b) $\sqrt{27} \times \sqrt{30}$ (c) $\frac{9\sqrt{75}}{\sqrt{15}}$

21.6 (a) $2\sqrt{3} \times \sqrt{21}$ (b) $(5\sqrt{7}) \times 2\sqrt{14}$ (c) $4\sqrt{33} \div 2\sqrt{27}$

21.7 (a) $\frac{3\sqrt{5}\times 2\sqrt{2}}{4\sqrt{30}}$ (b) $\frac{5\sqrt{10}\times 2\sqrt{20}}{4\sqrt{2}}$ (c) $\frac{2\sqrt{6}\times 4\sqrt{12}}{2\sqrt{2}}$

Expand the following, and simplify where possible.

21.8 (a) $(\sqrt{2}+\sqrt{7})(\sqrt{3}-\sqrt{7})$ (c) $(\sqrt{2}+\sqrt{7})(\sqrt{2}-\sqrt{7})$
(b) $(\sqrt{5}-2\sqrt{3})(\sqrt{5}-3\sqrt{3})$ (d) $(\sqrt{5}-2\sqrt{3})^2$

21.9 (a) $(3\sqrt{2}+5\sqrt{2})(3\sqrt{2}-2\sqrt{5})$ (c) $(2\sqrt{5}+5\sqrt{2})^2$
(b) $(\sqrt{5}-2\sqrt{3})(\sqrt{5}-2\sqrt{3})$ (d) $8(\sqrt{6}+2\sqrt{3})(\sqrt{6}-3\sqrt{3})$

When a fraction has a surd in the denominator, the value of the denominator is irrational. Rationalising the denominator means finding an equivalent fraction without a surd in the denominator. There are two cases.

The first case is fractions with denominators of the form $a\sqrt{b}$, such as $\frac{10}{3\sqrt{5}}$. These fractions can be rationalised by multiplying by $\frac{\sqrt{b}}{\sqrt{b}}$.

Example 5 - Rationalise the denominator of $\frac{10}{3\sqrt{3}}$.

Multiply the fraction by $\frac{\sqrt{3}}{\sqrt{3}}$.

$$\frac{10}{3\sqrt{3}} = \frac{10}{3\sqrt{3}} \times \frac{\sqrt{3}}{\sqrt{3}} = \frac{10 \times \sqrt{3}}{3\sqrt{3} \times \sqrt{3}} = \frac{10 \times \sqrt{3}}{3 \times 3} = \frac{10 \times \sqrt{3}}{9} = \frac{10\sqrt{3}}{9}$$

The second case is fractions with denominators of the form $a + b\sqrt{c}$, such as $\frac{3+2\sqrt{7}}{2+5\sqrt{7}}$. To understand how to rationalise denominators of this form, first consider multiplying out a pair of binomial brackets which differ only in the sign of one of the terms:

$$(x+y)(x-y) = x^2 - y^2$$

The result is the difference of two squares. This is rational even if one or both of x and y are surds. For example,

$$(\sqrt{5}+\sqrt{3})(\sqrt{5}-\sqrt{3}) = (\sqrt{5})^2 - \sqrt{5}\sqrt{3} + \sqrt{5}\sqrt{3} - (\sqrt{3})^2$$
$$\Rightarrow (\sqrt{5}+\sqrt{3})(\sqrt{5}-\sqrt{3}) = 5 - 3 = 2$$

Therefore, to rationalise a fraction with a denominator of the form $a + b\sqrt{c}$, multiply by $\frac{a-b\sqrt{c}}{a-b\sqrt{c}}$. This approach works even if a is itself a surd.

Example 6 - Rationalise the denominator of $\frac{3+2\sqrt{7}}{2+5\sqrt{7}}$.

Multiply the fraction by $\frac{2+5\sqrt{7}}{2+5\sqrt{7}}$.

$$\frac{3+2\sqrt{7}}{2+5\sqrt{7}} = \frac{3+2\sqrt{7}}{2+5\sqrt{7}} \times \frac{2-5\sqrt{7}}{2-5\sqrt{7}} = \frac{(3+2\sqrt{7}) \times (2-5\sqrt{7})}{(2+5\sqrt{7}) \times (2-5\sqrt{7})}$$

$$\therefore \frac{3+2\sqrt{7}}{2+5\sqrt{7}} = \frac{6-15\sqrt{7}+4\sqrt{7}-70}{4-10\sqrt{7}+10\sqrt{7}-175} = \frac{-64-11\sqrt{7}}{-171} = \frac{64+11\sqrt{7}}{171}$$

Expressions such as $(\sqrt{5}+\sqrt{3})$ and $(\sqrt{5}-\sqrt{3})$, which differ only in the sign of one of the terms, are called conjugate surds.

Rationalise the denominators of the following. Leave the numerators fully expanded and simplified as far as possible.

21.10 (a) $\frac{1}{\sqrt{7}}$ (b) $\frac{2}{\sqrt{11}}$ (c) $\frac{7}{3\sqrt{3}}$

21.11 (a) $\frac{4}{1+\sqrt{2}}$ (b) $\frac{3}{5-\sqrt{3}}$ (c) $-\frac{6}{7+\sqrt{5}}$

21.12 (a) $\frac{\sqrt{7}-\sqrt{3}}{\sqrt{7}+\sqrt{3}}$ (b) $\frac{1+\sqrt{5}}{\sqrt{5}-\sqrt{3}}$ (c) $\frac{\sqrt{2}-\sqrt{11}}{\sqrt{7}-\sqrt{11}}$

21.13 (a) $\frac{2\sqrt{5}+3\sqrt{3}}{3\sqrt{5}+2\sqrt{3}}$ (b) $\frac{1-3\sqrt{5}}{7\sqrt{3}-\sqrt{2}}$ (c) $\frac{2(\sqrt{5}-\sqrt{7})}{13(\sqrt{5}+\sqrt{2})}$

22 § Algebraic Fractions

Algebraic fractions such as $\frac{x}{x+1}$ can be manipulated and combined in an analogous way to numerical fractions such as $\frac{2}{5}$.

A fraction with the same expression in both the numerator and denominator has a value of 1.

$$\frac{3}{3} = \frac{1}{1} = 1 \qquad \text{Rule: } \frac{a}{a} = \frac{1}{1} = 1 \qquad \frac{3x^2}{3x^2} = \frac{1}{1} = 1$$

When fractions are multiplied, the numerators are multiplied and the denominators are multiplied. In the example below, note the use of brackets around each numerator and denominator.

$$\frac{3}{7} \times \frac{2}{5} = \frac{3 \times 2}{7 \times 5} \qquad \text{Rule: } \frac{a}{b} \times \frac{c}{d} = \frac{a \times c}{b \times d}$$

Example 1 – $\dfrac{x}{x+3} \times \dfrac{x+1}{x+2} = \dfrac{x \times (x+1)}{(x+3) \times (x+2)}$

Dividing one fraction by another is equivalent to multiplying the first fraction by the second fraction inverted.

$$\frac{2}{9} \div \frac{5}{11} = \frac{2}{9} \times \frac{11}{5} = \frac{2 \times 11}{9 \times 5} = \frac{22}{45} \qquad \text{Rule: } \frac{a}{b} \div \frac{c}{d} = \frac{a}{b} \times \frac{d}{c} = \frac{ad}{bc}$$

Example 2 – $\dfrac{x+5}{x+7} \div \dfrac{x+3}{x+4} = \dfrac{x+5}{x+7} \times \dfrac{x+4}{x+3} = \dfrac{(x+5)(x+4)}{(x+7)(x+3)}$

If both the numerator and denominator in a fraction have the same factor, this factor can be cancelled to leave a simpler equivalent fraction.

Example 3 – $\dfrac{2(x+2)}{3x(x+2)} = \dfrac{2}{3x} \times \dfrac{x+2}{x+2} = \dfrac{2}{3x} \times \dfrac{1}{1} = \dfrac{2}{3x}$

Note: A factor can only be cancelled when it multiplies every term in the numerator and every term in the denominator. Factorisation of the numerator and/or denominator is often needed before cancellation is possible.

Example 4 – Simplify the algebraic fraction $\frac{x(x+1)+2x}{(x+1)(x+3)}$ as far as possible:

$(x+1)$ multiplies every term in the denominator but not every term in the numerator, so it cannot be cancelled. The numerator needs to be properly factorised before cancellation is possible.

$$\frac{x(x+1)+2x}{(x+1)(x+3)} = \frac{x^2+x+2x}{(x+1)(x+3)} = \frac{x^2+3x}{(x+1)(x+3)} = \frac{x(x+3)}{(x+1)(x+3)}$$

$(x+3)$ multiplies every term in the denominator and every term in the numerator, so it can be cancelled. There are no further common factors. Hence, the answer is

$$\frac{x(x+1)+2x}{(x+1)(x+3)} = \frac{x}{x+1}$$

Addition or subtraction of algebraic fractions is analogous to addition of numerical fractions. First find a common denominator, then add or subtract the numerators, and finally simplify the result.

$$\frac{2}{5}+\frac{3}{7} = \frac{2\times 7}{5\times 7}+\frac{5\times 3}{5\times 7} = \frac{14+15}{35} = \frac{29}{35}$$

$$\text{Rule:} \quad \frac{a}{b}+\frac{c}{d} = \frac{a\times d}{b\times d}+\frac{b\times c}{b\times d} = \frac{ad+bc}{bd}$$

Example 5 – Sum $\frac{2}{x}$ and $\frac{4}{x+1}$ and simplify the result.

$$\frac{2}{x}+\frac{4}{x+1} = \frac{2(x+1)}{x(x+1)}+\frac{4x}{(x+1)x} = \frac{2(x+1)+4x}{(x+1)x}$$

$$\Rightarrow \frac{2}{x}+\frac{4}{x+1} = \frac{2x+2+4x}{(x+1)x} = \frac{6x+2}{(x+1)x} = \frac{2(3x+1)}{x(x+1)}$$

In this exercise leave your answers as fully factorised as possible.

22.1 Simplify:

(a) $\frac{2x}{x(x+1)}$ (b) $\frac{(x+1)(x+3)}{(x+3)(x+5)}$ (c) $\frac{x+1}{x^2+2x+1}$

22.2 Simplify:

(a) $4x^2 \div 2x^3$ (c) $6x \times 2x \div (x(x+2))$

(b) $3(x+1) \div 6(x+1)(x+2)$ (d) $a^2 \times (\frac{x^{\frac{1}{2}}a^{-\frac{1}{2}}}{ax}) \times (ax^{-\frac{5}{2}})^{-1}$

22.3 Simplify:

(a) $\frac{x}{x+5} \times \frac{x+5}{x+7}$ (b) $\frac{x^2}{x+3} \times \frac{2x+6}{x^3}$ (c) $\frac{x}{(x+3)(x+4)} \times \frac{x+4}{x(x+3)}$

22.4 (a) $\frac{x^2}{5x^2+15} \div \frac{x}{4x^3+6}$ (b) $\frac{x}{x+2} \div \frac{5x^2-7x}{2x+4}$ (c) $\frac{x^3}{4x^4} \div -\frac{x+1}{x^2}$

Express the following as a single fraction in as simple a form as possible.

22.5 (a) $\frac{1}{x} + \frac{1}{x}$ (b) $\frac{1}{x} + \frac{1}{2x}$ (c) $\frac{2}{x} - \frac{3}{4x}$

22.6 (a) $\frac{1}{x} + \frac{1}{x+1}$ (b) $\frac{1}{x-2} + \frac{2}{x+2}$ (c) $\frac{2x}{x-1} - \frac{15}{x+1}$

22.7 (a) $\frac{x+1}{x+2} + \frac{2x}{x+3}$ (b) $\frac{x+2}{x+3} - \frac{x-4}{x-5}$ (c) $\frac{x}{x-7} - \frac{2x}{3x+5}$

22.8 Simplify the following:

(a) $\frac{x^2+x}{x^2-1}$ (b) $\frac{x(x+2)}{x^2+5x+6}$ (c) $\frac{x^2+3x-10}{x^2+12x+35}$

22.9 Write as a single fraction, simplifying as far as possible:

(a) $\frac{6}{x^2-25} + \frac{3}{x-5}$ (b) $\frac{1}{x+3} + \frac{2}{x-3} + \frac{3}{x^2-9}$ (c) $\left(\frac{(x+a)^2}{x^2-a^2}\right)^{-1}$

22.10 Simplify:

(a) $\frac{x^2-1}{x+1}$ (b) $\frac{2x^4-32}{x^2-4}$ (c) $(x^3+9x^2+20x) \div (x^3-25x)$

Linear Functions

23 Solving Linear Equations

Solving equations follows the same procedures as changing the subject of an equation (see Chapter 17), but results in a numerical value. Proceed in steps. Identify an operation taking part in the equation, apply the inverse operation to both sides of the equation, and then repeat this process until the unknown variable is left on its own.

Example 1 – Solve the equation $15 - 3x = x + 7$ for x.

First collect all the terms containing x on the same side of the equation. On the left $3x$ is being subtracted. The inverse operation is to add $3x$, so add $3x$ to both sides.

$$15 - 3x = x + 7$$
$$15 - 3x + 3x = x + 7 + 3x$$
$$15 = 4x + 7$$

On the right hand side 7 is being added. The inverse operation is to subtract 7, so subtract 7 from both sides.

$$15 - 7 = 4x + 7 - 7$$
$$8 = 4x$$

On the right x is being multiplied by 4. The inverse operation is to divide by 4, so divide both sides by 4.

$$8 \div 4 = 4x \div 4$$
$$2 = x$$
$$\therefore x = 2$$

Solve the following equations:

23.1 (a) $2x = 6$ (b) $4x = x + 9$ (c) $3x + 4 = 1$

23.2 (a) $2x + 5 = 6$ (b) $5x - 1 = 2$ (c) $7x + 2 = 17$

23.3 (a) $2x + 5 = 3x - 1$ (b) $6x - 5 = 4x - 15$ (c) $5x - 2 = 8x - 1$

23.4 (a) $1 - 4x = 5$ (b) $6 - 3x = 5 + 4x$ (c) $2x + 6 = 9x - 10$

23.5 (a) $2(x - 5) = 12$ (b) $\frac{2}{3}x + 17 = 29$ (c) $\frac{x+1}{4} = 2$

23.6 The length of a rectangle is 4 times the width. The perimeter is 100 cm. By solving an equation, find the length of the rectangle.

23.7 There are six identical mugs on a tray. Together, the mugs and the tray have a mass of 2.95 kg. The tray has a mass of 1.03 kg.

(a) Let the mass of one mug be m. Write the information above as an equation involving m.

(b) Solve your equation from (a) to find the mass of one mug. Give your answer in grams.

23.8 If $X + Y + 2 = 4 + Y$ and $2Y + 3 = 9$, find X and Y.

23.9 A child experiments with balancing objects on scales. The child discovers that

- 2 blocks balance 3 pens
- 3 packets and 1 block balance 12 pens

The mass of 10 blocks is 300 g. Find the mass of one block, the mass of one pen, and the mass of one packet.

23.10 If $2T = 6$ and $7T + 5R - 1 = 30$, find the value of $\frac{3T+2R+1}{4}$.

23.11 Add 1 to a, and multiply by 3. Then add 4 and divide by 5. The answer is 17. What is a?

23.12 Solve

(a) $-3(x + 2) = 5(x - 2) - 2$ (b) $\frac{1}{2}(x + 3) = \frac{2}{3}(x + 4)$

23.13 Members of a club are bird-watching. They observe flocks of birds in four fields. In field A there are three times as many birds as in field B. In field C there are half the number of birds that are in field A. In field D the count is 4 less than the count in field B.

(a) The total number of birds is 256. How many birds are in field C?

(b) One week later it is claimed that the same relationship exists between the counts in the four fields, but that the total number of birds is 32. Explain why this cannot be correct.

23.14 Using an algebraic method, find x:

(a) $\frac{1}{x} + 2 = \frac{2}{5}$ (b) $\frac{1}{x+2} = \frac{2}{5}$ (c) $\frac{1}{3} + \frac{2}{3+x} = \frac{5}{6}$

24 Graphs and Co-ordinate Geometry of Straight Lines

$y = 2x + 1$ and $y = -x - 3$ are examples of linear functions. Linear functions have the general form $y = mx + c$. The graphs of linear functions are all straight lines. Example 1 shows how to plot a linear function.

Example 1 – Plot a graph of the function $y = \frac{1}{2}x + 1$.

First, create a table.

x	0	2	4	6	8
y	1	2	3	4	5

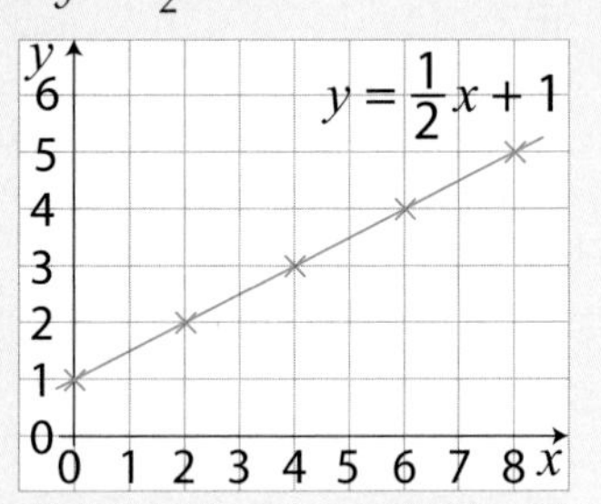

Next, plot the points (×).

Finally, draw a straight line through the points with a ruler.

When drawing straight line graphs there are a few special cases.

- Lines with $c = 0$ are straight lines through the origin.
  For example, $y = 2x$ and $y = -\frac{1}{3}x$.
- Lines of the form $y = c$ (no x term) are horizontal.
  For example, $y = 7$ and $y = -2$.
- Lines of the form $x = k$ (no y term) are vertical.
  For example, $x = 3$ and $x = -4$.

The x-axis is a horizontal line where $y = 0$ and it is said that "the equation of the x-axis is $y = 0$". Likewise, the y-axis is a vertical line where $x = 0$, and "the equation of the y-axis is $x = 0$".

Example 2 – Examples of sloping lines passing through the origin, horizontal lines and vertical lines.

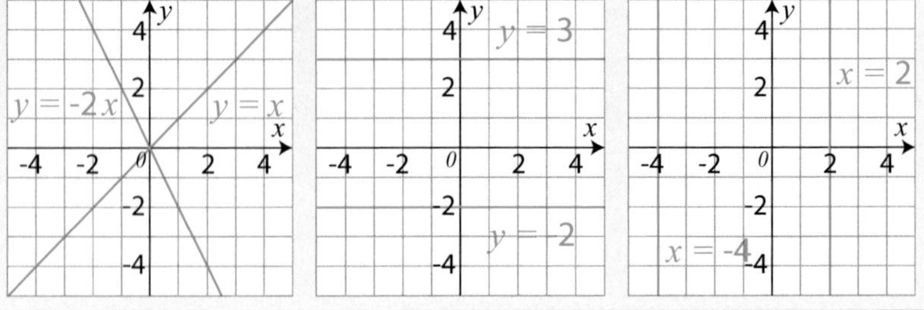

24.1 (a) The table on the right is for points on the line $y = 4x - 5$. Fill in the blanks in the table.

x	0	1		3	4
y			3		

(b) Use the values in the table to plot a graph of $y = 4x - 5$.

24.2 Fill in the table for points on the line $y = 3 - 2x$, and hence plot a graph of $y = 3 - 2x$.

x	-1	0	1	2	3	4	5
y			1				

24.3 (a) Draw the graph of $y = 2x - 3$ for x between -2 and 4.

(b) If $x = -7$, find y. (c) What is x if $y = 27$?

24.4 Points A and B are on the straight line $y = 2x + 5$.

(a) The x-coordinate of point A is 3. What is its y-coordinate?

(b) The y-coordinate of point B is 9. What is its x-coordinate?

24.5 (a) Draw a sketch to show the following lines:

$$x = 2 \qquad y = 5 \qquad y = -1 \qquad x = -3$$

(b) Which of these lines are parallel to the y-axis?

(c) What is the shortest distance between the two lines in the answer to part (b)?

The gradient of a line is a measure of its slope, and parallel lines have the same gradient. The gradient of a line is zero if it is horizontal, and large if it is steeply sloping. The gradient is positive if y increases as x increases, and negative if y decreases as x increases.

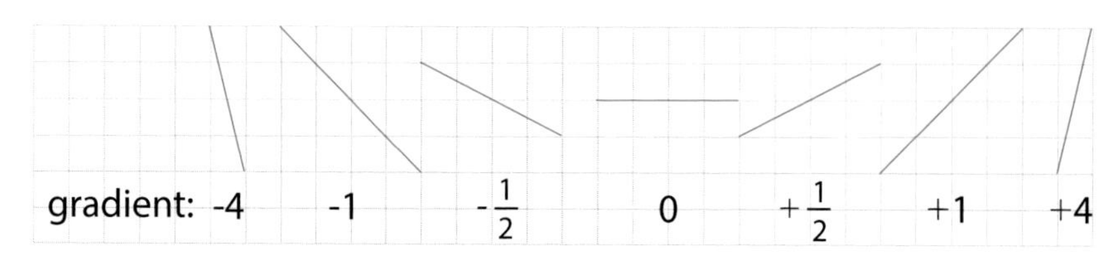

The gradient is calculated from the coordinates of two points on a line (x_1, y_1) and (x_2, y_2) using the formula:

$$\text{gradient} = \frac{\text{change in } y \text{ values}}{\text{change in } x \text{ values}} = \frac{y_2 - y_1}{x_2 - x_1}$$

Example 3 – Find the gradients of the lines shown.

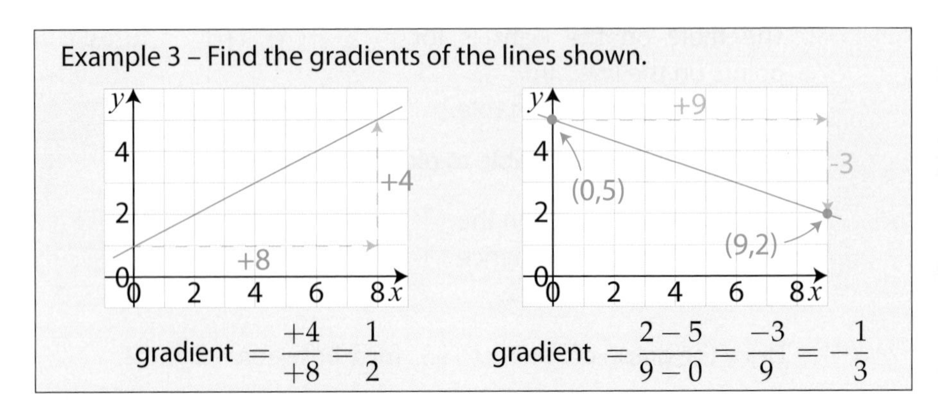

gradient $= \dfrac{+4}{+8} = \dfrac{1}{2}$ gradient $= \dfrac{2-5}{9-0} = \dfrac{-3}{9} = -\dfrac{1}{3}$

When the equation of a line is written in $y = mx + c$ form, m is the gradient, and c is the y-intercept. The y-intercept is where the line crosses the y-axis.

Example 4 – Find the gradient and y-intercept of $2y - 4x = 3$.

Start by re-arranging the equation into $y = mx + c$ form.

$$2y - 4x = 3$$ ↓ Add $4x$ to both sides

$$2y = 4x + 3$$ ↓ Divide both sides by 2

$$y = 2x + 1\frac{1}{2}$$ ↓ Compare the equation with $y = mx + c$

$$y = mx + c$$

$m = 2$ and $c = 1\frac{1}{2}$. The gradient is 2 and the y-intercept is at $y = 1\frac{1}{2}$.

The x-intercept is where a line crosses the x axis. On the x axis the value of y is 0. The x intercept can be found be putting $y = 0$ into the equation for the line and solving to find x.

Example 5 – Find where $y = 4x - 8$ cross the x axis.

On the x axis y is 0. Put $y = 0$ into the equation:

$$0 = 4x - 8$$ ↓ Add 8 to both sides

$$8 = 4x$$ ↓ Divide both sides by 4

$$x = 2$$

The line crosses the x axis at $x = 2$.

24.6 Find the gradient of each line.

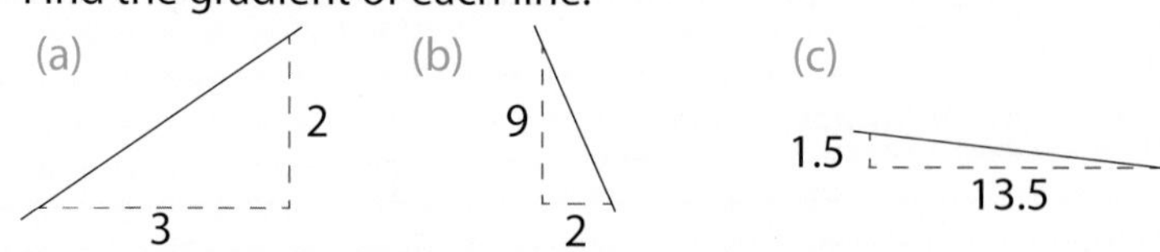

By matching these lines to $y = mx + c$, write down the values of the gradient and the y-intercept:

24.7 (a) $y = 4x + 3$ (b) $y = -2x + 5$ (c) $y = 7x - 6$

24.8 (a) $y = \frac{3}{4}x - 2$ (b) $y = -\frac{1}{2}x + 7$ (c) $y = \frac{1}{4}x - \frac{1}{3}$

Find the gradient and y-intercept for these lines:

24.9 (a) $2y = 3x - 2$ (b) $5y = -x + 4$

24.10 (a) $x + y = 5$ (b) $3x - y = 2$

24.11 Find the x intercept for these lines:

(a) $y = 2x - 4$ (b) $x + y = 7$ (c) $3y = 2x + 5$

24.12 You are given some equations of straight lines,

A: $y = -4x + 1$ B: $2y + x = -7x + 4$ C: $2y = \frac{1}{4}x + 3$

(a) Find the gradient and y-intercept for lines A, B and C.

(b) Which lines are parallel?

To find the equation of a straight line, you need to know either the coordinates of one point and the gradient, or the coordinates of two points.

Example 6 – Find the equation of the straight line with gradient 3 which passes through the point $(4, 15)$.

The equation will have the form $y = mx + c$, where m is the gradient.

We are told that the gradient is 3, so the equation of the line will be $y = 3x + c$. We have to find the value of c.

The point $(4, 15)$ is on the line. Putting these values into $y = 3x + c$:

$$15 = 3 \times 4 + c$$
$$\Rightarrow 15 = 12 + c$$
$$\therefore c = 3$$

The equation of the line is $y = 3x + 3$.

Example 7 – Find the equation of the straight line through the points $(1,7)$ and $(3,3)$.

First find the gradient of the line.

$$m = \frac{y_2 - y_1}{x_2 - x_1} = \frac{3-7}{3-1} = \frac{-4}{2} = -2$$

Putting this into $y = mx + c$ gives $y = -2x + c$. Now we need to find c. The point $(1,7)$ is on the line. Using these values in $y = -2x + c$:

$$\begin{aligned} 7 &= -2 \times 1 + c \\ \Rightarrow 7 &= -2 + c \\ \therefore c &= 9 \end{aligned}$$

The equation of the line is $y = -2x + 9$.

In this exercise give your answers in the form $y = mx + c$.

24.13 Find the equations of the straight lines from the information given.

(a) The coordinates of two points on the line, $(2,3)$ and $(5,9)$.

(b) The gradient 5 and the point $(-2,8)$.

(c) The points $(6,11)$ and $(8,10)$.

24.14 Find the equations of the following lines:

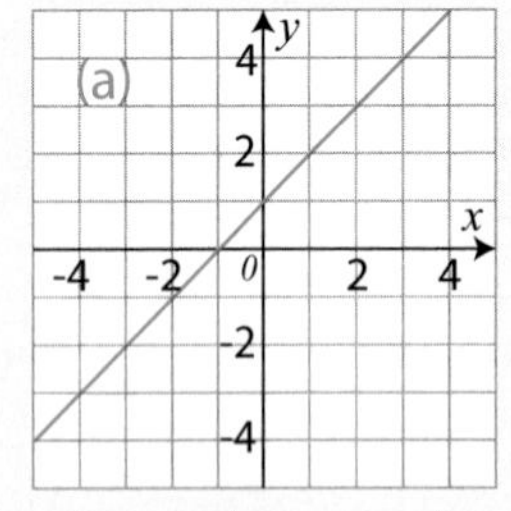

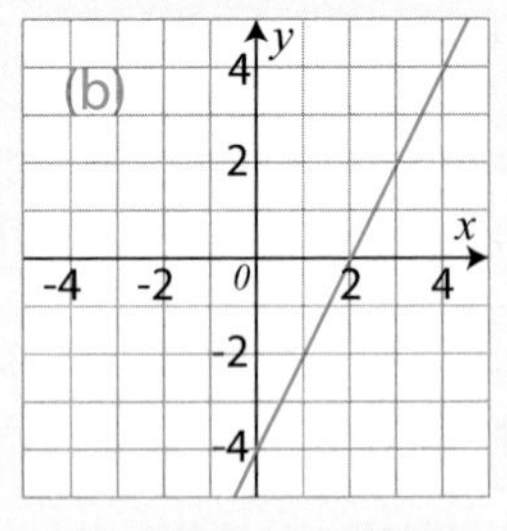

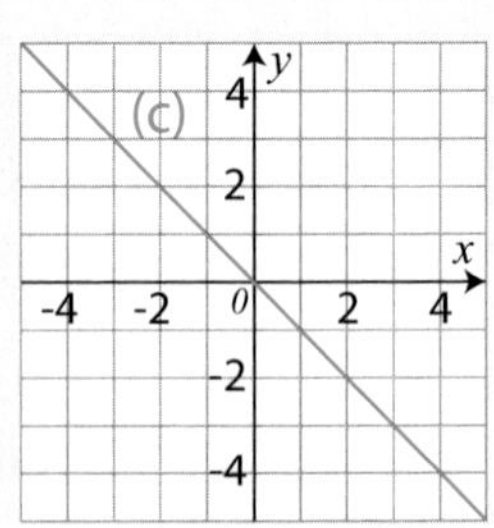

24.15 Find the equations of the following lines:

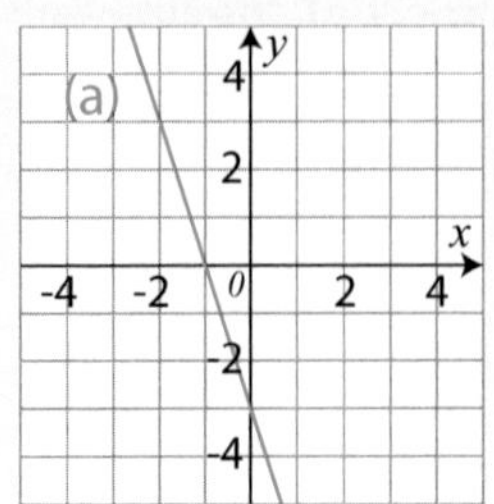

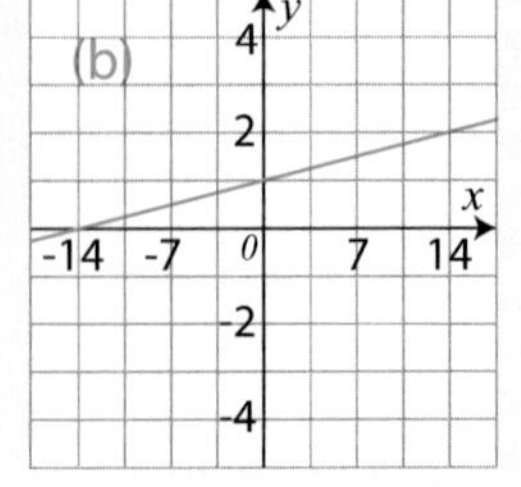

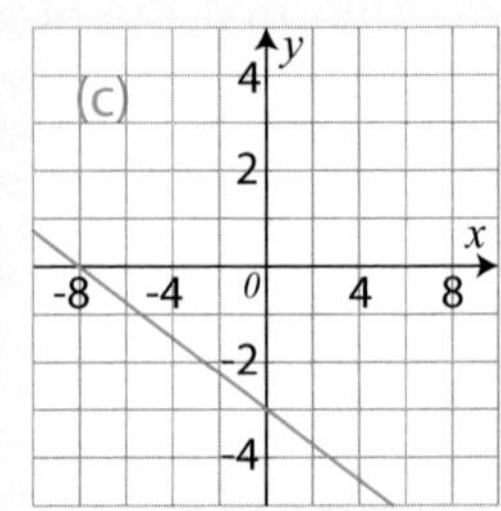

24.16 Find the equation of the straight line parallel to $y = 5x + 7$ which passes through the point $(2, 1)$.

24.17 Line A passes through the points $(-1, 6)$ and $(3, 18)$. Line B is parallel to line A and passes through $(9, -2)$. Find the equations of A and B.

§ Perpendicular lines make a right angle where they cross. Using m_1 and m_2 for the gradients of two lines, two lines are perpendicular if:

$$m_1 \times m_2 = -1 \qquad \text{or equivalently} \qquad m_2 = -\frac{1}{m_1}$$

Example 8 – Find the equation of the line perpendicular to $y = 2x + 4$ which passes through the point $(1, 6)$.

The gradient of $y = 2x + 4$ is 2. Therefore, the gradient of a line perpendicular to $y = 2x + 4$ is $-\frac{1}{2}$.

Putting this gradient into $y = mx + c$ gives $y = -\frac{1}{2}x + c$. We need to find c. Putting the coordinates $(1, 6)$ into $y = -\frac{1}{2}x + c$ gives:

$$6 = -\frac{1}{2} \times 1 + c \qquad \Rightarrow 6 = -\frac{1}{2} + c \qquad \therefore c = 6\frac{1}{2}$$

The equation of the line is $y = -\frac{1}{2}x + 6\frac{1}{2}$.

24.18 Are the lines $2y + 3x = -5$ and $y = \frac{2}{3}x + 6$ parallel, perpendicular, or neither?

24.19 (a) Find the equations of lines 1 and 2. Give your answers in the form $y = mx + c$.

(b) Add the line $y = 2x + 1$ to the graph.

(c) Which two lines are perpendicular?

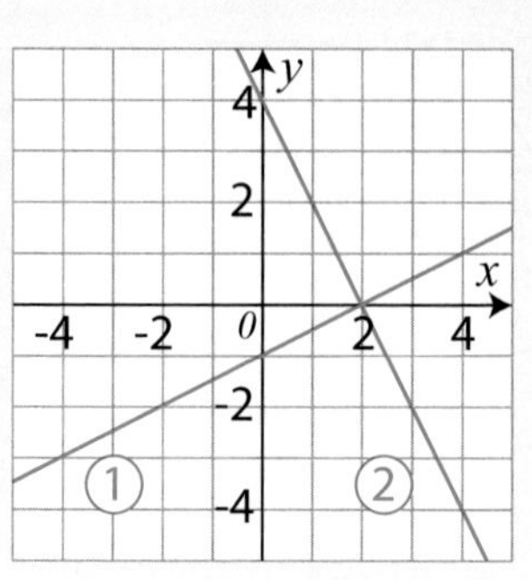

24.20 Find the line perpendicular to $y = 7x - 5$ which passes through the point $(3, 16)$.

25 Simultaneous Equations I - Two Linear Equations

Solving a pair of linear equations simultaneously means finding a pair of x and y values which satisfy both equations at the same time.

On a graph the solutions to simultaneous equations are the points where lines meet. The graphs of linear equations are straight lines. A pair of simultaneous equations has 0 solutions if the lines are parallel and separate from one another. There is 1 solution if the lines are not parallel.

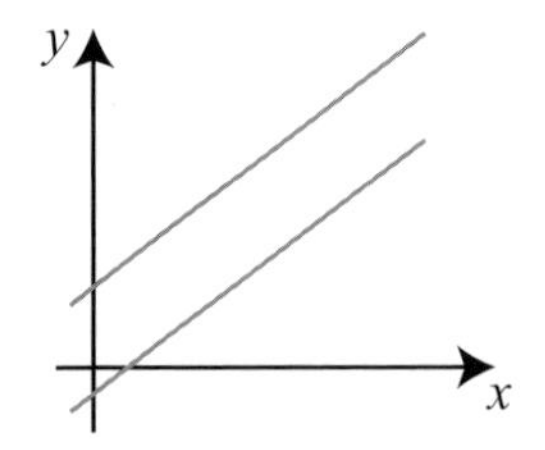

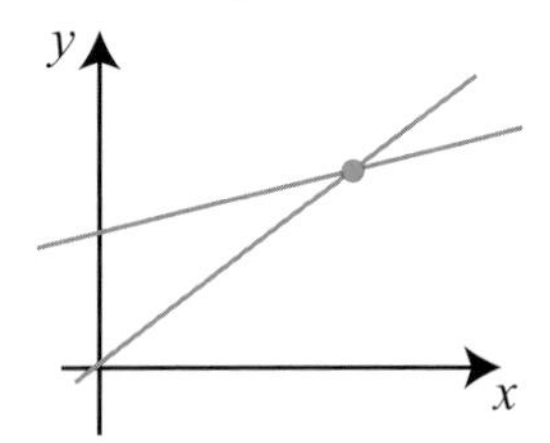

You can therefore tell how many solutions a pair of simultaneous equations has by finding out whether the lines are parallel.

Example 1 shows how to solve a pair of simultaneous linear equations by the method of eliminating a variable. In this example x is the variable that is eliminated, but either variable can be chosen.

Example 1 – Solve the simultaneous equations

$$3x + 2y = 5 \quad \text{and} \quad 4x - 3y = 18.$$

Label the equations:

$$3x + 2y = 5 \qquad \text{A}$$
$$4x - 3y = 18 \qquad \text{B}$$

Scale equation A by 4, and equation B by 3, to get $12x$ in both cases. This gives

$$12x + 8y = 20 \qquad \text{C}$$
$$12x - 9y = 54 \qquad \text{D}$$

By subtracting equation D from equation C, x is eliminated.

$$12x - 12x + 8y - (-9y) = 20 - 54$$
$$17y = -34$$
$$y = -2 \qquad \text{(dividing by 17)}$$

Find x by substituting this value for y into A and solving.

$$3x + 2 \times (-2) = 5 \quad \text{gives} \quad 3x = 9 \quad \therefore x = 3$$

Test the values of x and y in equation B to check that they work.

$$4 \times (3) - 3 \times (-2) = 12 + 6 = 18 \quad \checkmark$$

Therefore the solution is $x = 3, y = -2$.

An alternative method of solving a pair of simultaneous equations is to rearrange one equation into the form $y = ...$ or $x = ...$, and substitute for this variable in the second equation. The two methods are equivalent.

25.1 State, without working out coordinates for intersections, whether the graphs of each pair of equations have 0 or 1 intersections.

(a) $y = 3x + 5, y = 2x - 1$

(b) $2y = x + 4, y - \frac{1}{2}x = 9$

(c) $2x + 3y = 1, 5x - 4y = 14$

25.2 Solve the following pairs of simultaneous equations:

(a) $x - y = 4, 2x + y = 5$

(b) $x + 2y = 9, 2x - y = -2$

25.3 Solve the following pairs of simultaneous equations:

(a) $2x + 3y = 11, x - 3y = -8$

(b) $3x - 4y = 1, 2x + 2y = 10$

(c) $y = 2x + 3, 2y = x - 6$

25.4 Solve the simultaneous equations $4x - 3y = 4, y = 2x$.

25.5 By drawing graphs, find where $y + x = 7$ and $y = x - 3$ intersect.

25.6 By drawing graphs, find approximate values for where $y + 2x = 7$ and $2y = 3x + 1$ intersect.

25.7 Solve the following pairs of simultaneous equations:

(a) $4x + 3y = 7, 3x + 2y = 4$

(b) $5x + 3y = -2, 3x - 5y = 9$

(c) $2y - 3x = 4, 6x + 5y = 10$

25.8 (a) By drawing graphs, find an approximate solution to the simultaneous equations $y = 3x - 11.5$ and $2x + y = 3$.

(b) Use algebra to solve the simultaneous equations $y = 3x - 11.5$ and $2x + y = 3$ exactly.

25.9 Electricity bills often have two components: a fixed supply charge S, plus a fuel charge which is proportional to the power used. The fuel charge is equal to the cost per unit of power, c, multiplied by the number of units of power used, W. The total cost, T, is

$$T = S + cW$$

Company A offers a contract with a fixed charge $S = £30.50$ and cost per unit $c = 0.04\,£/\text{unit}$.

Company B offers a contract with a fixed charge $S = £25.00$ and cost per unit $c = 0.05\,£/\text{unit}$.

(a) Which company would be cheaper for a household which used 1000 units? And by how much?

(b) For what number of units W would the contracts cost the same amount?

25.10 Find:

(a) The equations of lines 1 and 2.

(b) The exact coordinates of point A.

(c) The area of the shaded region M.

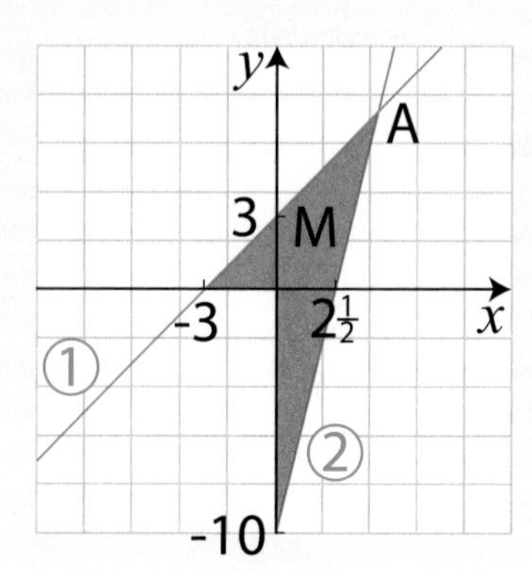

Quadratic Functions

26 Solving Quadratic Equations I - By Factorising

A common source of confusion with quadratic equations is understanding when an equation can be solved and when it cannot.

- An equation which contains only one variable can be solved.
  For example, $0 = x^2 + 3x + 2$, has solutions $x = -2$ and $x = -1$.
- On its own, an equation which contains both x and y cannot be solved.
  For example, $y = x^2 - x - 6$ cannot be solved.
- An equation which contains both x and y can be solved if extra information is provided.
  For example, if we are told y is 0, we can put this into $y = x^2 - x - 6$ to get $0 = x^2 - x - 6$, which has solutions $x = -2$ and $x = 3$.

Examples 1 and 2 show how to solve a quadratic equation by factorising.

Example 1 – Solve the equation $x^2 + 7x + 12 = 0$.

The left hand side of the equation can be factorised.

$$(x+3)(x+4) = 0$$

If the value of either bracket is zero, the whole of the left hand side is zero and the equation balances. Therefore

$$(x+3) = 0 \quad \Rightarrow x = -3, \qquad \text{or} \qquad (x+4) = 0 \quad \Rightarrow x = -4$$

The solutions to the quadratic equation are $x = -3$ and $x = -4$.

Example 2 – Solve the equation $x^2 - 8x = 0$.

The left hand side factorises to $x(x-8) = 0$.

If $x = 0$, or if the value of the bracket is zero, the whole of the left hand side is zero and the equation balances.

$\therefore$ The solutions are $x = 0$ and $x = 8$.

Note: When solving a quadratic equation which has no constant term, such as the equation $x^2 - 8x = 0$ in Example 2, it is tempting to simplify by dividing both sides by x. This gives $x - 8 = 0$, which rearranges to $x = 8$. Although this is a correct solution, it is not the only solution: the solution $x = 0$ gets lost in the division process.

Dividing an equation through by a constant can be done without losing any solutions, and is often a useful first step before factorising.

26.1 Which of these equations can be solved without further information being provided?
(a) $x^2 + y^2 = 25$ (b) $2x^2 - 11x - 6 = 0$ (c) $y = 8x^2 - 1$

Solve the following quadratic equations by factorising:

26.2 (a) $x^2 + 3x + 2 = 0$ (b) $x^2 - 7x + 10 = 0$ (c) $x^2 + x - 2 = 0$

26.3 (a) $x^2 + 7x = 0$ (b) $2x^2 - 3x = 0$ (c) $5x^2 - 25x = 0$

26.4 (a) $x^2 - 5x - 14 = 0$ (c) $2x^2 + 20x + 48 = 0$
(b) $x^2 - 18x - 63 = 0$

26.5 (a) $x^2 + 6x - 6 = 1$ (b) $2x^2 - 4x - 13 = x^2 - 1$

Solve the following quadratic equations by factorising:

26.6 (a) $3x^2 - x - 2 = 0$ (c) $4x^2 - 2x - 2 = x^2 + 2x + 2$
(b) $10x^2 + 13x - 3 = 0$ (d) $9x + 6 = -\frac{1}{x}$

26.7 (a) $x^2 - 25 = 0$ (b) $16x^2 - 9 = 0$

26.8 (a) $4x^2 + 24x + 20 = 0$ (c) $0.01x^2 - 0.2x - 3 = 0$
(b) $\frac{1}{2}x^2 - \frac{1}{2}x - 1 = 0$

26.9 (a) $3x^2 - \frac{27}{4} = 0$ (b) $\frac{1}{4} = \frac{4}{x^2}$ (c) $\frac{x}{3} - \frac{12}{x} = 0$

26.10 The solutions of a quadratic equation are $p = -1$ and $p = 5$. Write the equation with these solutions in the form $ap^2 + bp + c = 0$, where a, b and c are the smallest possible integers.

26.11 The solutions to the following equations are all integers. In each case p is either $-1, 2,$ or 5. Work out the correct values of p.
(a) $x^2 + px + 6 = 0$ (b) $x^2 + p = 0$ (c) $x^2 + px = 15$

27 Graphs of Quadratic Functions

$y = x^2 + 1$, and $y = -x^2 + 2x + 5$ are examples of quadratic functions. A quadratic function can be plotted using a table of values.

Example 1 – Plot a graph of $y = x^2 - 2$.

First, create a table.

x	-3	-2	-1	0	1	2	3
y	7	2	-1	-2	-1	2	7

Next, plot the points ($\times$).

Finally, draw a smooth curve through the points.

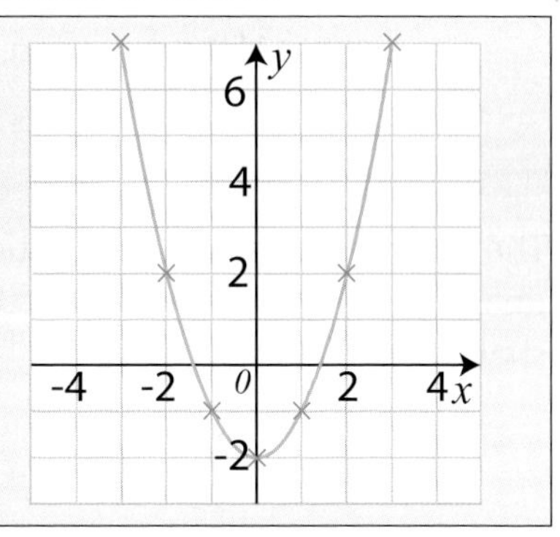

The shape of a quadratic function is called a parabola. A parabola has a minimum or maximum point. This is called the vertex or turning point of the graph. A parabola is symmetrical. The line of symmetry is parallel to the y-axis and passes through the vertex.

27.1 You are given the function $y = x^2 - 2x - 8$.

x	-3	-2	-1	0	1	2	3	4	5
y				-8				0	

(a) Complete the table of values.
(b) Use the table of values to draw the graph of the function.
(c) Where does the curve cross the x and y axes?
(d) Give the coordinates of the turning point.

27.2 For the function $y = x^2 - 6x + 8$:

x	-4	-2	0	2	4	6	8	10
y	48		8	0	0	8	24	

(a) Fill in the missing values.
(b) Predict the x-coordinate of the minimum.
(c) Find the y value of the minimum.
(d) Plot the curve, showing the position of the minimum.

27.3 For the function $y = (x-3)^2$,

(a) Construct a table of values for $-1 \leqslant x \leqslant 5$.

(b) Plot a graph of $y = (x-3)^2$

(c) What is the y-intercept?

(d) What is the equation of the line of symmetry?

(e) Give the coordinates of the vertex.

The general form of a quadratic function is $y = ax^2 + bx + c$. When a quadratic function is written in this form, the sign of a determines the overall shape of the curve:

- If a is positive the curve has a minimum ◡ shape.
  For example, $y = 3x^2 + 4$ has a ◡ shape because 3 is positive.
- If a is negative the curve has a maximum ⌒ shape.
  For example, $y = -2x^2 + 7$ has a ⌒ shape because -2 is negative.

A quadratic function always crosses the y-axis once. The value of c is the y-intercept.

A quadratic function meets the x-axis in 2, 1 or 0 places. It crosses the x-axis, just touches it, or lies entirely above or below it.

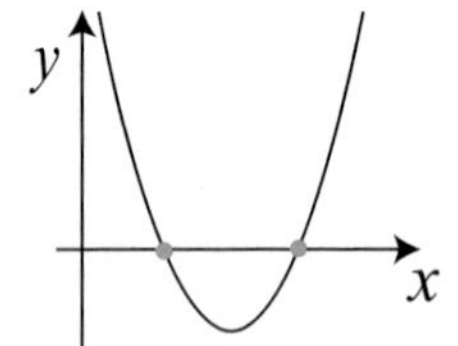

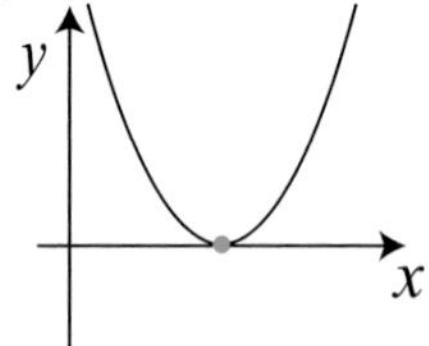

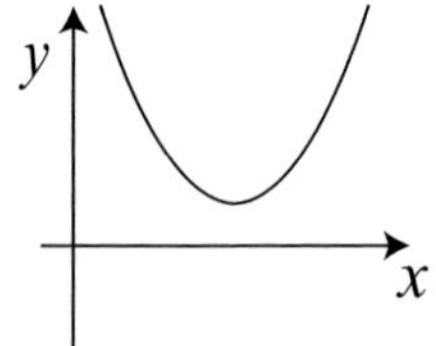

On the x-axis the value of y is 0. To find where a quadratic function meets the x-axis, put $y = 0$ into the equation for the function and solve for x. The solutions are the roots of an equation with the form $0 = ax^2 + bx + c$.

Example 2 – Find where the curve $y = x^2 + 5x + 6$ crosses the x-axis.

On the x axis $y = 0$:

$0 = x^2 + 5x + 6 \quad \Rightarrow 0 = (x+2)(x+3) \quad \Rightarrow x = -2$ or $x = -3$

Therefore, the curve crosses the x-axis at $x = -2$ or $x = -3$.

27.4 Without drawing graphs, find for each function:
(i) the y-intercept (ii) where the graph crosses the x-axis.
(a) $y = x^2 + x - 2$ (b) $y = x^2 + 6x + 5$ (c) $y = x^2 - 8x + 15$

27.5 (a) Plot a graph of the function $y = x^2 - 4x - 4$ for $-2 \leqslant x \leqslant 6$.
(b) Where does the graph cross the x-axis?

Sketching a graph is quicker than creating a table of values and putting them accurately onto graph paper. The goal is to identify the position of key points such as intercepts with the axes, and use these to draw a rough diagram showing the form of the graph.

To sketch a quadratic function, you need to find:

- the overall shape of the curve ($\smile$ or $\frown$)
- where the curve intercepts the y axis
- where the curve meets the x axis
- the position of the vertex

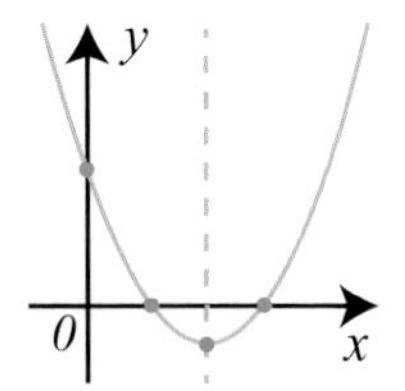

Example 3 – The curve $y = x^2 - 2x - 8$ crosses the x-axis at $x = -2$ and $x = 4$. Use this information to sketch $y = x^2 - 2x - 8$.

The curve is written in $y = ax^2 + bx + c$ form.

- $a = +1$, which is positive, so the basic shape is $\smile$.
- $c = -8$, so the y-intercept is at $y = -8$.

The curve is symmetrical. The curve crosses the x-axis at $x = -2$ and $x = 4$. The line of symmetry must be half-way between these x values at $x = 1$.

The vertex is on the line of symmetry, so it has $x = 1$. Putting this value into $y = x^2 - 2x - 8$ gives $y = -9$.

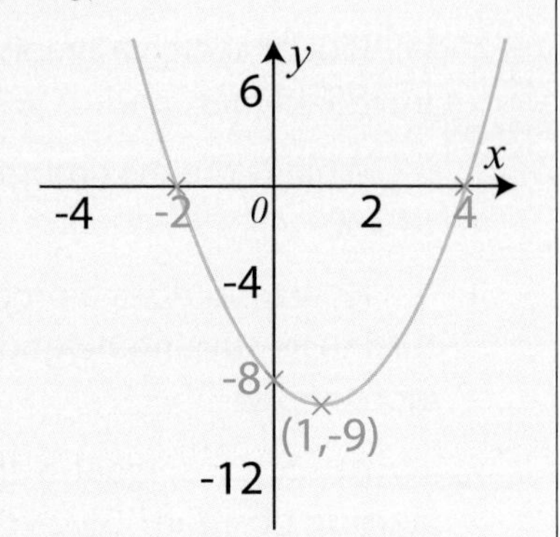

27.6 Find where the graphs of these quadratic equations meet or cross the x-axis, and use this information to sketch the graphs.

(a) $y = x^2 + 3x - 10$ (b) $y = -x^2 - 3x + 4$

27.7 (a) Sketch the graphs of $y = x^2$ and $y = -x^2$.

(b) Sketch the graph of $y = x^2 + 2$. Where does the curve cross the y-axis?

(c) Sketch the graph of $y = -x^2 - 2$. Where does the curve cross the y-axis?

27.8 Find where the graphs of these quadratic equations meet or cross the x-axis, and use this information to sketch the graphs.

(a) $y = 4x^2 - 24x + 27$ (b) $y = 3x^2 - 12$

27.9 The general form of a quadratic function is $y = ax^2 + bx + c$. You are told that a particular quadratic function intersects the x-axis at $x = 4$ and $x = 5$. For the given values of a, find: (i) the y-intercept (ii) the position of the vertex.

(a) $a = 1$ (b) $a = -1$

27.10 The graph of the equation $y = ax^2 + bx + 12$ intercepts the x-axis at $x = -3$ and $x = -2$. Find the values of the constants a and b.

27.11 The formula $s = ut + \frac{1}{2}at^2$ is used to calculate the height s of projectiles (such as balls) as a function of time.

(a) Plot or sketch a graph of s against t for $0 \leqslant t \leqslant 7$, given that $u =$29.43 m/s and $a =-$9.81 m/s^2.

(b) What is the maximum height reached? Give your answer to 3 sf.

(c) How long does a projectile modelled by this graph take to return to its starting height? You may assume the projectile was launched at $t = 0$.

(d) At $t =$7 s, what is the height of the projectile relative to its starting position? Give your answer to 3 sf.

28 § Solving Quadratic Equations II - The Quadratic Formula

When a quadratic equation is written in the form $ax^2 + bx + c = 0$, the solutions can be found using the quadratic formula:

$$x = \frac{-b \pm \sqrt{b^2 - 4ac}}{2a}$$

The number of solutions depends upon the value of the expression $b^2 - 4ac$ under the square root sign:

- if $b^2 - 4ac > 0$ the number under the square root sign is positive. It is possible to take the square root, and there are two real solutions.
- if $b^2 - 4ac = 0$ the number under the square root is 0. There is one real solution, which has a value $x = -\frac{b}{2a}$.
- if $b^2 - 4ac < 0$ the number under the square root is negative. It is not possible to take the square root of a negative number and get a real answer, so there are no real solutions.

Example 1 – Find the solutions to $7x^2 - 16x + 2 = 0$ to 2 dp.

This equation has $a = 7$, $b = -16$ and $c = 2$. Putting these numbers into the formula,

$$x = \frac{-(-16) \pm \sqrt{(-16)^2 - 4 \times 7 \times 2}}{2 \times 7} = \frac{16 \pm \sqrt{200}}{14}$$

$$\therefore x = \frac{16 - \sqrt{200}}{14} = 0.13 \qquad \text{and} \qquad x = \frac{16 + \sqrt{200}}{14} = 2.15$$

Give your answers to 2 decimal places unless told otherwise.

28.1 By evaluating $b^2 - 4ac$ for the following equations, determine how many real solutions they each possess.

(a) $5x^2 - 14x + 7 = 0$

(b) $11x^2 - 13x = -10$

(c) $4x^2 = 20x - 25$

28.2 Solve the following quadratic equations.

(a) $2x^2 - 17x + 4 = 0$

(b) $3x^2 - 10x - 7 = 0$

28.3 Solve the following quadratic equations.

(a) $4x - 12x + 9 = 0$ (c) $7x^2 + 5x = 11$

(b) $11x^2 - 21x + 3 = 0$

28.4 How many real roots does $7x^2 + bx + 4 = 0$ have if

(a) $b = 12$ (b) $b = 2$

(c) For what value(s) of b does the equation have exactly one numerical solution? Give your answer(s) in surd form, simplified as far as possible.

28.5 Solve the following quadratic equations.

(a) $3x^2 + 5x - 1 = 0$, to 2 dp (b) $5x^2 - \frac{1}{2}x - \frac{1}{3} = 0$, to 3 dp

(c) Solve $a^2x^2 + a^2x - a = 0$ for x, simplifying your answers as far as possible.

28.6 A farmer wants to set aside a small strip along every boundary of a rectangular field to provide a habitat for wildlife. He can afford to set aside a maximum of 5 % of the growing area. If the field is 100 m long and 50 m wide, and the strip has the same width on each side of the field, find the maximum width of the strip.

28.7 A golfer strikes a ball with a golf club. You are given the following formula for calculating the height of the ball above the ground:

$$s = ut + \frac{1}{2}at^2$$

- s is the height above the position where the ball was struck
- u is the initial upward component of the ball's velocity
- a is acceleration due to gravity, -9.81 m/s^2
- t is the time since the ball was struck

The golfer plays his shot on sloping ground. The ball comes down on a spot that is 2.00 m higher than where the ball was struck.

(a) Re-arrange the equation into a quadratic equation for t in the form $at^2 + bt + c = 0$.

(b) Solve your equation to find the time at which the ball lands, given that u =30.0 m/s.

29 § Solving Quadratic Equations III - Completing the Square

The goal of completing the square is to re-write a quadratic expression as a single squared bracket containing the variable, plus a constant. An example of an expression in completed square form, and the general form, are

$$2(x+3)^2+27 \qquad\qquad a(x+b)^2+c$$

Completing the square is easiest when the co-efficient of x^2 is 1.

Example 1 – Complete the square for the expression x^2+8x+9.

The co-efficient of x in this expression is 8. Half of 8 is 4. Use this 4 by considering the bracket $(x+4)^2$. Expanding this gives

$$(x+4)^2 = (x+4)(x+4) = x^2+8x+16.$$

We can re-arrange this to get an expression for x^2+8x by subtracting 16 from both sides:

$$x^2+8x = (x+4)^2-16$$

Substituting this for the x^2+8x in the expression in the question gives

$$x^2+8x+9 = ((x+4)^2-16)+9 = (x+4)^2-16+9$$

$$\therefore x^2+8x+9 = (x+4)^2-7$$

When the co-efficient of x^2 is not equal to 1, there is an extra step. It is necessary to first factorise out the co-efficient of x^2 from the x^2 and x terms.

Example 2 – Complete the square for the expression $3x^2+18x+11$.

First, factorise out the 3 from the x^2 and x terms.

$$3x^2+18x+11 = 3(x^2+6x)+11$$

The co-efficient of x in the bracket in this expression is 6. Half of 6 is 3. Use this 3 by considering the expansion of $(x+3)^2$:

$$(x+3)^2 = (x+3)(x+3) = x^2+6x+9.$$

$$\therefore x^2+6x = (x+3)^2-9$$

Substituting this into the expression in the question, we get

$$3x^2+18x+11 = 3((x+3)^2-9)+11 = 3(x+3)^2-27+11$$

$$\therefore 3x^2+18x+11 = 3(x+3)^2-16$$

Express the following in completed square form:

29.1 (a) $x^2 - 2x - 8$ (b) $x^2 + 6x - 5$

29.2 (a) $x^2 - x - 5$ (b) $x^2 - 5x + 4$

29.3 (a) $2x^2 - 8x + 2$ (b) $3x^2 - 18x - 7$

29.4 (a) $2x^2 + 5x + 1$ (b) $3x^2 - x - 7$

When an equation is written in completed square form, finding the vertex of the graph of the equation is straightforward.

For $y = a(x+b)^2 + c$ **the vertex is at** $(-b, c)$.

Example 3 – Find the vertex of the graph of $y = 2x^2 - 12x + 13$.

In completed square form, the equation is

$$y = 2(x-3)^2 - 5$$

The vertex of the graph is where the bracket is zero. The vertex has coordinates $(3, -5)$.

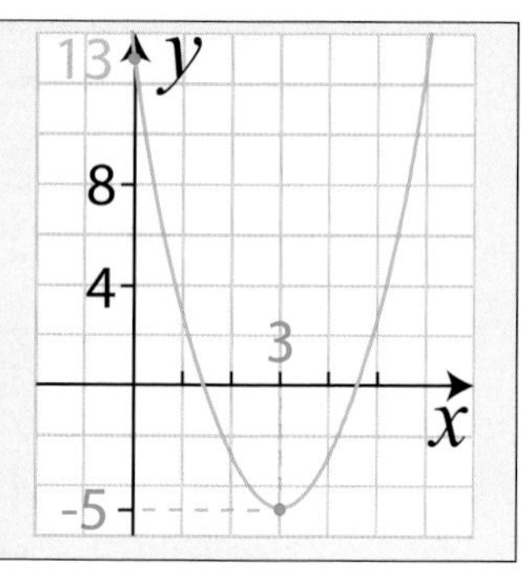

Completing the square can be used to solve quadratic equations.

Example 4 – Solve the equation $x^2 + 14x + 24 = 0$ by completing the square.

First, complete the square for the expression $x^2 + 14x + 24$:

$$x^2 + 14x + 24 = (x+7)^2 - 25$$

Now solve the equation in the question. $x^2 + 14x + 24 = 0$ becomes

$$(x+7)^2 - 25 = 0 \quad \Rightarrow (x+7)^2 = 25 \quad \Rightarrow x + 7 = \pm 5$$

$$\therefore x = -7 \pm 5, \qquad \text{so } x = -2 \text{ or } x = -12.$$

29.5 For each of these curves, find the position of the vertex by completing the square.

(a) $y = x^2 - 3x - 6$ (b) $y = 2x^2 - 4x + 7$

Solve these equations by completing the square, leaving your answers in surd form where necessary.

29.6 (a) $x^2 - 4x - 5 = 0$ (b) $x^2 + 6x - 1 = 0$

29.7 (a) $2x^2 + 8x + 1 = 0$ (b) $2x^2 - 6x + 3 = 0$

29.8 (a) $x^2 = 21 - 8x$ (b) $x^2 - x - \frac{4}{3} = 1$

29.9 For each of the following curves,
(i) Complete the square to find the position of the vertex.
(ii) Sketch the curve. Include on your sketch the y-intercept, x-intercepts, and the position of the vertex.
(a) $y = x^2 + 8x + 7$ (c) $y = -2x^2 + 2x + 12$
(b) $y = \frac{1}{2}x^2 - x - 7\frac{1}{2}$ (d) $y = x^2 - 4x + 9$

29.10 Find the equation of the quadratic curve shown in the sketch below, giving your answer in the form $y = ax^2 + bx + c$.

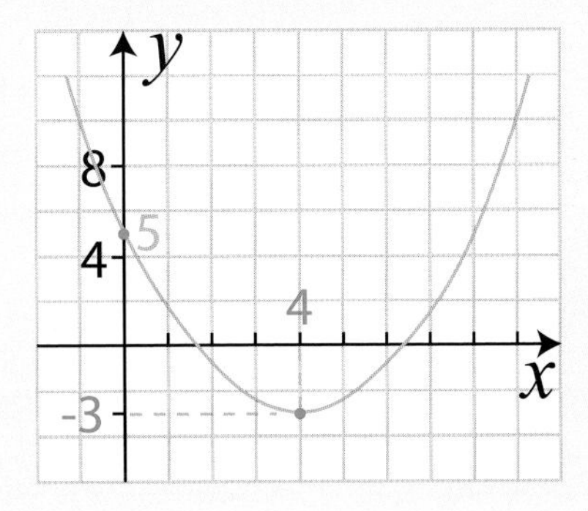

30 § Simultaneous Equations II - Where One Is Quadratic

To solve simultaneous equations when one is linear and one is quadratic,

1. Rearrange the linear equation into the form $y = ...$
2. Substitute the linear equation into the quadratic equation.
3. Solve the quadratic equation to find value of x.
4. Substitute into the linear equation to find values of y.
5. Check your solutions by substituting into the quadratic equation.

Example 1 – Solve the simultaneous equations

$$y - 2x = -5 \qquad \text{and} \qquad y = 2x^2 + 12x + 7.$$

Re-arrange the first equation into the form $y = ...$

$$y - 2x = -5 \qquad \Rightarrow y = 2x - 5$$

Substitute for y in the second equation:

$$\begin{aligned} 2x - 5 &= 2x^2 + 12x + 7 && \downarrow \text{Subtract } 2x \text{ and add } 5 \\ 0 &= 2x^2 + 10x + 12 && \downarrow \text{Divide both sides by } 2 \\ 0 &= x^2 + 5x + 6 && \downarrow \text{Factorise} \\ 0 &= (x+2)(x+3) \end{aligned}$$

$$\therefore x = -2 \quad \text{or} \quad x = -3$$

Substitute the values of x into the linear equation to find values of y:

When $x = -2, \ y = 2(-2) - 5 = -9$
When $x = -3, \ y = 2(-3) - 5 = -11$

Check the solutions by substituting their values into the quadratic equation:

$$-9 = 2(-2)^2 + 12(-2) + 7 = 8 - 24 + 7 \quad \checkmark$$
$$-11 = 2(-3)^2 + 12(-3) + 7 = 18 - 36 + 7 \quad \checkmark$$

The solutions are $x = -2, y = -9$ and $x = -3, y = -11.$

The graph of a linear equation is a straight line. A straight line passes through a quadratic curve twice, just touches it once, or misses it. Hence, the number of numerical solutions is always 2, 1 or 0. If the straight line just touches the curve, it is a tangent at the point where it touches.

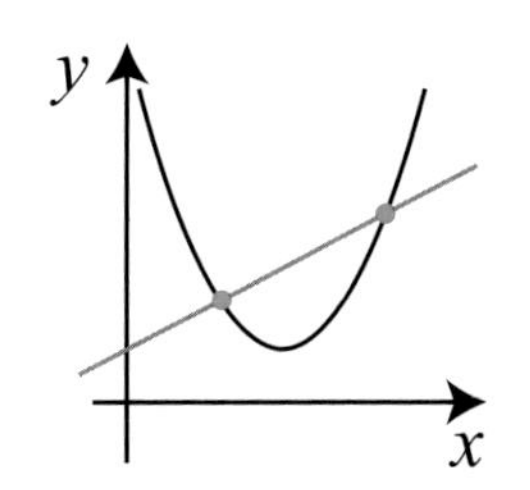

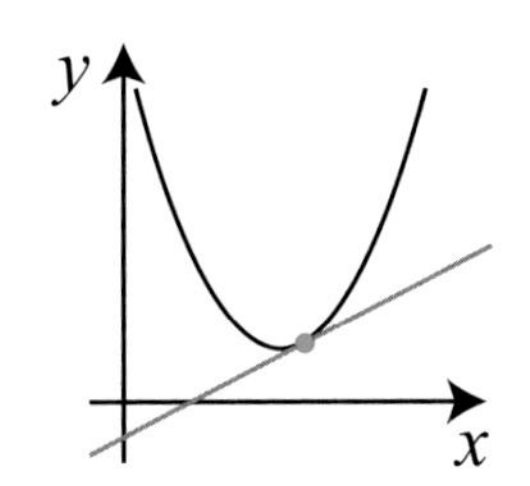

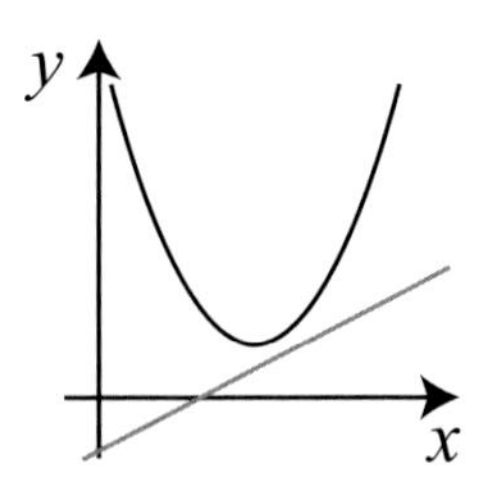

Finding where a quadratic meets the x-axis can be thought of as a simultaneous equations problem. In this case the linear equation is $y = 0$.

The method used in Example 1 can also be applied to other problems, such as finding where two quadratic curves intersect.

Solve the following pairs of simultaneous equations:

30.1 $y = 2x + 3$ $\quad y = x^2 + 5x - 1$

30.2 $6y = x - 3$ $\quad 3y = 3x^2 + x - 2$

30.3 $y = x^2 + 4x - 6$ $\quad 2y = 3x$

30.4 $y = 4x - 40$ $\quad y = x^2 - 10x + 9$

30.5 By drawing graphs, find approximate solutions to the simultaneous equations $y = x^2 - 7x + 10$ and $3y = 2x + 1$.

30.6 Find the value of a, such that the line $y = 5x + a$ is a tangent to $y = x^2 - 11x + 14$.

30.7 Find the solution(s) to the following pair of simultaneous equations: $y = 2x^2 + 13x + 8, \quad y = 5x^2 - 12x - 10$

30.8 Find where the line $y - x = 4$ intersects the circle $x^2 + y^2 = 58$.

30.9 $x^2 + y^2 = 25$ is the equation of a circle of radius 5 centred on the origin. $(x - 5)^2 + y^2 = 25$ is the equation of a circle of radius 5 centred on $(5, 0)$. Using algebra or otherwise, find where the circles intersect.

30.10 Find the points of intersection of $x = \frac{y^2}{2} - 3$ with $(x - 2)^2 + y^2 = 25$ (a circle of radius 5 with centre $(2, 0)$.)

(You will get three answers. Can you work out why?)

Inequalities

31 Inequalities

There are four inequality signs, $>$, $<$, $\geqslant$ and $\leqslant$. Their meaning is as as follows:

$A>B$	A is greater than B	$A\geqslant B$	A is greater than or equal to B
$A<B$	A is less than B	$A\leqslant B$	A is less than or equal to B

On a number line the range of values satisfying an inequality is shown with a thick line. At the end of a line,

- A filled-in circle • is used for $\geqslant$ and $\leqslant$ inequalities to indicate that the value at the position of the circle is included in the inequality.
- An empty circle ∘ is used for $>$ and $<$ inequalities to indicate that the value at the position of the circle is not included in the inequality.

Example 1 – Show the following inequalities on a number line:
(i) $x \geqslant 1$ (ii) $-3 < x \leqslant 3$ (iii) $x < -2$ or $x \geqslant 4$

(i) the value of x is greater than or equal to 1.

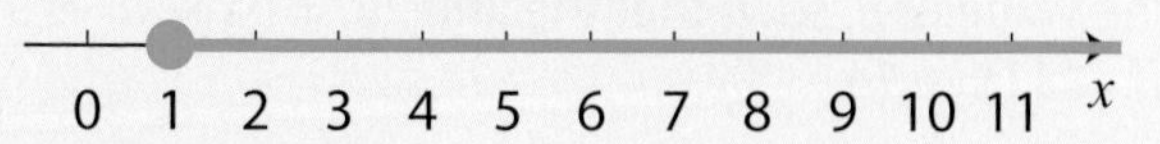

(ii) the value of x is greater than -3 and less than or equal to $+3$.

-5 -4 -3 -2 -1 0 1 2 3 4 5 6 x

(iii) the value of x is less than -2, or greater than or equal to $+4$.

-5 -4 -3 -2 -1 0 1 2 3 4 5 6 x

31.1 List the integer values satisfying the following inequalities:
(a) $-2 \leqslant x < 5$ (b) $6 \geqslant x > -1$ (c) $-1 < x < +1$

31.2 Plot the following inequalities on a number line:
(a) $x > 5$ (b) $x < 4$ (c) $x \leqslant 1$ or $x > 4$ (d) $2 \leqslant x < 6$

In a linear inequality such as $6x + 2 > 14$ the variable only appears to the first power.

Solving linear inequalities is similar to solving linear equations. Addition, subtraction, multiplication by a positive number and division by a positive number can all be used in the same way. However, when multiplying or dividing by a negative number, the sign of the inequality has to be reversed. For example, $\leqslant$ becomes $\geqslant$.

To see why it is necessary to reverse the sign, consider the inequality $-x < 0$. In order for $-x$ to have a value less than 0, x on its own must be positive. In other words, $x > 0$. This is equivalent to multiplying both sides of $-x < 0$ by -1 and reversing the inequality sign.

Example 2 – Solve (i) $4x - 6 \geqslant 2$ (ii) $-3 \leqslant -5x + 12$

(i)
$$\begin{aligned} 4x - 6 &\geqslant 2 \\ 4x &\geqslant 2 + 6 \\ 4x &\geqslant 8 \\ x &\geqslant 2 \end{aligned}$$

(ii)
$$\begin{aligned} -3 &\leqslant -5x + 12 \\ -15 &\leqslant -5x \\ 3 &\geqslant x \\ \therefore x &\leqslant 3 \end{aligned}$$

You may see inequalities written in set notation using curly brackets $\{...\}$. For example, $\{x : x \geqslant 3\}$ is the set of all numbers greater than or equal to 3.

31.3 Solve the following inequalities:
(a) $5x \leqslant 15$ (b) $3x < -4.5$ (c) $-5P < 10$

31.4 Solve these linear inequalities:
(a) $2x + 7 < 8$ (b) $3y + 5 \geqslant 9y - 6$ (c) $4(3x + 1) < 5x - 3$

31.5 (a) When 7 is added to 4 times p the result is greater than 14. What values can p take?

(b) Add 3 to a quantity a, multiply by 6 and then take away 5. The answer is less than or equal to 19. What values can a take?

31.6 x is a whole number such that $2 \leqslant x < 5$, and y is a whole number such that $-1 \leqslant y \leqslant 3$.

(a) What is the maximum value of $x + y$?

(b) What is the minimum value of $x + y$?

(c) What is the maximum value of xy?

(d) What is the minimum value of xy?

(e) What is the maximum value of $x - y$?

31.7 Solve the following inequalities:

(a) $3 \leqslant 2x + 1 \leqslant 9$

(b) $5 < \frac{15a+6}{3} < 20$

(c) $2(x - 3) < 4x + 1$ and $4x < 10$

31.8 It is given that $0 < x < 4$ and $1 \leqslant y \leqslant 4$, where x and y are integers.

(a) Write down the pairs (x, y) which are possible given these constraints.

(b) Another constraint is added: $x + y \leqslant 3$. List the pairs which satisfy all three constraints.

31.9 Amy wants to grow flowers in tubs. Each tub take 5 plants, and she has 7 tubs. Amy knows that some plants come in poor condition, and last year she wasted 4 plants while she was planting up the tubs.

(a) Amy assumes that she will waste at least as many plants this year as last year. Let the number of plants Amy buys be P. Use the above information to write an inequality for P.

The flowers are sold in trays which each contain 9 plants, and trays cannot be split up before purchase.

(b) Let the number of trays Amy buys be T. Use the above information to write an inequality for T. What is the minimum number of trays Amy buys?

31.10 Two runners start 900 metres apart on a straight path and run towards each other. Runner A runs twice as fast as runner B. They meet after no more than $2\frac{1}{2}$ minutes. Write an inequality for the speed of runner A in metres per second, and solve it.

32 § Plotting Inequalities and Solving Quadratic Inequalities

Linear equations such as $y = 2x + 3$ are straight lines on an x-y graph. Linear inequalities such as $y > 2x + 3$ are regions bounded by straight lines.

When sketching an inequality, start by drawing the straight line on which the inequality is based. Use a solid line for $\leqslant$ and $\geqslant$ inequalities to show that points on the line satisfy the inequality. Use a dotted line for $<$ and $>$ inequalities to show that points on the line do not satisfy the inequality. The region satisfying an inequality is usually shaded in.

It may be helpful to be reminded that

- Lines of form $x = k$, such as $x = 3$, are vertical lines in an x-y plot.
- Lines of form $y = c$, such as $y = 2$, are horizontal lines in an x-y plot.

Example 1 – Draw sketches of the inequalities (i) $y < 2x + 4$ (ii) $x \geqslant 3$.

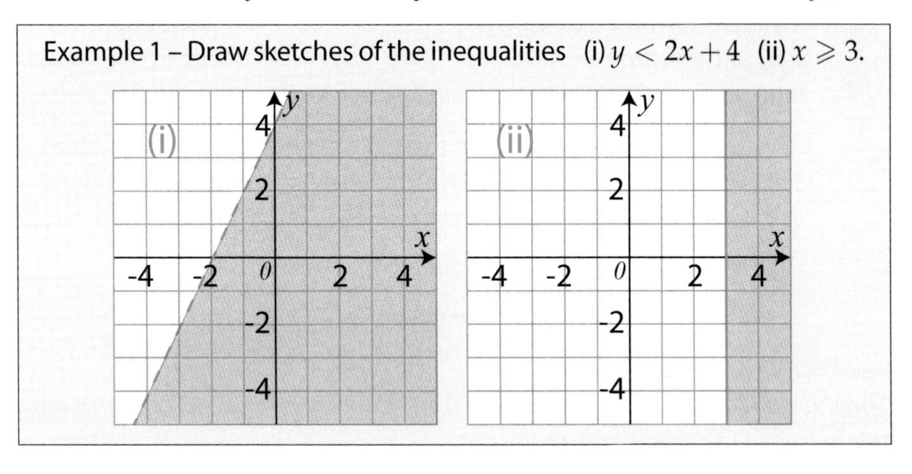

Example 2 – Shade the region bounded by the following inequalities:

$$y \leqslant 2x + \frac{1}{2}, \quad y < -\frac{1}{2}x + 5\frac{1}{2},$$
$$y \geqslant 0,$$
$$x \geqslant 1, \quad x < 3$$

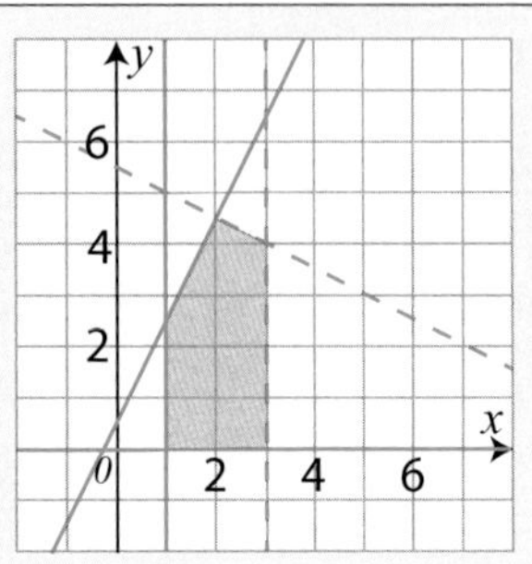

32.1 On separate graphs sketch the following inequalities:

(a) $y \leqslant x+3$ (b) $y > -x-2$ (c) $x > 4$ (d) $y \leqslant 3$

32.2 State the inequalities satisfied by the shaded regions.

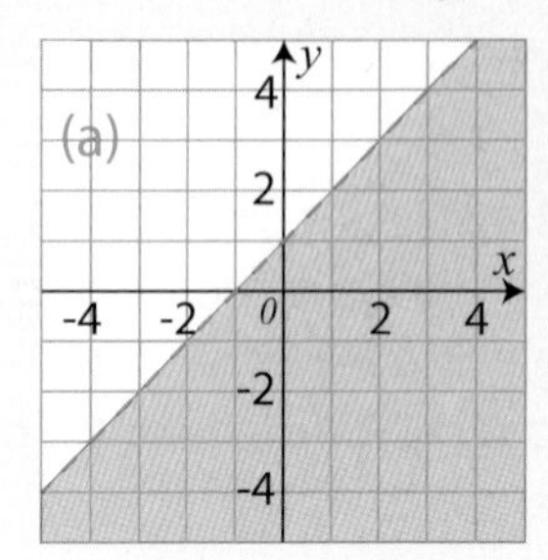

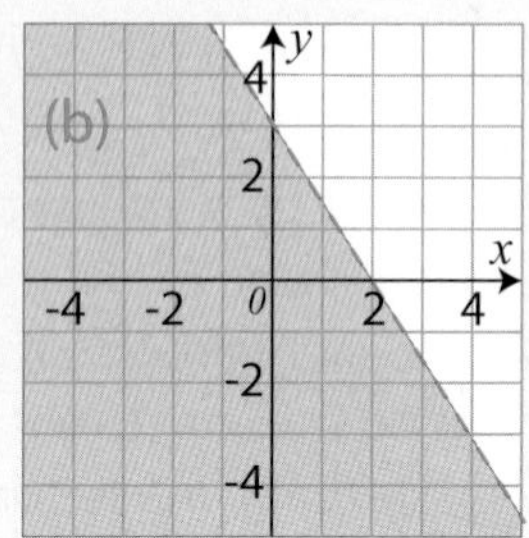

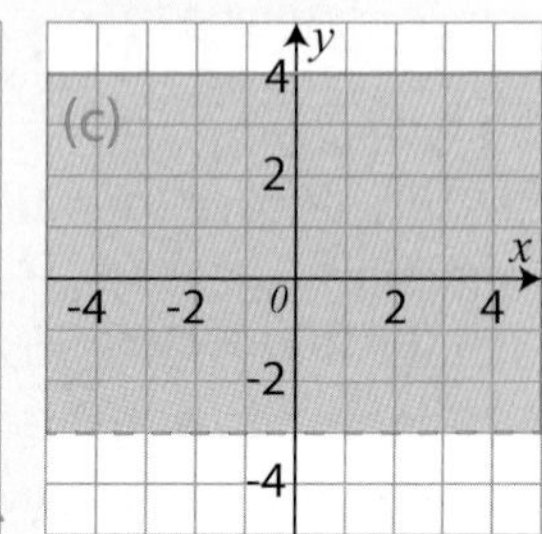

32.3 Show on a graph the region B satisfying the following inequalities:

$$y < \frac{1}{2}x+8 \quad y < -\frac{1}{2}x+8 \quad y \geqslant 0$$

32.4 A mathematician is sowing two kinds of seed in her flower bed. The area of her flower bed is 20 m^2. She sows x m^2 of the first kind of seed, and y m^2 of the second kind. Therefore, $x+y \leqslant 20$.

The mathematician knows that the second type of seed always produces a colourful display, so she covers at least half of the flower bed with this kind of seed. Therefore, $10 \leqslant y \leqslant 20$.

(a) Write down one other inequality that x must satisfy.

(b) Sketch all the inequalities on a graph, and shade the region which shows the possible amounts of the two types of seeds.

Solving quadratic inequalities can be done entirely by logical means, or with the help of a graphical argument.

Example 3 – Solve the inequality $x^2 - 64 \leqslant 0$.

First re-arrange the inequality by adding 64 to both sides: $x^2 \leqslant 64$.

The equation $x^2 = 64$ has solutions $x = -8$ and $x = +8$, and due to the "=" in $\leqslant$ these values of x are part of the solution.

For values of x that are less then -8 or greater $+8$, $x^2 > 64$. For values of x between -8 and $+8$, $x^2 \leqslant 64$.

$$\therefore -8 \leqslant x \leqslant 8$$

Example 4 – Solve the inequality $x^2 - x - 6 > 0$.

Let $y = x^2 - x - 6$. Substituting this into the inequality gives $y > 0$. This means that solving the inequality is equivalent to finding the values of x for which $y > 0$.

Next, sketch the graph of $y = x^2 - x - 6$. This curve cuts the y-axis at $y = -6$. It cuts the x-axis ($y = 0$) where

$$0 = x^2 - x - 6 = (x+2)(x-3)$$

This equation has solutions $x = -2$ or $x = +3$.

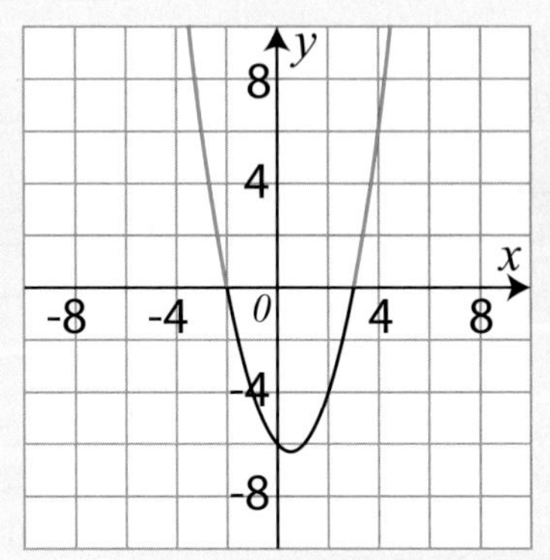

The graph shows that $y > 0$ for $x < -2$ and $x > +3$. Therefore, the solution to the inequality is

$$x < -2 \text{ and } x > +3$$

32.5 For what values of x are the following true?

(a) $x^2 - 7x + 12 < 0$ (b) $x^2 - 8x + 14 \geqslant -1$

32.6 Plot the solutions to the following inequalities on a number line.

(a) $x^2 < 16$ (b) $x^2 - 4x + 3 \geqslant 0$

32.7 Find the range of values of x for which the value of $f(x) = (x-3)^2 - 6$ is greater than $g(x) = x - 7$.

32.8 You are told that $(x-a)^2 + (y-b)^2 = r^2$ is the equation of a circle with centre (a, b) and radius r. Points satisfying the inequality $(x-a)^2 + (y-b)^2 < r^2$ occupy the interior of this circle.

On a diagram, show the region A which satisfies the following inequalities:

$$y + x < 9 \quad x < 6 \quad y \geqslant 0 \quad x \geqslant 0 \quad (x-4)^2 + (y-3)^2 < 5^2$$

Graphs

33 Graphs of Standard Functions

In addition to graphs of linear and quadratic functions you need to be familiar with the graphs of $y = \frac{1}{x}$ and $y = x^3$.

The graph of the reciprocal function $y = \frac{1}{x}$ has two parts. For $x < 0$ there is a part in the lower left quadrant, and for $x > 0$ there is a part in the upper right quadrant. The value of the reciprocal function is undefined when $x = 0$ as it is not possible to divide by 0.

As the value of x gets larger in the positive or negative direction, the curve gets closer to the x axis but never quite reaches it. The x axis is an asymptote of the curve. Similarly, as the value of x gets closer to zero, the curve gets closer to the y axis but never quite reaches it. The y axis is also an asymptote.

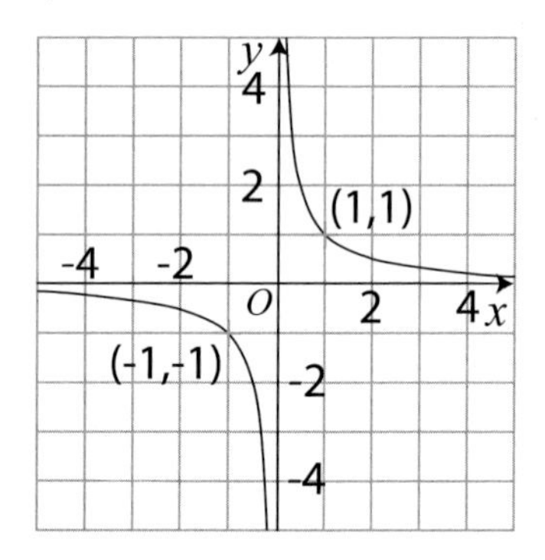

Cubic functions are polynomials in which the highest power of x is 3. The graph of the simplest cubic function, $y = x^3$, is shown on the left. It has a turning point called a point of inflexion at the origin $(0, 0)$.

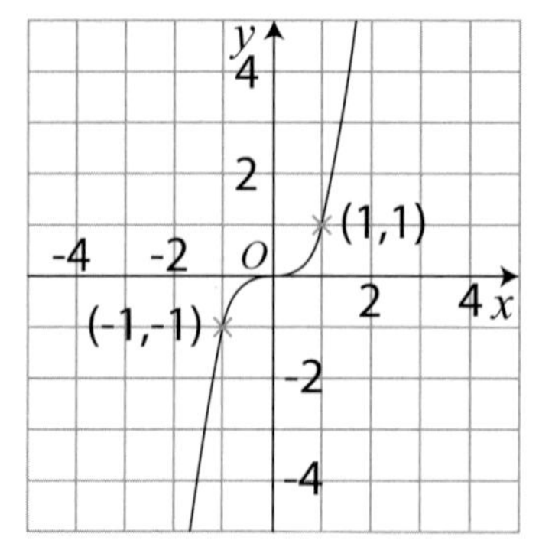

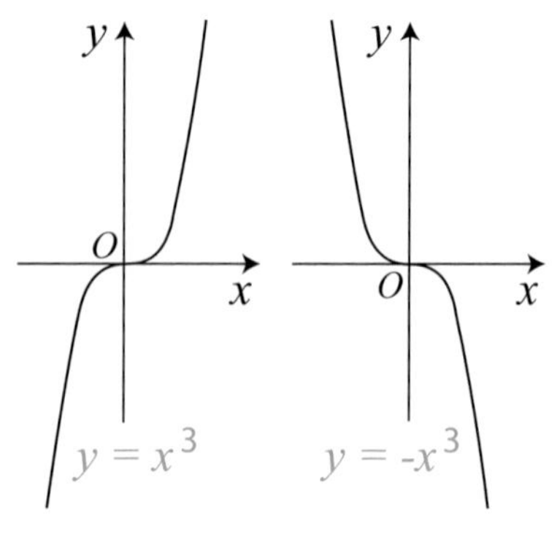

The graph of $y = -x^3$ is the mirror image of $y = x^3$ in either the x or y axis.

33.1 Match the functions to the correct graph.

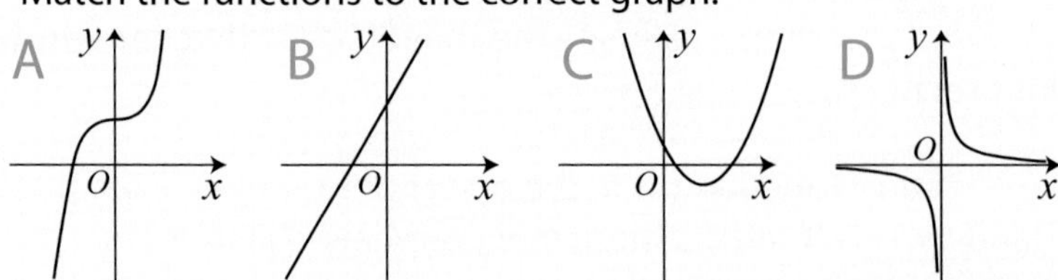

(a) $y = 2x + 3$ (b) $y = \frac{2}{x}$ (c) $y = x^3 + 2$ (d) $y = x^2 - 7x + 6$

33.2

x	-2	-1.5	-1	-0.5	0	0.5	1	1.5	2
x^3	-8								
$\frac{1}{x}$	-0.5				X				

(a) Complete the table of values.

(b) Why is no value required for $\frac{1}{x}$ when $x = 0$?

(c) Plot the graphs of $y = x^3$ and $y = \frac{1}{x}$ on the same axes and write down where the curves intersect.

33.3 For the function $y = \frac{1}{x} + 2$, where $x \neq 0$:

(a) Make a table of values of this function for $-4 \leqslant x \leqslant 4$.

(b) Plot a graph using the values in the table.

(c) Use your graph to obtain approximate values for x when (i) $y = 1.6$ (ii) $y = 2.6$.

33.4 For the function $y = x^3 + \frac{1}{2}$:

(a) Make a table of values of this function for $-3 \leqslant x \leqslant 3$.

(b) Plot a graph using the values in the table.

(c) Use your graph to obtain approximate values for x when (i) $y = 12$ (ii) $y = -22$

33.5 (a) Complete the table of values.

x	-3	-2	-1	-0.5	0	0.5	1	2	3
$\frac{1}{x}$	$-\frac{1}{3}$		-1		X		1		
$-\frac{1}{x}$	$\frac{1}{3}$				X		-1	$-\frac{1}{2}$	$-\frac{1}{3}$
$-\frac{1}{x} - 3$	$-2\frac{2}{3}$		-2		X				$-3\frac{1}{3}$

(b) On the same axes plot $y = \frac{1}{x}$ and $y = -\frac{1}{x} - 3$.

(c) From your graph, estimate the coordinates where the two graphs intersect.

§ In an exponential function x is in the power of a number. Examples are $y = 2^x$ and $y = -3 \times 4^x$. These functions have the form:

$$y = a \times k^x \quad \text{where} \quad a \text{ and } k \text{ are constants} \quad \text{and} \quad k > 0$$

Graphs of exponentials always cross the y-axis once. The y-intercept is at $x = a$ because $k^0 = 1$. Exponentials do not cross the x axis. The x axis is an asymptote.

An exponential shows growth if $k > 1$ and decay if $0 < k < 1$. A real-world example of exponential growth is compound interest, and a real-world example of exponential decay is radioactive decay.

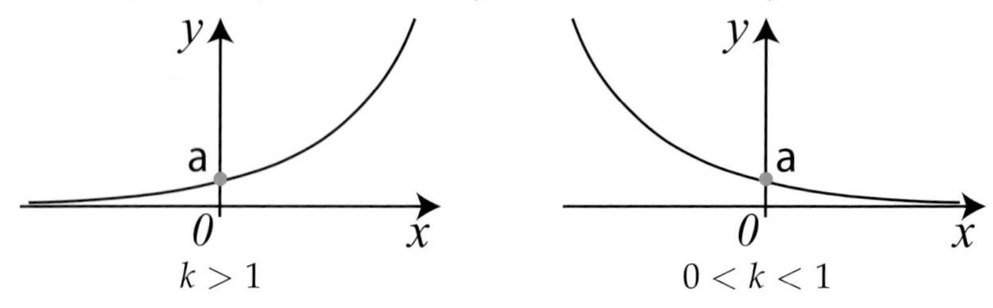

Note: Remember that negative indices are used for reciprocals of powers. Hence, the exponential $y = (\frac{1}{2})^x$ can also be written in the alternative form $y = 2^{-x}$. More generally, $y = (\frac{1}{k})^x$ is the same as $y = k^{-x}$

The general equation of a circle of radius r, centred at the origin, is:

$$x^2 + y^2 = r^2$$

Example 1 – Sketch the circle $x^2 + y^2 = 36$ and state where it meets the axes.

Compare $x^2 + y^2 = 36$ with the general equation of a circle to find the radius.

$$r^2 = 36 \qquad \Rightarrow r = 6$$

The circle meets the x axis at $x = -6$ and $x = 6$, and the y axis at $y = -6$ and $y = 6$.

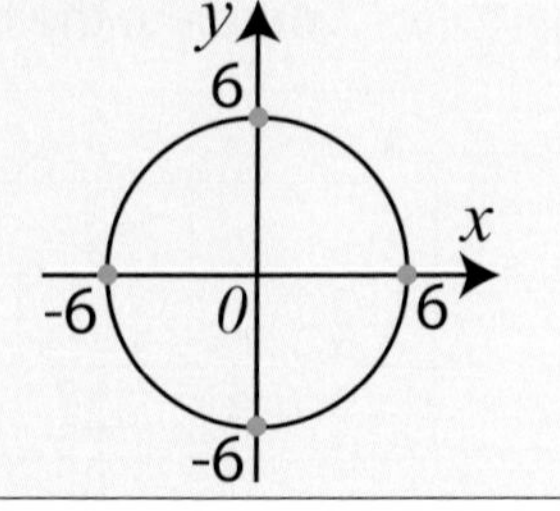

33.6 Fill in the tables of values and plot graphs of these functions for values of x from 0 to 4.

(a)

x	0	1	2	3	4
2^x		2		8	

(b)

x	0	1	2	3	4
$(\frac{1}{2})^x$		$\frac{1}{2}$		$\frac{1}{8}$	

33.7 (a) If $y = 3k^x$ and $k = 1.2$, fill in this table of values, giving your values to 3 sf. Hence plot the function.

x	0	1	2	3	4	5	6
$3k^x$		3.6	4.32				

(b) Use your graph to find a value for x when $y = 7.0$.

33.8 Sketch the following circles, stating the value of the radius.

(a) $x^2 + y^2 = 49$ (b) $x^2 + y^2 = 27$ (c) $y^2 = 32 - x^2$

33.9 (a) Sketch the circle $x^2 + y^2 = 8$.

(b) Give the coordinates of the intercepts with the axes.

(c) What is the area enclosed by the circle? Leave your answer in terms of π.

33.10 A curve has the equation $y = a \times b^t$, where a and b are constants. It passes through the points $(0, 400)$ and $(2, 625)$.

(a) Find a. (b) Find b. (c) Find y to 3 sf when $t = 5$.

33.11 $y = x^3$ is the simplest cubic function. More complicated cubic functions, such as $y = x^3 - x$, can have two turning points. One is a maximum, the other a minimum. For the function $y = x^3 - x$,

(a) What is the y-intercept?

(b) Factorise $x^3 - x$, and hence find where the function crosses the x-axis.

(c) The function has two turning points. Their x coordinates are $x = \pm\frac{1}{\sqrt{3}}$. Find their y coordinates.

(d) Sketch the function, labelling the intercepts and turning points.

34 Proportionality

When two quantities are directly proportional, they increase and decrease in the same ratio. If one quantity doubles, the other doubles; if one is divided by 3, the other is divided by 3; etc.

The sign $\propto$ means "proportional to". If y is directly proportional to x, this is written $y \propto x$. A proportionality relationship can be turned into an equation using a constant of proportionality, k:

$$y \propto x \qquad \Rightarrow \qquad y = kx$$

Example 1 – The total number of potatoes a restaurant serves each day, p, is directly proportional to the number of customers, q. 156 potatoes are needed to serve 26 customers.

(i) Write the proportionality relationship as an equation, and find the constant of proportionality.

$p \propto q$ and so $p = kq$. We are told that $p = 156$ when $q = 26$, so

$$156 = k \times 26 \qquad \Rightarrow k = \frac{156}{26} = 6$$

The restaurant serves 6 potatoes per customer. $p = 6q$

(ii) Find how many potatoes would be needed to serve 38 customers.

$$p = 6 \times 38 = 228 \text{ potatoes}$$

The graph of $y = kx$ is a straight line through the origin with gradient k. Hence, when the quantities on the axes of a graph are directly proportional to one another, the graph is a straight line through the origin.

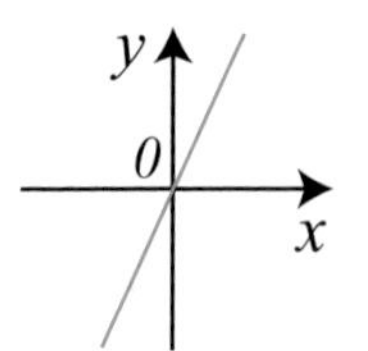

The equation $y = kx$ rearranges to $\frac{y}{x} = k$. If (x_1, y_1) and (x_2, y_2) are the coordinates of two points on the same line, both $\frac{y_1}{x_1}$ and $\frac{y_2}{x_2}$ are equal to k, and hence they are also equal to one another:

$$\frac{y_1}{x_1} = \frac{y_2}{x_2}$$

A second type of relationship is inverse proportionality. If one quantity doubles, the other halves; if one is divided by three, the other is multiplied by three; etc. This type of proportionality can be written:

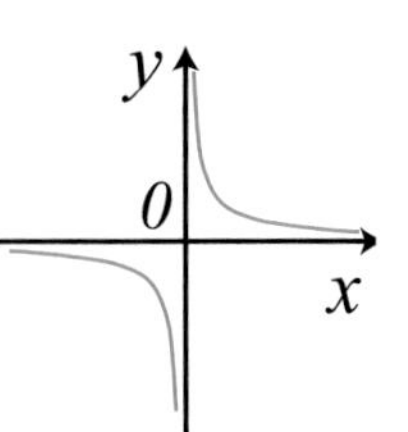

$$y \propto \frac{1}{x} \qquad \Rightarrow \qquad y = \frac{k}{x}$$

The graph shows a sketch of an equation with the form $y = \frac{k}{x}$.

Example 2 – Quantities A and B are inversely proportional to one another. When $A = 12$, $B = 6$. What is A when $B = 5$?

$A \propto \frac{1}{B}$ and so $A = \frac{k}{B}$. We are told that $A = 12$ when $B = 6$, so

$$12 = \frac{k}{6} \qquad \Rightarrow k = 12 \times 6 = 72$$

This gives the equation $A = \frac{72}{B}$. When $B = 5$, $A = \frac{72}{5} = 14.4$.

The equation $y = \frac{k}{x}$ rearranges to $yx = k$. Hence, a relationship of inverse proportionality can also be written $y_1 x_1 = y_2 x_2$.

34.1 The graph has three lines, A, B and C.
If k is a positive constant,

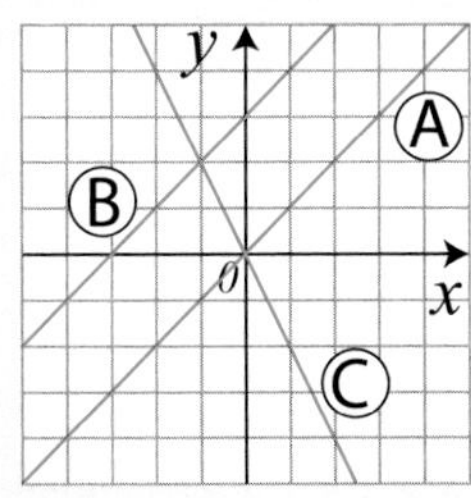

(a) For which line is $y = kx$?
(b) For which line is $y = -kx$?
(c) Which lines are of the form $y = mx + c$?
(d) Which lines demonstrate direct proportionality?

34.2 (a) $R \propto Q$ Write this as an equation by including a constant k.
(b) If $Q = 10$ when $R = 4$, find the value of k.
(c) If $Q = 20$, what is R? (d) If $R = 18$, what is Q?

34.3 (a) The quantities F and G are directly proportional to one another. When $G = 10$, $F = 25$. Write an equation for F in terms of G.
(b) Find F when $G = \frac{3}{4}$. (c) If $F = 55$, what is G?

34.4 (a) It is given that $z \propto \frac{1}{h}$. Write an equation for z in terms of h using constant of proportionality k.
(b) Find k if $z = 8$ when $h = 3$. (c) Find h when $z = 6$.

34.5 A nurse is calculating the amount of painkilling medication to give to her young adult patients. For patients with a body mass of up to 50 kg, the dose of medicine is 15 mg per kilogram of body mass.

(a) What is the dose for a 44 kg patient?

(b) Sketch the graph of dose against body mass for patients between 30 and 50 kg.

(c) If the dose is 540 mg, what is the mass of the patient?

(d) The medication can be administered up to 4 times per day. What is the overall maximum daily dose for a 50 kg patient?

34.6 A shop has a sale in which the cost of every item is reduced by 20%. If £N is the sale price of an object which originally cost £O, then

$$N \propto O$$

(a) Write this proportionality relationship as an equation using a constant k, and find the value of k.

(b) Re-write your equation to make O the subject, giving your answer in the form $O = mN$, where m is a constant.

(c) What is the original price of an item with a sale price of £12.80?

34.7 (a) A train travels at a steady speed v. Using a formula triangle, or otherwise, write an equation for t, the time it takes the train to travel a distance d.

(b) On the first part of its journey, the train travels 20 km. Is the time for this part of the journey directly proportional or inversely proportional to the speed?

(c) On the second part of its journey, the train travels for 30 minutes at 80 km/hour. How long would this part of the journey take if the train could travel at its maximum speed of 200 km/hour?

34.8 If a gas is in a sealed container which cannot expand, the pressure of the gas is proportional to its temperature in Kelvin:

$$\frac{p_1}{T_1} = \frac{p_2}{T_2}$$

(a) A gas starts at a pressure of 1 atm (1 atmosphere). Its temperature is doubled from 300 K to 600 K. What is its new pressure?

(b) A gas changes pressure from 1 atm to 0.4 atm. If the final temperature of gas was 200 K, what was its original temperature?

§ The idea of proportionality can be extended to more complicated relationships. The examples in the table are for y proportional to x^2, x^3, $\frac{1}{x^2}$, $\sqrt{x}$, and a^x.

Relationship	Equation
$y \propto x^2$	$y = kx^2$
$y \propto x^3$	$y = kx^3$
$y \propto \frac{1}{x^2}$*	$y = \frac{k}{x^2}$
$y \propto \sqrt{x}$	$y = k\sqrt{x}$
$y \propto a^x$	$y = ka^x$

y does not have to be to the first power. For example, if y^2 is proportional to x^3, we could write $y^2 \propto x^3$ and turn this into the equation $y^2 = kx^3$.

*$y \propto \frac{1}{x^2}$ is known as an "inverse square" relationship.

Example 3 – p is proportional to $\sqrt{q}$. When $q = 81$, $p = 18$. What is q when $p = 7$?

$p \propto \sqrt{q}$ and so $p = k\sqrt{q}$. We are told $p = 18$ when $q = 81$, so

$$18 = k\sqrt{81} \qquad \Rightarrow 18 = k \times 9 \qquad \Rightarrow k = \frac{18}{9} = 2$$

This gives the equation $p = 2\sqrt{q}$. When $p = 7$,

$$7 = 2\sqrt{q} \qquad \Rightarrow \frac{7}{2} = \sqrt{q} \qquad \Rightarrow q = \left(\frac{7}{2}\right)^2 = \frac{49}{4} = 12\frac{1}{4}$$

Knowing that two quantities have a proportionality relationship is useful when plotting a graph. If the expressions separated by the "∝" sign are used for the axes, the graph that results is a straight line. For example, if $y \propto \sqrt{x}$, a graph of y against x is a curve; but a graph of y against $\sqrt{x}$ is a straight line.

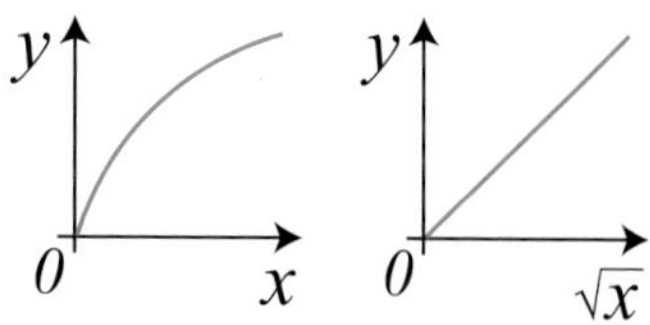

34.9

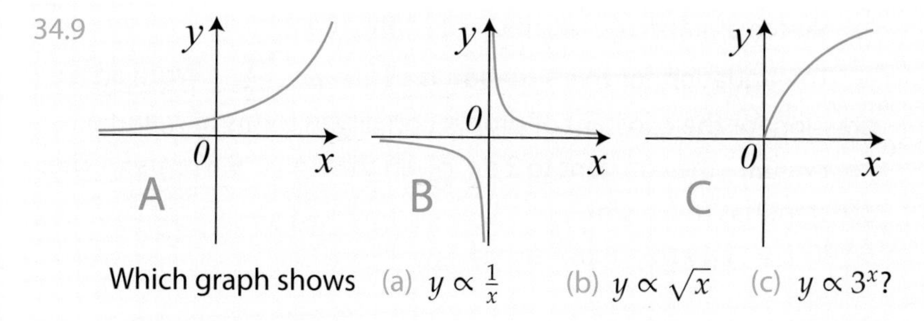

Which graph shows (a) $y \propto \frac{1}{x}$ (b) $y \propto \sqrt{x}$ (c) $y \propto 3^x$?

34.10 Connect the relationship between y and x to the equation.

(a) Directly proportional to x	(i) $y = \frac{7}{x}$
(b) Proportional to $\frac{1}{x^2}$	(ii) $y = \frac{3}{5}x^4$
(c) Proportional to x^4	(iii) $3y = -2x^2$
(d) Proportional to $\sin x$	(iv) $y = 0.28 \sin x$
(e) Proportional to x^2	(v) $yx^2 = \frac{5}{2}$
(f) Inversely proportional to x	(vi) $\frac{y}{x} = 8 \times 10^{-2}$

34.11 (a) A quantity F is proportional to the square root of the variable x. Write this as an equation with a constant of proportionality K.

(b) Find the value of K if $F = 14$ when $x = 49$.

(c) What value of x gives a value of 3 for F?

34.12 In the early stages of growth, the number of bacteria in a bacterial colony, N, after t minutes of growth is given by

$$N \propto 2^{t/T}$$

The constant T is the time it takes the colony to double in size.

(a) Write this information as an equation for N in terms of t, using A for the constant of proportionality.

(b) After $5T$ minutes there are 8 000 bacteria. Find A.

(c) How many bacteria were present initially?

(d) It takes 20 minutes for each doubling in size. How long does it take to reach 64 000 bacteria, assuming none die?

34.13 The period of a pendulum, T, is proportional to the square root of the length of the string, l.

(a) Write an equation for T in terms of l.

(b) Sketch a graph of T against (i) l (ii) $\sqrt{l}$.

(c) The equation for this situation is $T = 2\pi\sqrt{\frac{l}{g}}$. Write an expression for the constant of proportionality in terms of π and g.

(d) Evaluate the constant to 2 dp, given that $g = 9.81$ m/s^2. The constant has units s/m$^{\frac{1}{2}}$.

(e) If $l = 1.44$ m, find T to 3 sf.

35 § Function and Graph Transformations

Sometimes one function can be written in terms of another. For example, if $g(x) = x^2$ and $h(x) = x^2 + 2$, then $h(x) = g(x) + 2$. The functions $g(x)$ and $h(x)$ are related: a function transformation turns $g(x)$ into $h(x)$.

The graphs of $y = g(x)$ and $y = h(x)$ are shown on the right. The graph of $y = h(x)$ is the same as the graph of $y = g(x)$, but moved 2 units in the positive y direction. A graph transformation has taken place.

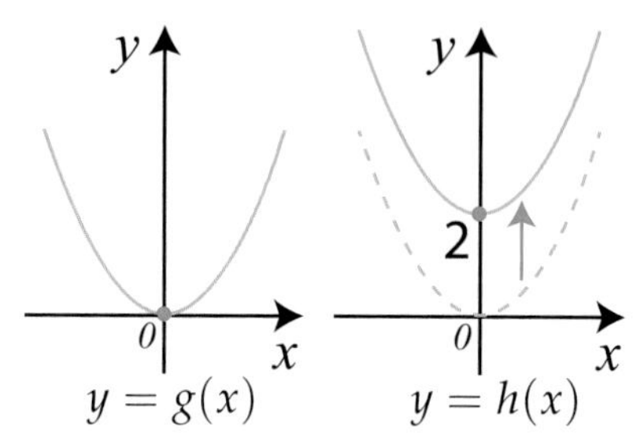

A translation moves a graph up-and-down or left-and-right. A description of a translation has two parts: the direction in which the graph is moved, and the distance. For any function $f(x)$,

- $y = f(x) + a$ is a translation of $y = f(x)$ parallel to the y axis in the positive-y direction by a units.
- $y = f(x - a)$ is a translation of $y = f(x)$ parallel to the x axis in the positive-x direction by a units.

If a is negative the translation is in the negative-y or negative-x direction.

Example 1 – The graph below left shows a sketch of the function $f(x)$. Sketch (i) $f(x) + 3$ (ii) $f(x - 4)$ (iii) $f(x) - 3$ (iv) $f(x + 6)$

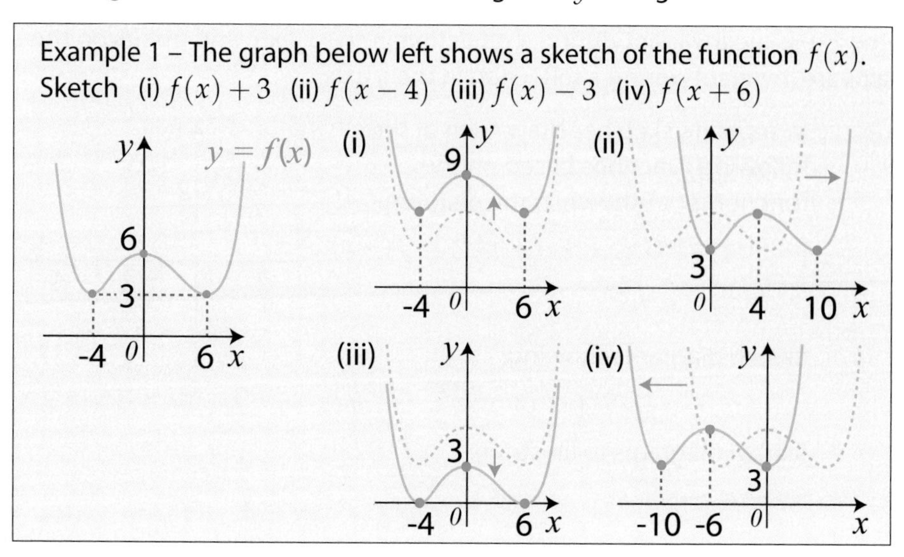

The notation $f(x-a)$ can be confusing. What it means in practice is that $x-a$ occurs in $f(x-a)$ wherever x occurs in $f(x)$. For example,

- If $f(x) = 2x^3$, $f(x-3) = 2(x-3)^3$
- If $g(x) = -\frac{4}{x}$, $g(x+7) = -\frac{4}{x+7}$

To see why $y = f(x-a)$ is a translation in the positive x direction, consider moving the graph of $f(x) = x^2$ along the x axis to place the vertex at $x = 2$. $x = 2$ is the solution to the equation $(x-2)^2 = 0$. Hence, the function becomes $g(x) = (x-2)^2$.

A graph can also be reflected in the x or y axis:

- $y = -f(x)$ is a reflection of the curve $y = f(x)$ in the x-axis.
- $y = f(-x)$ is a reflection of the curve $y = f(x)$ in the y-axis.

Example 2 – The graph below left shows a sketch of the function $f(x)$. Sketch (i) $-f(x)$ (ii) $f(-x)$

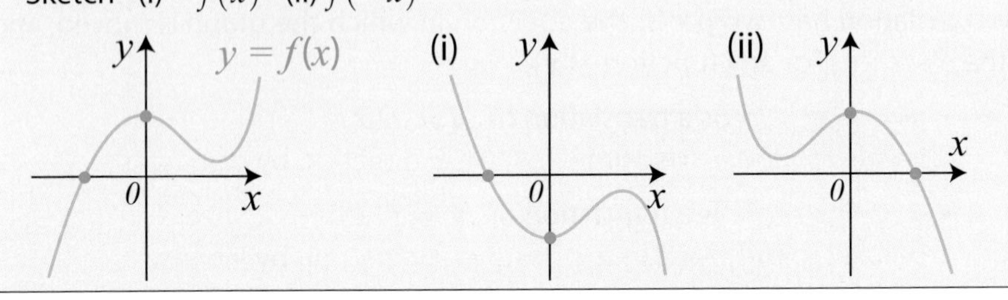

Points which do not move under a transformation are invariant. Points on the x axis are invariant during a reflection in the x axis, and points on the y axis are invariant during a reflection in the y axis.

35.1 In separate sketches draw each of the following functions based on the function $f(x)$ shown in the diagram:

(a) $p(x) = f(x) + 3$ (c) $r(x) = f(-x)$

(b) $q(x) = -f(x)$

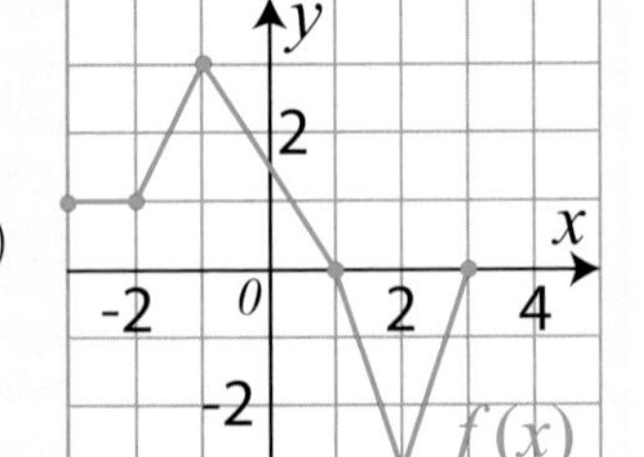

35.2 Sketch diagrams showing:

(a) $y = x^3$ (b) $y = (x-2)^3$ (c) $y = x^3 - 3$ (d) $y = -x^3$

35.3 Sketch diagrams to illustrate:

(a) $y = -\frac{1}{x}$ (b) $y = \frac{1}{x-1}$ (c) $y = 2 + \frac{1}{x}$

35.4 The diagram shows a sketch of the function $y = f(x)$, where $f(x) = k^x$. Copy the graph and add to your copy sketches of the following functions based on $f(x)$:

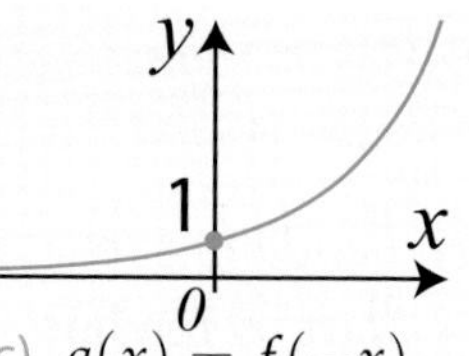

(a) $g(x) = k^x + 2$ (b) $h(x) = -f(x)$ (c) $q(x) = f(-x)$

35.5 Sketch the following equations, marking the value(s) of the intercepts with the axes on your diagram.

(a) $y = -\frac{1}{x} + 2$ (b) $y = \frac{1}{x+2} - 4$

35.6 The diagram shows a sketch of $f(x) = x^3 - x$.

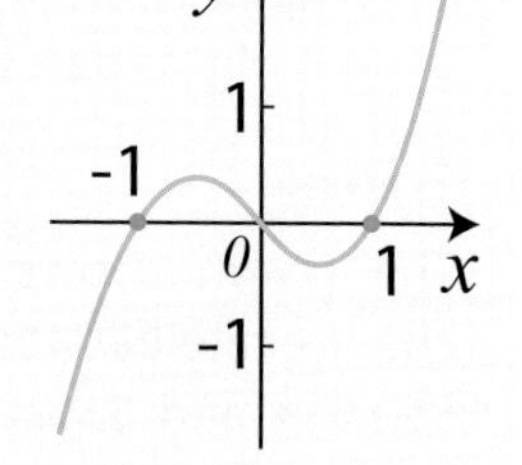

(a) Copy the diagram and add to your sketch $g(x) = x^3 - x - 2$. The x intercept is at 1.52.

(b) $h(x)$ is the translation of $g(x)$ by $+3$ units parallel to the x axis in the positive x-direction. Write an expression for $h(x)$ in terms of x.

(c) Sketch $h(x)$.

35.7 In this question you are going to plot a graph of the function $f(x) = x^3 - 6x^2 + 12x - 7\frac{1}{2}$.

(a) Expand the bracket $(x-2)^3$.

(b) Use your answer to (a) to write $f(x)$ in terms of $(x-2)^3$.

(c) Write down the transformations that turn the graph of $g(x) = x^3$ into the graph of $f(x)$. Hence sketch $y = f(x)$. The x intercept of $f(x)$ is at $x = 1.21$.

35.8 (a) Find the solutions to the equation $x^2 - 8x + 15 = 0$.

(b) Give the coordinates of the vertex of the graph of $y = f(x)$, where $f(x) = x^2 - 8x + 15$.

(c) Sketch the graph, labelling all intersections with the axes.

(d) On a separate graph sketch $y = g(x)$, where $g(x) = 8x - 15 - x^2$, labelling the vertex and the intersections with the axes.

(e) What transformation relates the graphs of $f(x)$ and $g(x)$?

(f) List the points that are invariant under the transformation.

36 Real-World Graphs and Kinematics

When handling a real-world graph,

- Start by reading the axes to find out what quantities are plotted and their units.
- Consider whether the shape of the graph corresponds to a function with which you are familiar. If not, can the graph be split up into smaller shapes, for example a number of straight lines?
- Decide if there is anything you can measure from the graph. For example, if part of a graph is a straight line, you could measure the gradient of this part of the graph.

Example 1 -

The graph shows the exchange rate between pence Sterling and Japanese Yen on one particular day. For how many yen could £165 be exchanged?

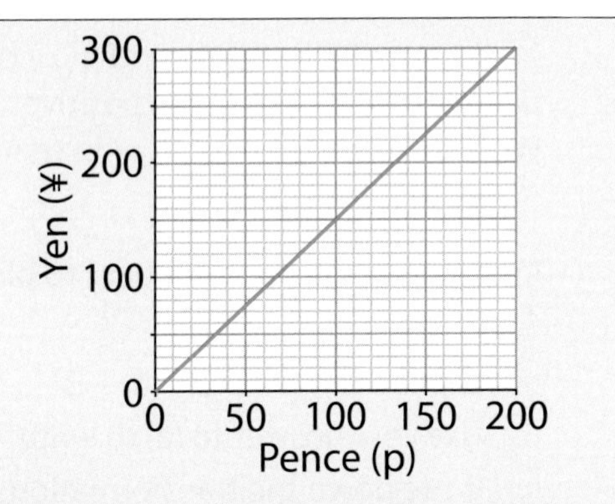

First read the axes. The y axis shows the number of yen. The size of one rectangle in the y direction is 10 ¥. The x axis shows the number of pence. The size of one rectangle in the x direction is 10 p.

Next, look at the shape of the line. It is a straight line through the origin. The number of yen is proportional to the number of pence.

£1 is 100 p. Reading from the graph, 100 p is worth 150 ¥.

Therefore, £165 could be exchanged for $165 \times 150 = 24\,750$¥.

A distance-time graph or travel graph shows distance travelled on the y axis and time on the x axis. The gradient of a straight part of the graph is the speed at which the person or object was travelling during that part of the journey. Where the graph is horizontal, the speed was 0 and the person or object was stationary.

For a person or object travelling at a constant speed,

$$\text{speed} = \frac{\text{distance covered}}{\text{time taken}}$$

Over a time interval where the speed of an object varies,

$$\text{average speed} = \frac{\text{total distance covered}}{\text{total time taken}}$$

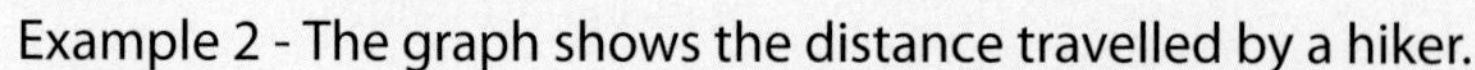

Example 2 - The graph shows the distance travelled by a hiker.

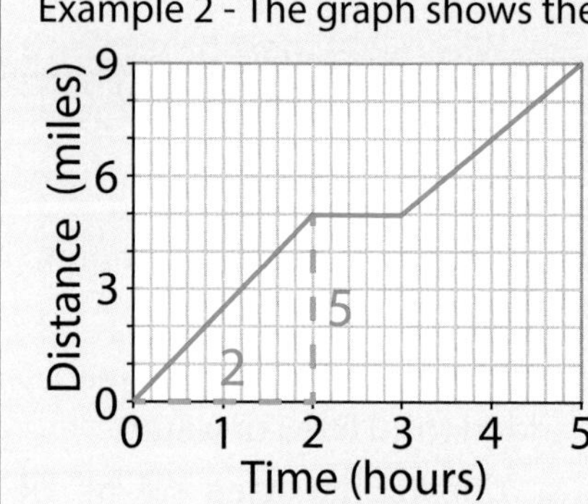

(i) What was the speed of the hiker during the first part of their walk?

$$\text{speed} = \frac{5}{2} = 2.5 \text{ miles/hour}$$

(ii) What was their average speed over the whole 5 hours?

$$\text{average speed} = \frac{9}{5} = 1.8 \text{ miles/hour}$$

A speed-time graph shows how the speed of an object varies during a journey. The gradient of a straight part of a speed-time graph is the acceleration during that part of the journey. The acceleration is negative if the speed is decreasing and positive if the speed is increasing. Where the graph is horizontal, the acceleration is 0 and the object is travelling at constant speed.

Over a time interval where the acceleration of an object varies,

$$\text{average acceleration} = \frac{\text{change in speed}}{\text{time for change}}$$

Example 3 - The graph shows a speed-time graph for a car. Between 10 and 25 seconds into the motion, how fast was the car decelerating?

$$\text{acceleration} = \frac{-7.5}{15}$$

$$\text{acceleration} = -0.5 \text{ m/s}^2$$

The car was decelerating (slowing down) at 0.5 m/s^2.

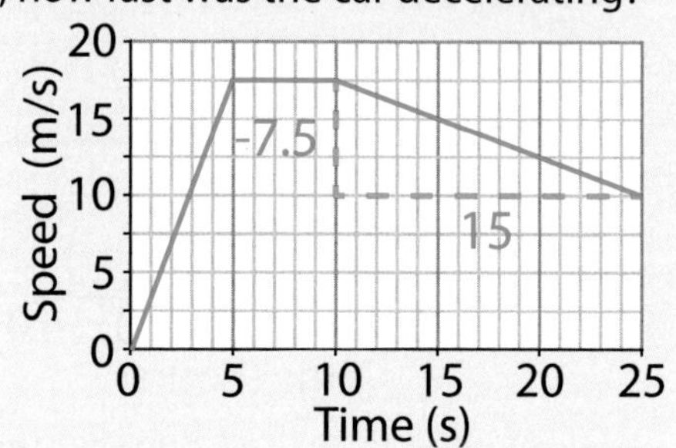

36.1 The graph below shows how the number of cars per minute passing a traffic monitoring camera varies over the course of a day.

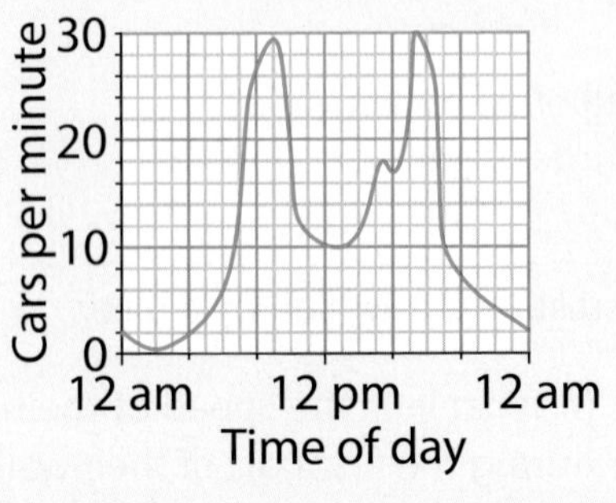

(a) What was the maximum number of cars per minute passing the camera on this day?

(b) When was the flow of traffic at its lowest value?

(c) Why might there have been a peak between 3 and 4 pm?

36.2 Plant feed comes as a concentrated liquid. It has to be diluted before it can be used to water plants. The graph shows the amount of plant feed to use with volumes of water of up to 20 litres.

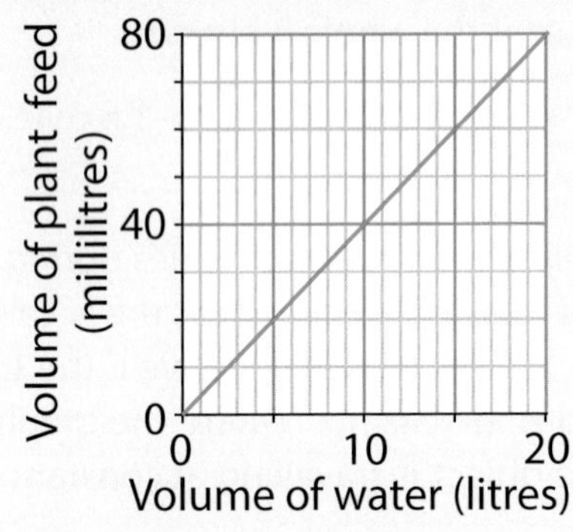

(a) What volume of plant feed is added to 10 litres of water?

(b) Christopher used 60 ml of plant feed. What volume of water did he use?

(c) To water their stock a garden centre uses 250 litres of water. How many litres of plant feed will they need?

36.3 Heidi leaves Marhampton at 11:30 and hikes to Scorville. On the way she stops for lunch at a cafe for 30 minutes. Ben cycles the same route and reaches Scorville 20 minutes before Heidi.

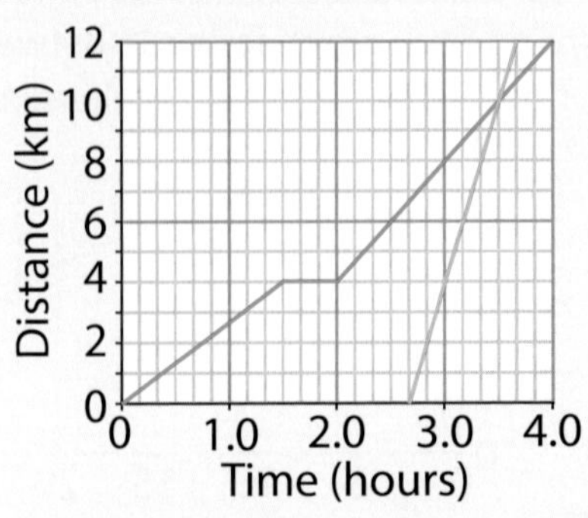

(a) How far is it from Marhampton to the cafe?

(b) How far is it from the cafe to Scorville?

(c) What is Heidi's speed on her way to the cafe? Give your answer in km/hour to 2 sf.

(d) How long after Heidi leaves does Ben leave?

(e) At what time does Ben overtake Heidi?

36.4 A cyclist goes out for ride. They travel downhill and then uphill.

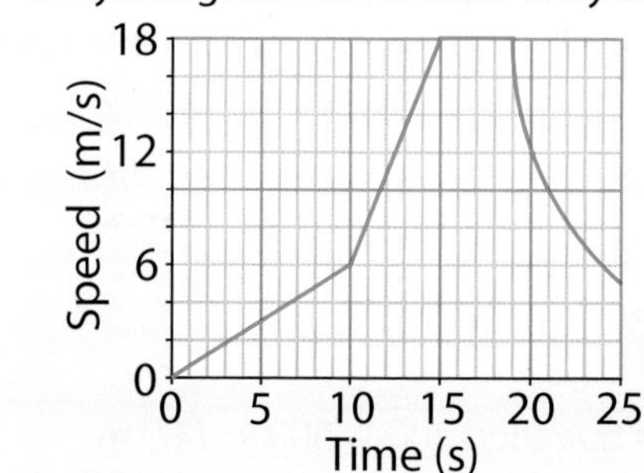

(a) What is the cyclist's acceleration during the first 10 s?

(b) What is the cyclist's average acceleration during the first 15 s?

(c) How many seconds into the ride is it before the cyclist starts going uphill?

36.5 The graphs below shows a linear conversion between pounds and dollars, and between dollars and Euros.

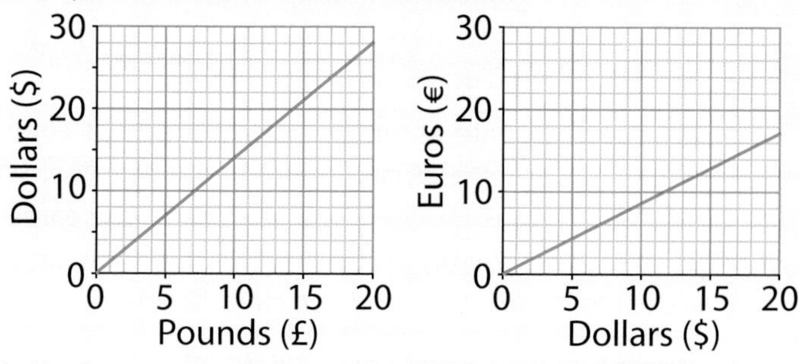

(a) For how many dollars can £780 be exchanged?

(b) Draw a graph to show the conversion between pounds and Euros if pounds were converted into dollars and then into Euros. You may assume there are no additional charges of any kind.

In mathematics two pairs of related concepts are distance and displacement and speed and velocity.

The diagram shows a long straight road. One direction is chosen to be positive, and the other negative. A car starts at the 0 m mark and travels at 10 m/s in the positive direction to the 300 m mark at A. The car then travels at 10 m/s in the negative direction to the -200 m mark at B.

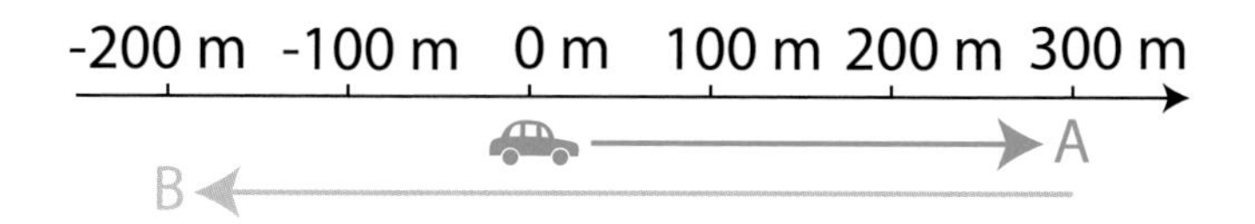

The distance between two points is the number of metres (or kilometres, miles, etc) between them. Point A is a distance of 300 m from the 0 m mark, and B is 200 m from the 0 m mark. Distance is a positive quantity.

Displacement makes use of the sign of the coordinates. The displacement of point A is $+300$ m, and the displacement of point B is -200 m.

- When the car reaches A it has travelled 300 m and its displacement is $+300$ m.
- When the car reaches B it has travelled $300 + 500 = 800$ m and its displacement is -200 m.

The speed of the car is the number of metres of ground that it covers per second (or km per hour, miles per hour, etc). The speed of the car is 10 m/s on its way to A, and also 10 m/s on its way to B.

The velocity of the car is the rate at which its displacement changes. The size of the velocity is the car's speed, and the sign of the velocity indicates the direction in which the car is moving. The velocity of the car is $+10$ m/s on its way to A as the car is moving in the positive direction, and -10 m/s on its way to B as the car is moving in the negative direction.

For a person or object travelling at a constant velocity,

$$\text{velocity} = \frac{\text{change in displacement}}{\text{time for change}}$$

A displacement-time graph shows how the displacement of a person or object changes with time. The gradient of a straight part of the graph is the velocity during that part of the journey.

Note: The y axis may be labelled "displacement". However, if the displacement never takes a negative value, the y axis is often given a label such as "distance from start point" or "distance along road" instead.

Example 4 - A drone is flown along a straight path to take aerial photos for a nature documentary. What is the velocity of the drone after 2.4 hours?

$$\text{velocity} = -\frac{4}{0.5} = -8 \text{ m/s}$$

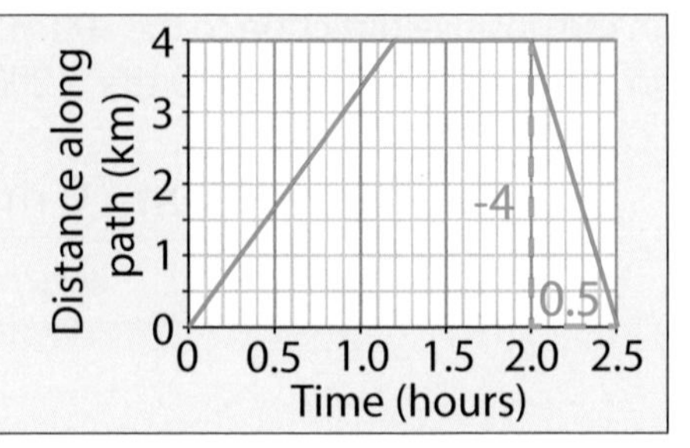

A velocity-time graph is similar to a speed-time graph. The gradient of a straight part of the graph is the acceleration of the object during that part of the motion. The acceleration is positive if the velocity of the object is becoming more positive, and negative if the velocity of the object is becoming more negative.

For situations where an object is accelerating at a constant rate, the displacement s, initial velocity u, final velocity v, acceleration a and the time over which the acceleration occurs t are related by the kinematic ("$suvat$") equations below. These equations assume that the displacement is 0 when $t = 0$.

$$v = u + at \qquad v^2 = u^2 + 2as \qquad s = ut + \frac{1}{2}at^2 \qquad s = \left(\frac{u+v}{2}\right)t$$

To use these equations, start by writing down the values of s, u, v, a and t that you know. Then identify which equation has as its only unknown the quantity which you wish to find.

Example 5 - At $t = 0$ s, the displacement of a car is 0 m and the car is moving with a velocity of $+5$ m/s. The car accelerates at 20 m/s². What are the velocity and displacement of the car after 2 s?

First, draw a diagram.

+5 m/s

0 10 20 30 40 s (m)

From the question, we know that $u = +5$ m/s and $a = 20$ m/s². When $t = 2$ s, the velocity v and displacement s are

$$v = u + at \qquad s = ut + \frac{1}{2}at^2$$

$$v = 5 + (20 \times 2) \qquad s = (5 \times 2) + \frac{1}{2}(20 \times 2^2)$$

$$v = 5 + 40 = 45 \text{ m/s} \qquad s = 10 + 40 = 50 \text{ m}$$

36.6 A window-cleaner is cleaning the windows on one side of a small block of flats using a hoist. It takes them 25 minutes to do all of the windows. The graph shows their journey.

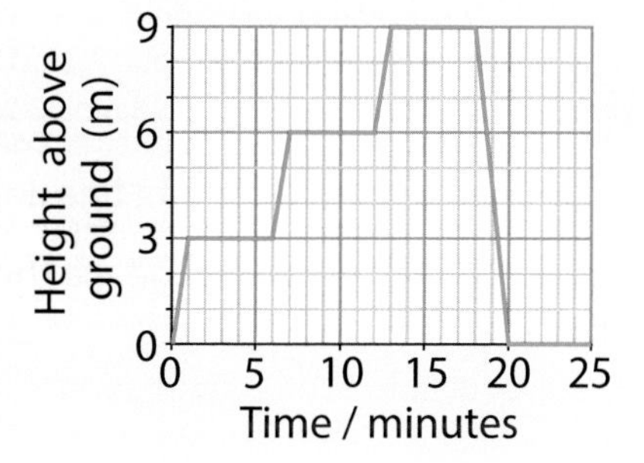

(a) How many floors are there, including the ground level?

(b) Do they clean the windows at ground level first or last?
(c) How long does it take to clean the windows on one floor?
(d) What is the velocity when going upwards between floors?
(e) What is the velocity of the hoist at a time of 19 minutes?

36.7 Use the suvat equations to find the following quantities.
(a) $u = 2$ m/s, $a = 3.5$ m/s^2, and $t = 6$ s. Find v.
(b) If $v = 22$ m/s, $a = 0.5$ m/s^2, and $t = 7$ s,
find the initial velocity u.
(c) Find, to 3 sf, the displacement of a particle starting from rest ($u = 0$ m/s) and accelerating at $a = 2.2$ m/s^2 for $t = 15$ s.

36.8 Use the suvat equations to find the following quantities.
(a) A ball is accelerated at 50 m/s^2 for half a second. The initial velocity of the ball was 15 m/s. What is its final velocity?
(b) A ball with a starting velocity of 1 m/s accelerates at a rate of 4 m/s^2. The displacement of the ball changes from 0 m to 10 m. What is the final velocity of the ball?
(c) A particle accelerates from rest ($u = 0$) at 6 km/s^2. What is the displacement of the particle from its original position when its velocity is 24 km/s?

A rate of change is calculated from a graph by finding its gradient. For example, velocity is the rate of change of displacement with respect to time. The rate of change of a straight line is the same everywhere on the line.

§ Along a curve the rate of change varies:

- The instantaneous rate of change at a point can be found by drawing the tangent at that point and finding the gradient of the tangent.
- An average rate of change can be found by connecting two points on a curve with a straight line and finding the gradient of the line.

The units of a rate of change are the units on the y axis divided by the units on the x axis.

Example 6 - For the graph, find:

(i) The acceleration at $t = 8$ s.

$$a = \frac{5}{10} = \frac{1}{2} \text{ m/s}^2$$

(ii) The average acceleration between $t = 16$ s and $t = 23$ s.

$$a = -\frac{4}{7} \text{ m/s}^2$$

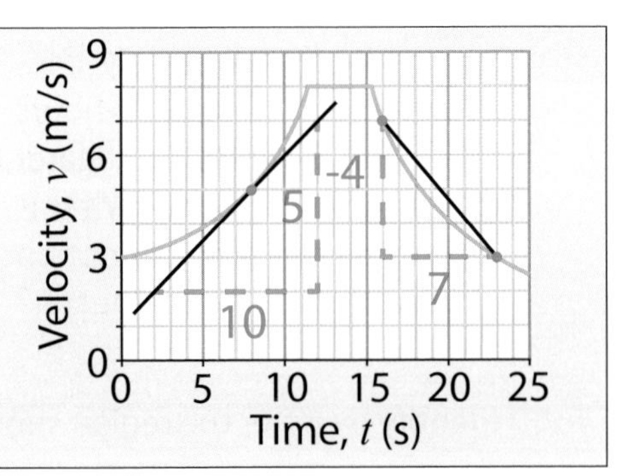

The area under a speed-time graph is the distance travelled. When the graph is made up of straight lines you can work out the area by splitting it up into triangles, rectangles and trapezia. When the graph is a curve you can estimate the area under the curve by counting rectangles. Include in your estimate every rectangle where at least half of the rectangle is under the curve.

The units of distance are the units on the y axis multiplied by the units on the x axis.

Example 7 - Find the distance travelled

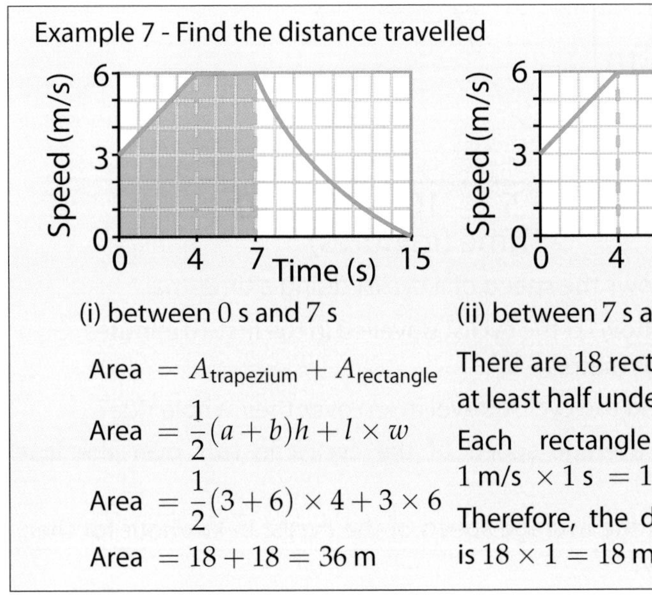

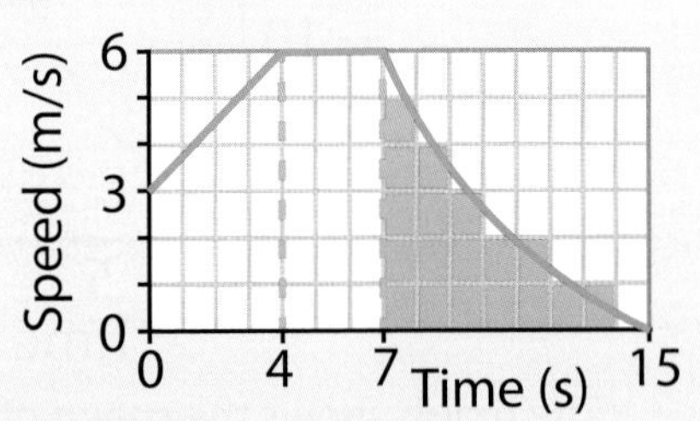

(i) between 0 s and 7 s

$$\text{Area} = A_{\text{trapezium}} + A_{\text{rectangle}}$$

$$\text{Area} = \frac{1}{2}(a+b)h + l \times w$$

$$\text{Area} = \frac{1}{2}(3+6) \times 4 + 3 \times 6$$

$$\text{Area} = 18 + 18 = 36 \text{ m}$$

(ii) between 7 s and 15 s

There are 18 rectangles which are at least half under the curve.

Each rectangle has the size $1 \text{ m/s} \times 1 \text{ s} = 1 \text{ m}$.

Therefore, the distance travelled is $18 \times 1 = 18$ m.

36.9 The graph shows energy consumption in kilowatt-hours (kWh) for an electric heater against time in hours. What is the rate of energy consumption in kilowatts (kW) for this heater?

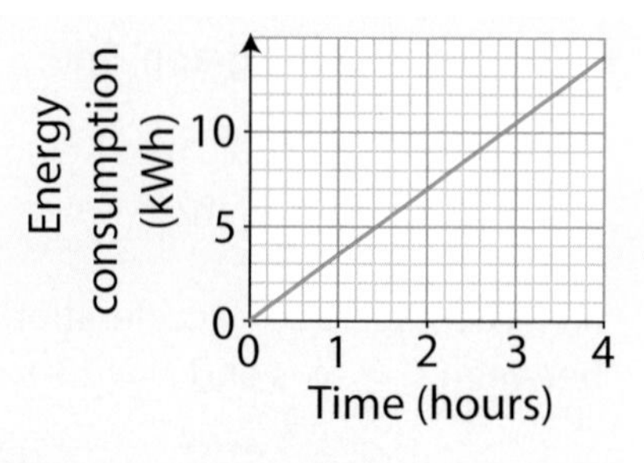

36.10 Identify by letter the region showing:

(a) Constant velocity

(b) Constant rate of change of velocity

(c) Variable rate of change of velocity

(d) Constant acceleration (positive or negative)

(e) Constant rate of change of distance

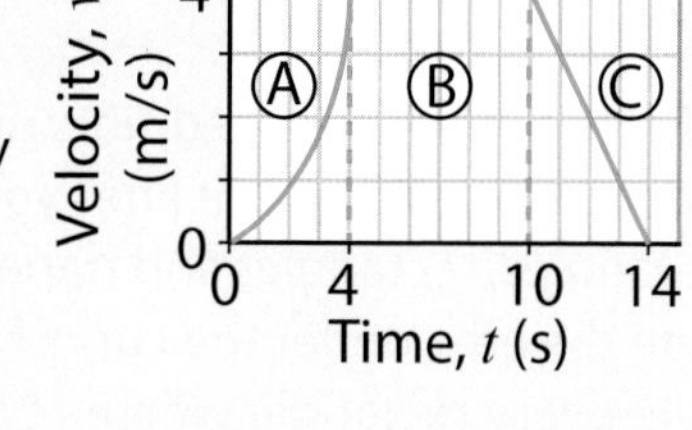

36.11

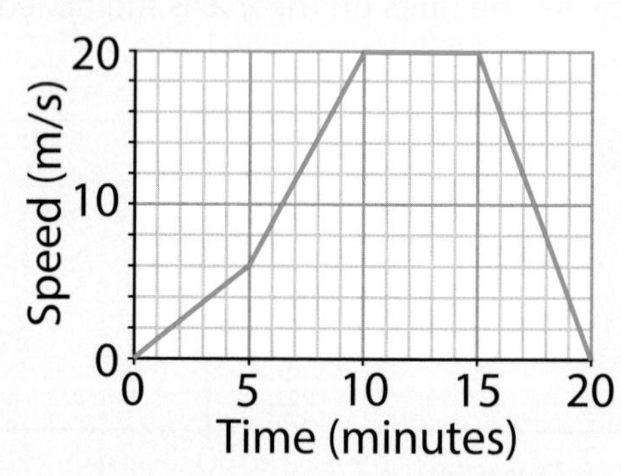

The graph shows the speed of a cyclist doing a time-trial.

(a) Work out how far the cyclist travelled in the first 10 minutes. Give your answer in metres.

(b) How far did the cyclist travel in km over their whole ride?

(c) Find the average speed of the cyclist in m/s over the first 10 minutes.

(d) What was the average speed of the cyclist in km/hour for their entire journey?

36.12 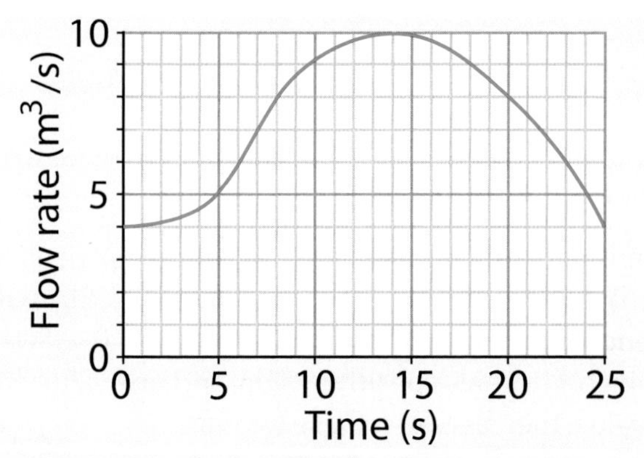

The graph shows the rate of flow of water through a sluice gate over a 25 s period.

(a) What is the maximum flow rate?

(b) Estimate the rate of change of the flow rate at $t = 5$ s.

(c) Estimate the average rate of change of the flow rate over the first 10 s. The units are m^3/s^2.

(d) Estimate the total volume of water flowing through the sluice gate during the 25 s measurement period.

36.13 The graph shows how the number of bacteria in a sample, N, increases over 1 hour.

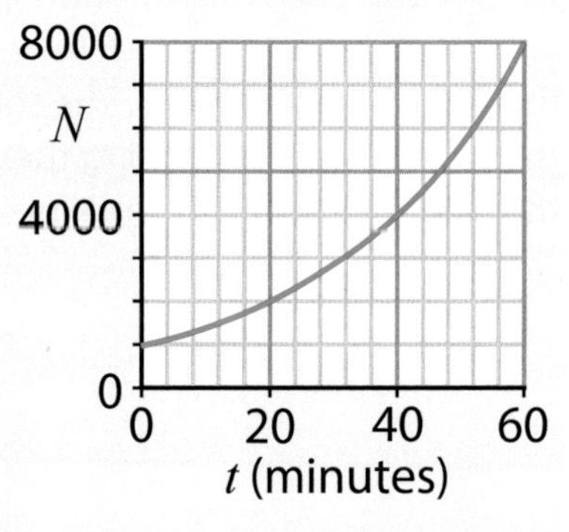

(a) Find the number of bacteria
(i) initially (ii) after 20 minutes

(b) Find the average rate at which the number of bacteria increases during the first 40 minutes.

(c) Estimate the instantaneous rate of increase of the number of bacteria 40 minutes into the experiment.

(d) If N is the number of bacteria after t minutes, which is the best model for the growth of the bacteria?
(i) $N = mt + c$ (ii) $N = 1000 \times 2^{\frac{t}{20}}$

37 § Numerical Methods

Numerical methods are techniques for finding approximate solutions to equations when finding an exact answer is very difficult or impossible.

The three numerical methods covered in this chapter all need a pair of starting values of x between which the solution must lie. Suppose we have a function $f(x)$ and wish to solve the equation $f(x) = 0$. If we can find one value of x for which $f(x)$ has a positive value, and one value for $f(x)$ which has a negative value, then between these two values of x there should be a value of x for which $f(x) = 0$.

The graph on the right shows a sketch of the function $f(x) = 2x^3 - 2x - 3$. When $x = 1$, $f(x) = -3$; and when $x = 2$, $f(x) = 9$. There is a value of x between $x = 1$ and $x = 2$ for which $f(x) = 0$. This value of x is the solution to $2x^3 - 2x - 3 = 0$.

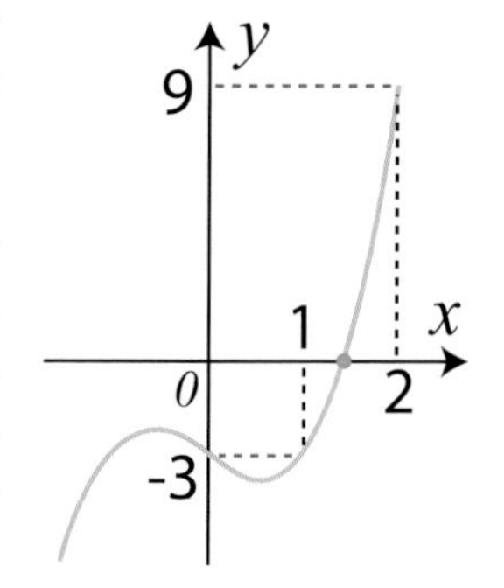

Decimal search involves methodically scanning through decimal numbers one a time. For example, if the starting values are $x = 1$ and $x = 2$, start at $x = 1.0$ and work through the possible values for the first decimal place one after another ($x = 1.1$, $x = 1.2$, ...), calculating values of $f(x)$ until the sign of $f(x)$ changes. The solution then lies between the last two values that were tried. Next, using these two values as a new starting point, work through the second decimal places until the sign changes, and so on.

Example 1 - Use decimal search with the starting values $x = 1$ and $x = 2$, find a solution to $2x^3 - 2x - 3 = 0$ to 2 dp.

$f(x) = 2x^3 - 2x - 3$. The starting values are $x = 1$ and $x = 2$.

1. Work through the first decimal places until $f(x)$ changes sign.

value	$f(x)$
1.0	-3
1.1	-2.538
1.2	-1.944
1.3	-1.206
1.4	-0.312
1.5	+0.75

The solution lies between $x = 1.4$ and $x = 1.5$.

2. Next, using $x = 1.4$ as the starting value, work through the second decimal places.

value	$f(x)$
1.40	-0.312
1.41	-0.213558
1.42	-0.113424
1.43	-0.011586
1.44	+0.091968

The solution lies between $x = 1.43$ and $x = 1.44$.

To 2 dp the solution is either $x = 1.43$ or $x = 1.44$. To decide between them, calculate $f(x)$ for the value of x mid-way between them. When $x = 1.435$, $f(x) = 0.0399$, which is positive. The solution is therefore between $x = 1.43$ and $x = 1.435$, so the solution is $x = 1.43$ to 2 dp.

A second numerical method is interval bisection. The interval in which the solution lies is repeatedly bisected (halved) to close in on the solution.

Example 2 – Use interval bisection to find a solution to $7x^3 - 20x + 5 = 0$ to 2 dp.

The equation is already in the form $f(x) = 0$. $f(x) = 7x^3 - 50x + 5$.

When $x = 1$, $f(x) = -8$, and when $x = 2$, $f(x) = 21$. Therefore, one solution lies between $x = 1$ and $x = 2$.

Now divide the interval into two. When $x = 1.5$, $f(x) = -1.375$. Therefore, the solution lies between $x = 1.5$ and $x = 2$.

Keep halving the interval, recording the results in a table.

x	$f(x)$	**solution is in the interval:**
1	-8	-
2	21	1 to 2
1.5	-1.375	1.5 to 2
1.75	7.5156...	1.5 to 1.75
1.625	2.537...	1.5 to 1.625
1.5625	0.4528...	1.5 to 1.5625
1.53125	-0.4924...	1.53125 to 1.5625
1.546875	-0.0277...	1.546875 to 1.5625
1.5546875	0.2105...	1.546875 to 1.5546875

There is a solution to $7x^3 - 20x + 5 = 0$ at $x = 1.55$, to 2 dp.

A third method of finding numerical solutions is to use an iterative sequence. The steps are outlined in Example 3.

Example 3 – Use an iterative sequence to find the value of the positive root of the equation $x^2 - 5x - 1 = 0$ to 3 dp. The root lies between $x = 5$ and $x = 6$.

First, rearrange the equation so that it has the form $x = \dots$. This is a quadratic equation, so there will be an x on both sides.

$$x^2 - 5x - 1 = 0 \qquad x^2 = 5x + 1 \qquad x = 5 + \frac{1}{x}$$

Based on the form of this equation we make a sequence:

$$x_{n+1} = 5 + \frac{1}{x_n}$$

As we know that a solution to the equation lies between 5 and 6, we take $x_1 = 5.0$ as a starting value for the sequence. Here are the first six terms:

$$x_1 = 5.0 \qquad x_4 = 5.192592...$$
$$x_2 = 5.2 \qquad x_5 = 5.192582...$$
$$x_3 = 5.192307... \qquad x_6 = 5.192582...$$

The sequence converges quickly to a value for x of 5.19258.... To 3 dp, the positive root of $x^2 - 5x - 1 = 0$ is $x = 5.193$.

Note: Not all iterative sequences made by re-arranging an equation converge towards a solution to the equation. Some sequences diverge away from a solution.

37.1 Use decimal search to find a root of each of these equations to 2 dp, starting from the values of x given.

(a) $x^2 - x - 3 = 0$ Starting values: $x = 2$, $x = 3$.

(b) $3x^2 - 9x - 2 = 0$ Starting values: $x = 3$, $x = 4$.

37.2 Starting from the initial estimates given, use decimal search to find a value of x, accurate to 1 dp, which solves each equation.

(a) $x^2 - 4x - 11 = 0$ Initial estimate is 5.

(b) $x^3 - 2x^2 + x = -5$ Initial estimate is -2.

37.3 Use interval bisection to find the root in the given interval to 2 dp:

$$3x^2 - 7x - 1 = 0 \qquad 2 < x < 3$$

37.4 Use interval bisection to find the root in the given interval to 2 dp:

$$x^3 - 6x^2 + 12x - 13 = 0 \qquad 3 < x < 4$$

37.5 Use the iterative sequence $x_{n+1} = \frac{1}{x_n} + 4$ with $x_1 = 4.0$ to find the positive root of the equation $x^2 - 4x - 1 = 0$ to 3 dp.

37.6 Use the iterative sequence $x_{n+1} = 5 - \frac{3}{x_n}$ with $x_1 = 5.0$ to find a root of the equation $x^2 - 5x + 3 = 0$ to 3 dp.

37.7 Adapt the method of decimal search to find the values of these roots to 1 dp.

(a) $\sqrt{11}$ (b) $\sqrt{13}$ (c) $\sqrt[3]{12}$ (d) $\sqrt[3]{22}$

37.8 You are given the equation $x^2 - 5x + 2 = 0$.

(a) Rearrange the equation into the form $x^2 = \dots$. Hence suggest an iterative sequence, involving a constant and a reciprocal, that could be used to find a root of this equation.

(b) By considering integer values of x that are greater than 2, find a suitable starting value of x for finding a root of the equation.

(c) Use your iterative sequence to find a root of the equation to 3 dp.

Geometry

38 Pythagoras' Theorem

The longest side of a right-angled triangle is called the hypotenuse. If c is the length of the hypotenuse, and a and b are the lengths of the other two sides, Pythagoras' Theorem states that

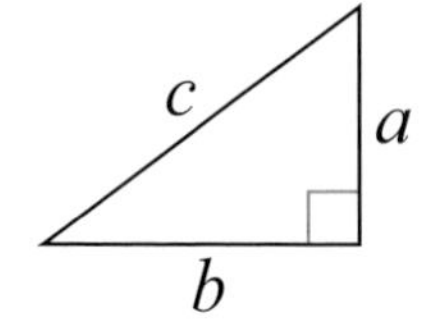

$$a^2 + b^2 = c^2$$

In some triangles a, b and c are all integers. These integer combinations are called Pythagorean triples, and include:

3, 4, 5:

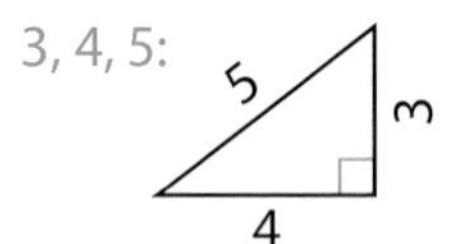

5, 12, 13:

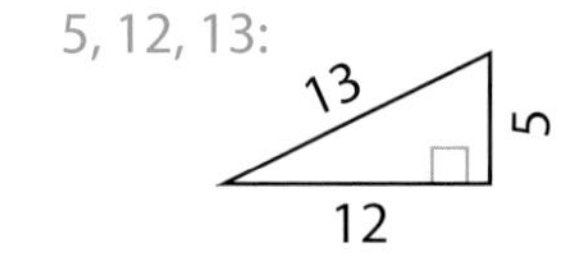

7, 24, 25:

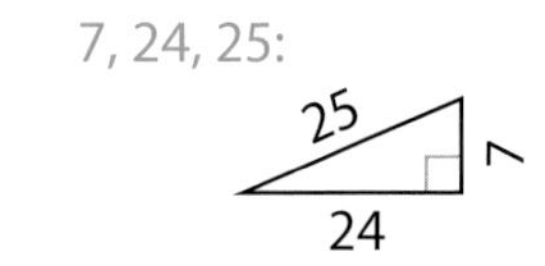

Multiples of Pythagorean triples, such as $6, 8, 10$, are also Pythagorean triples.

Example 1 – Find the missing length for this triangle.

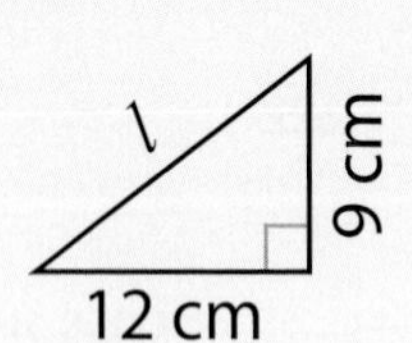

This triangle is a 3,4,5 triangle scaled up by a factor of 3 (as $9 = 3 \times 3$ and $12 = 4 \times 3$).

Hence, the length of the hypotenuse is

$$5 \times 3 = 15 \text{ cm}.$$

Example 2 shows how to use Pythagoras' Theorem to determine if a triangle is right-angled.

Example 2 –

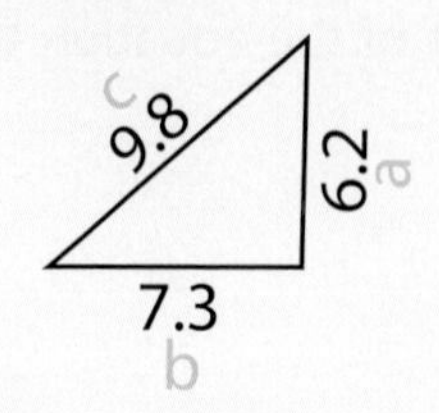

If this triangle is right-angled, the lengths of the sides obey Pythagoras' Theorem, $a^2 + b^2 = c^2$.

$$a^2 + b^2 = 7.3^2 + 6.2^2 = 91.73$$

$$c^2 = 9.8^2 = 96.04$$

The value of $a^2 + b^2$ is not the same as the value of c^2. Hence the triangle is not right-angled.

Example 3 – Find the missing lengths for these triangles.

In this question neither triangle is a scaled version of a Pythagorean triple, so a calculation using Pythagoras' Theorem has to be done in full.

(i)

$$p^2 = 16^2 + 42^2$$
$$\Rightarrow p = 256 + 1764 = 2020$$
$$\therefore p = \sqrt{2020} = 44.9 \text{ m, to 3 sf}$$

(ii)

$$1.11^2 + q^2 = 1.35^2$$
$$\Rightarrow q^2 = 1.35^2 - 1.11^2$$
$$\Rightarrow q^2 = 1.8225 - 1.2321 = 0.5904$$
$$\therefore q = \sqrt{0.5904} = 0.768 \text{ km, to 3 sf}$$

In this exercise give your answers to 3 sf when rounding is required.

38.1 By considering Pythagorean triples, write down the lengths of the missing sides:

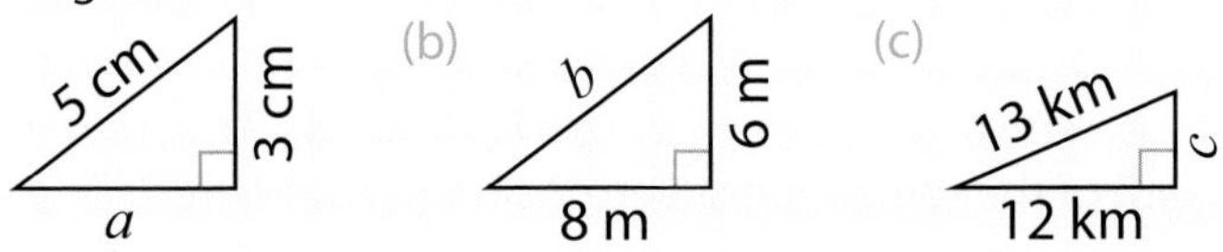

38.2 Find the length of the hypotenuse for each of these triangles.

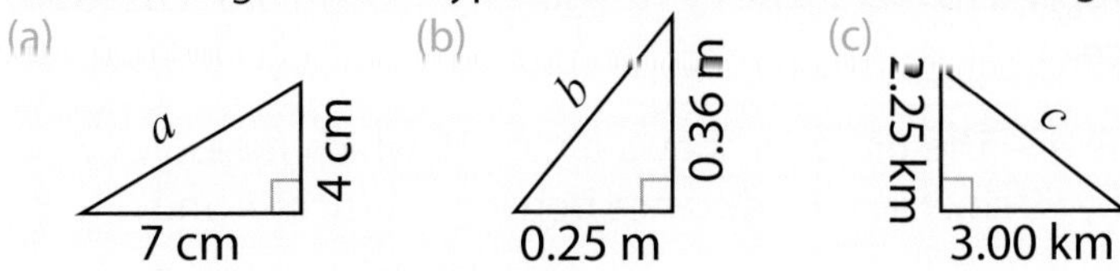

38.3 Find the lengths of the missing sides:

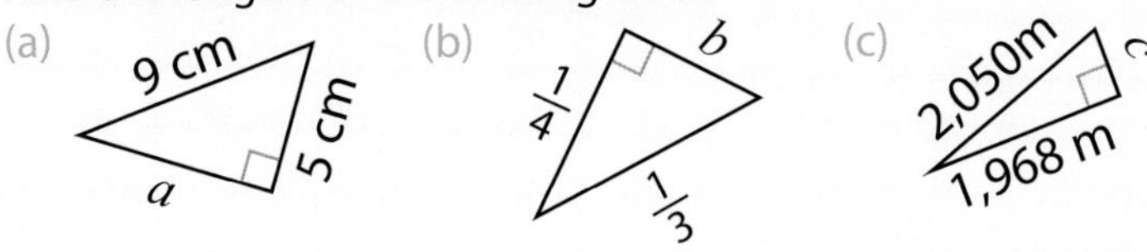

38.4 Which of these triangles are right-angled?

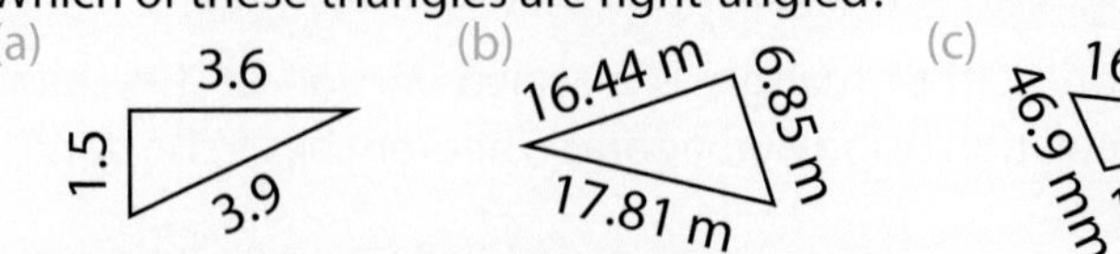

38.5 Rick needs to do some shopping. He starts at his home at H. He walks along a straight footpath to a shop at A, then along the main road to a second shop at B, then returns home along a straight side road. How far does he walk in total?

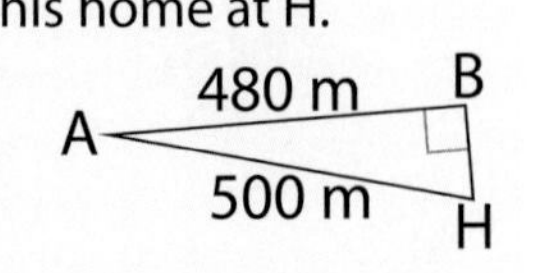

38.6 Rhys constructs a rectangle with sides in the ratio $3 : 4$. He draws in a diagonal and measures its length. It is 8.0 cm. Find the lengths of the sides of the rectangle.

38.7 The diagram shows a lamp shade in the shape of a frustum (a truncated cone).
The top has a radius of 5 cm, the bottom has a radius of 12.5 cm, and the slant height of the side of the shade is 19.5 cm as shown. What is the height of the shade, AB?

38.8 A right-angled triangle has three sides l, m and n. $l = 9.5$ cm, $n = 5.5$ cm, and $l > m > n$. Use Pythagoras' Theorem to find the length of the remaining side to 2 significant figures.

§ When applied to 3-D shapes, Pythagoras' Theorem often needs to be applied twice.

Example 4 – The diagram shows a cuboid which measures 70 cm by 60 cm by 50 cm. Find the distance between vertices A and G to 3 sf.

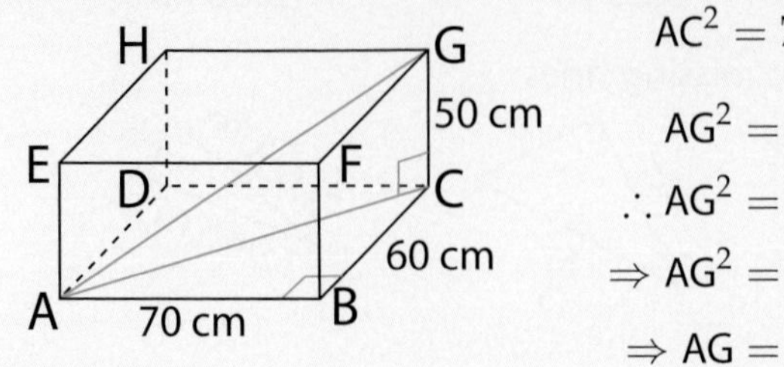

$$\mathrm{AC}^2 = 70^2 + 60^2$$

$$\mathrm{AG}^2 = \mathrm{AC}^2 + 50^2$$

$$\therefore \mathrm{AG}^2 = (70^2 + 60^2) + 50^2$$

$$\Rightarrow \mathrm{AG}^2 = 70^2 + 60^2 + 50^2 = 11\,000$$

$$\Rightarrow \mathrm{AG} = \sqrt{11\,000} = 105 \text{ cm, to 3 sf}$$

38.9 For the cuboids below, find to 3 sf the length of (i) AB and (ii) AC.

(a)

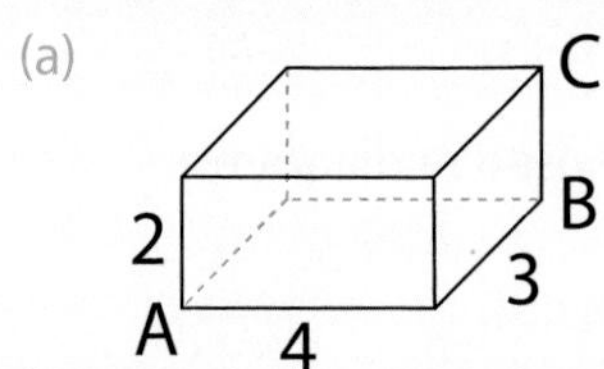

(b)

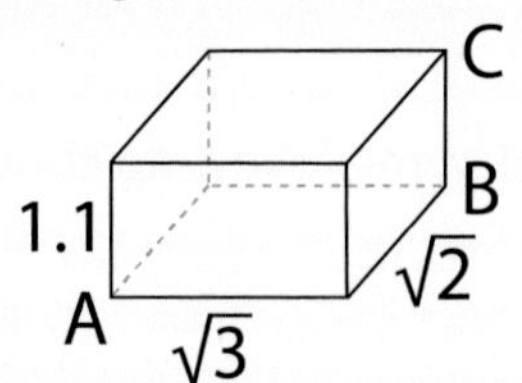

38.10 At one corner of a flat, rectangular patio is a vertical pole, at the top of which is a loudspeaker.

What is the distance from:

(a) A to the loudspeaker at the top of the pole.

(b) B to the loudspeaker at the top of the pole. (Give your answer to 3 sf.)

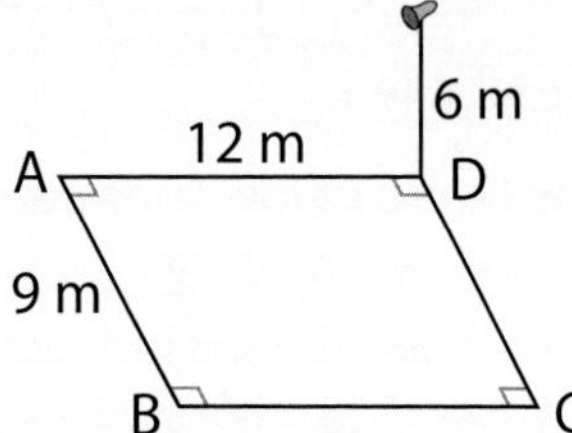

38.11 The diagram shows a cuboid with a square base.

(a) Find the length of AB.

(b) AC has a length of 25. Find the value of a, leaving your answer as a surd.

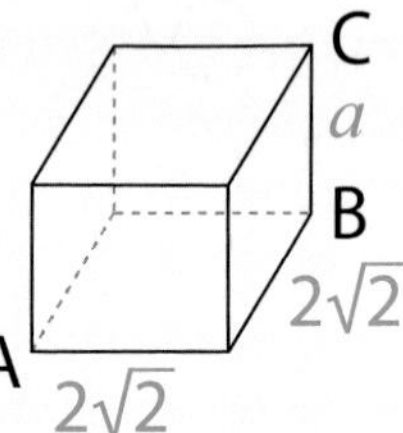

38.12 The diagram shows a cube of side length p. AC has a length of $\sqrt{48}$ cm.

(a) Find the value of p.

(b) Find the length of AB, leaving your answer in surd form.

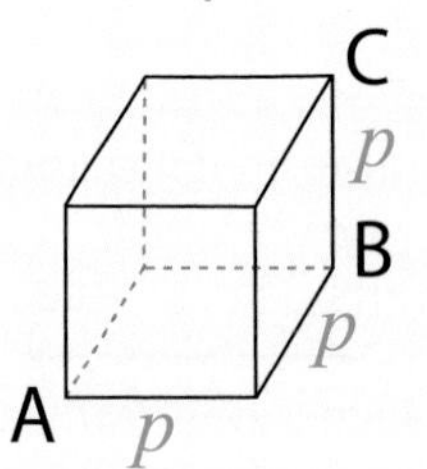

39 Angles and Shapes

In geometry, the following conventions are used in diagrams:

1. Lines that are parallel have the same number of arrows.
2. Lines of equal length have the same number of dashes.
3. A right-angle is drawn as a small square.

In some diagrams angles of equal size are drawn with the same number of arcs. In other diagrams all angles are drawn with a single arc, and the arcs are labelled.

The figure below summarises angle properties for parallel lines.

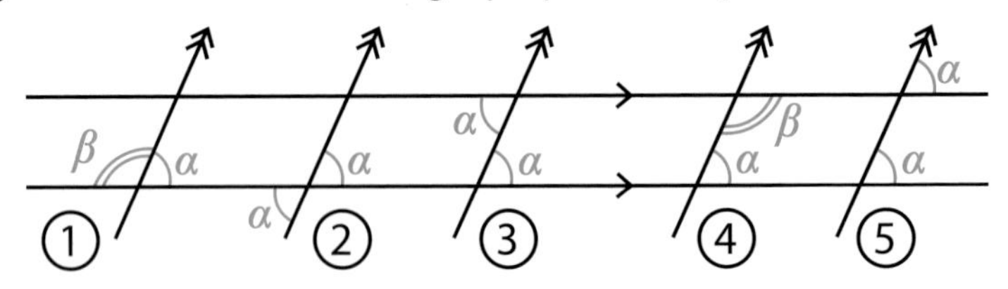

1. Angles on a straight line add up to $180°$: $\alpha + \beta = 180°$.
2. Vertically opposite angles are equal.
3. Alternate angles are equal.
4. Co-interior or allied angles add up to $180°$: $\alpha + \beta = 180°$.
5. Corresponding angles are equal.

Example 1 – Find angles α, β, γ and δ.

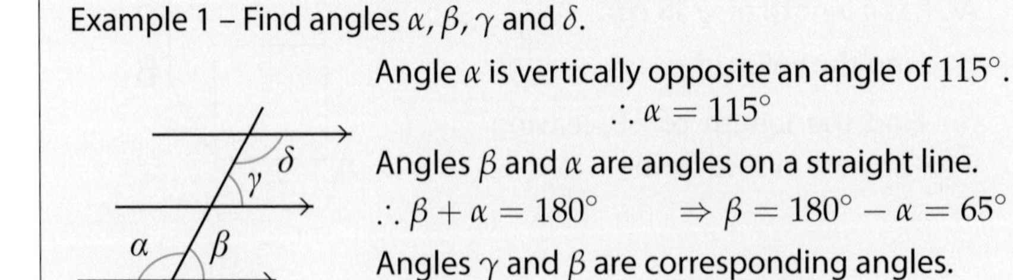

Angle α is vertically opposite an angle of $115°$.

$$\therefore \alpha = 115°$$

Angles β and α are angles on a straight line.

$\therefore \beta + \alpha = 180° \qquad \Rightarrow \beta = 180° - \alpha = 65°$

Angles γ and β are corresponding angles.

$$\therefore \gamma = \beta = 65°$$

Angles δ and γ are allied angles.

$\therefore \delta + \gamma = 180° \qquad \Rightarrow \delta = 180° - \gamma = 115°$

The figure below summarises the properties of three types of triangle:

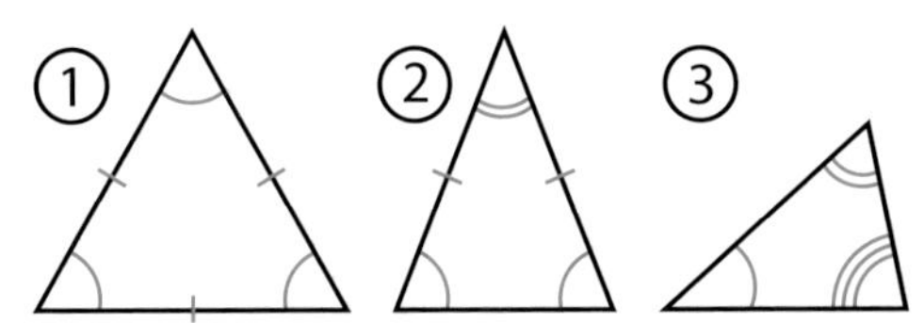

1. Equilateral: three sides the same length, all angles 60°.
2. Isosceles: two sides and two angles the same size.
3. Scalene: no sides of angles the same size.

The interior angles of any triangle add up to 180°.

The figure below summarises six different types of quadrilateral:

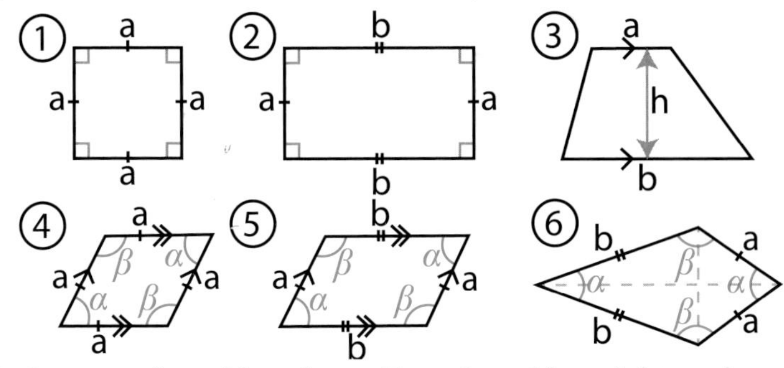

1. A square: four sides of equal length and four right angles.
2. A rectangle: two pairs of sides of equal length and four right angles.
3. A trapezium: one pair of parallel sides.
4. A rhombus: two pairs of parallel sides, and all sides have equal length.
5. A parallelogram: two pairs of parallel sides, parallel sides have equal length.
6. A kite: two pairs of adjacent sides of equal length.

39.1 Find the stated angles, giving your reasoning.

(a) Find α and β. (b) Find α, β, γ and δ.

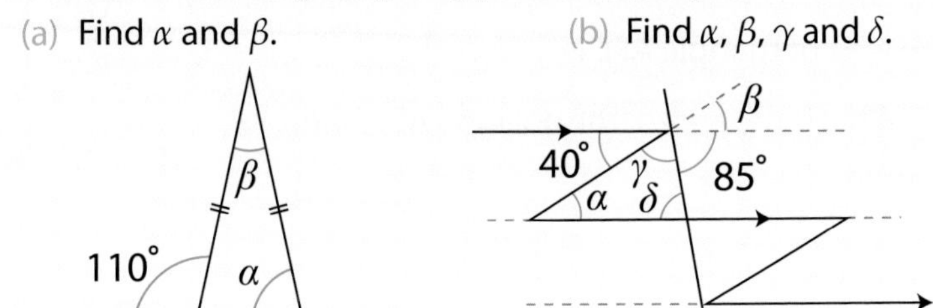

39.2 Find the stated angles, giving your reasoning.

(a) Find α.

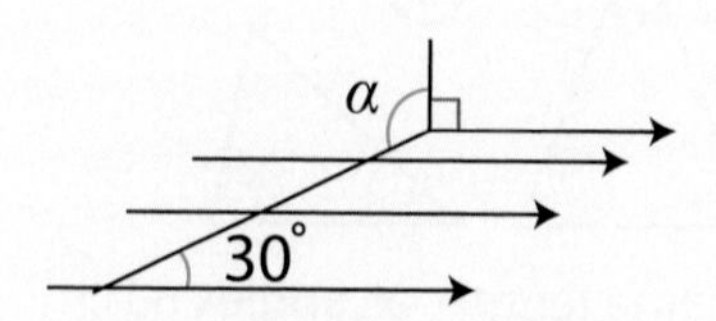

(b) Find α and β.

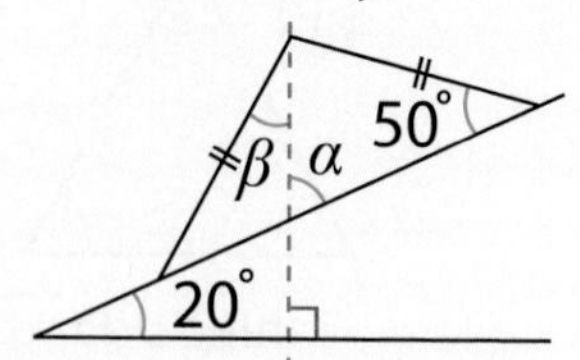

39.3 (a) Write down the sum of the internal angles of a triangle.

(b) Use your answer to (a) to write an equation involving α.

(c) Solve your equation from (b) to find the value of α.

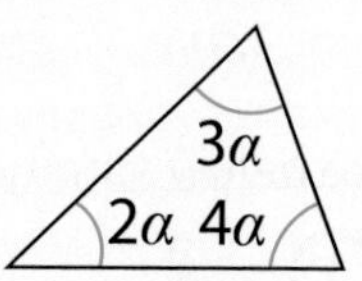

39.4 Find the values of

(a) $A\hat{B}C$ (c) $C\hat{B}E$

(b) $D\hat{B}A$ (d) β

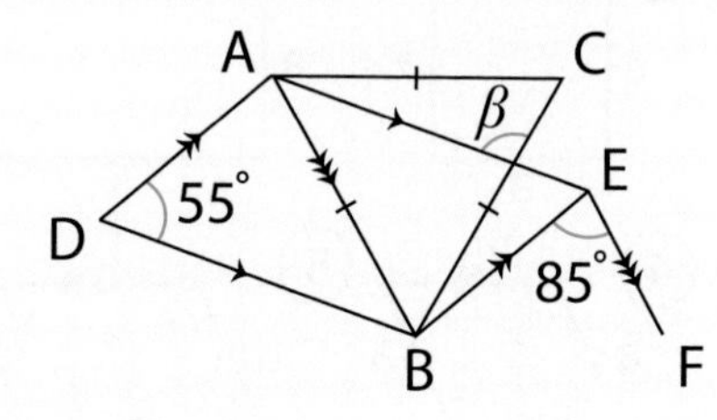

39.5 A kite is drawn as shown. AB $=10$ cm. Find:

(a) Angle $A\hat{D}C$.

(b) The length of DC, to 3 sf.

(c) The length of AC, to 3 sf.

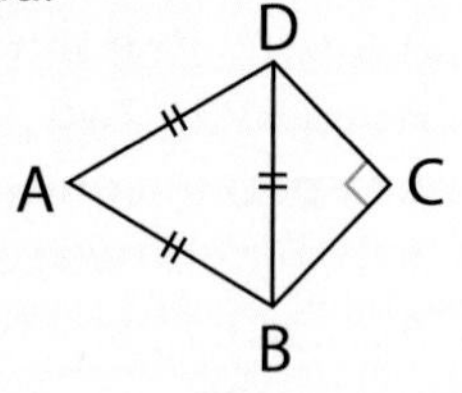

39.6 In the diagram below E, F and C lie on a straight line.

(a) What type of quadrilateral is AFDE?

(b) What is angle $D\hat{F}C$?

The area of triangle AFE is 6.92 cm^2.

(c) What is the area of the polygon ABCDE?

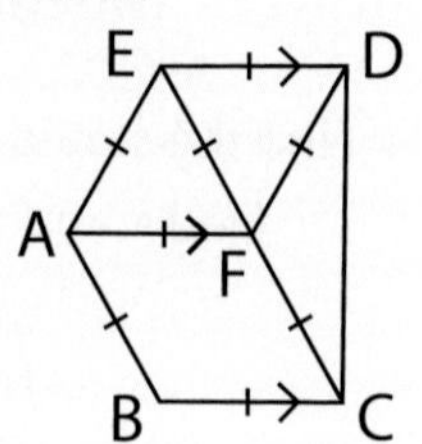

A polygon is a closed, flat shape with straight sides. If all the sides of a polygon are the same length, and all internal angles the same size, the polygon is regular. Otherwise it is irregular.

The diagram shows the internal angles (left) and external angles (right) of a regular pentagon.

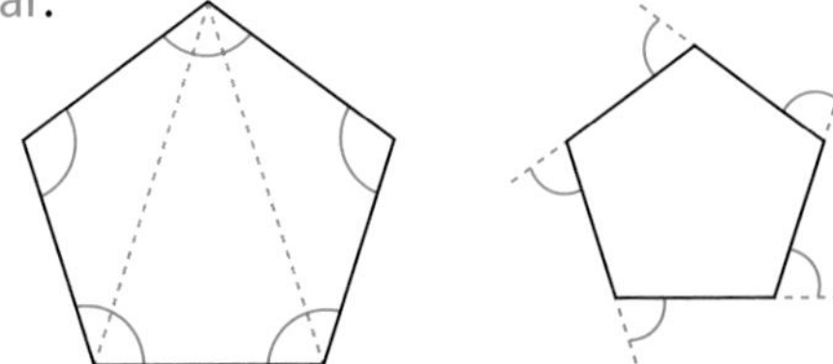

To find the sum of the interior angles of a polygon, subdivide the polygon into a fan of triangles. For the pentagon above, 3 triangles are needed. For a polygon with n sides, $n-2$ triangles are needed. The sum of the interior angles of one triangle is 180°. Therefore,

$$\text{Sum of internal angles} = 180(n-2)^\circ$$

Also, for any polygon the sum of the external angles is 360°, and at any vertex the sum of the internal and external angles is 180°.

Example 2 – The sum of the interior angles of a regular polygon is 1260°. What is the value of the exterior angle?

Use the formula for the sum of the interior angles to find the number of sides, n.

$$\begin{aligned} \text{Sum of internal angles} &= 180(n-2)^\circ \\ 1260^\circ &= 180(n-2)^\circ \qquad \downarrow \div 180 \\ 7 &= n-2 \\ \therefore n &= 9 \end{aligned}$$

The sum of the exterior angles of a polygon is always 360°. Therefore,

$$\text{Exterior angle} = \frac{360^\circ}{9} = 40^\circ$$

39.7 The shape shown is a regular octagon.

(a) Find the value of α.

(b) Find the value of β.

(c) Find the value of γ.

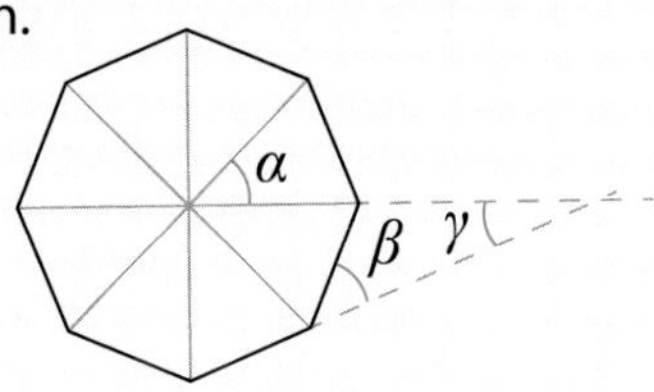

39.8 a, b and c are three sides of a regular polygon with 18 sides.

(a) Find the value of α, the exterior angle.

(b) Find the value of the angle β formed by extending sides a and c.

(c) What is the sum of the interior angles of this polygon?

(d) What is the size of one interior angle?

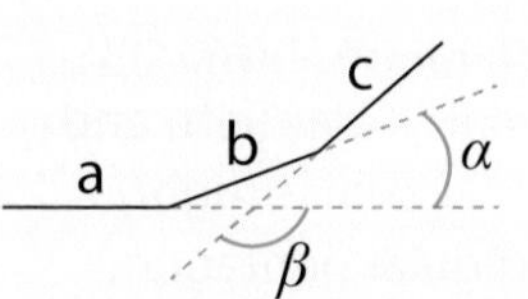

39.9 Calculate angles α and β, giving your reasoning.

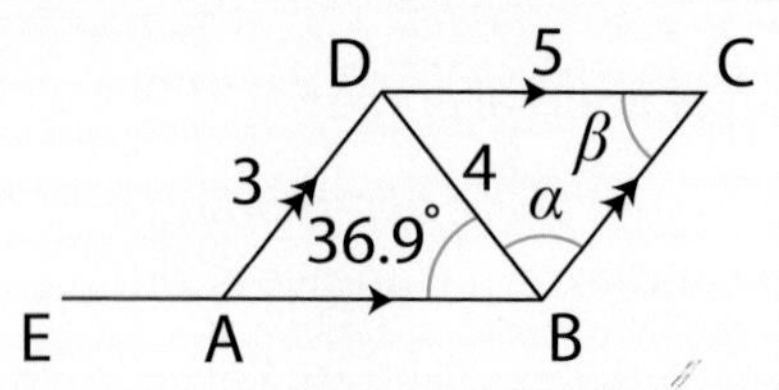

39.10 ABCDE is an irregular pentagon. x and y are in degrees.

(a) Angle $B\hat{C}D$ is $20°$ bigger than angle $A\hat{E}D$. Write this information as an equation involving x and y. Simplify the equation as far as possible.

(b) By considering the value of the sum of the internal angles of a pentagon, write a second equation involving x and y. Simplify the equation as far as possible.

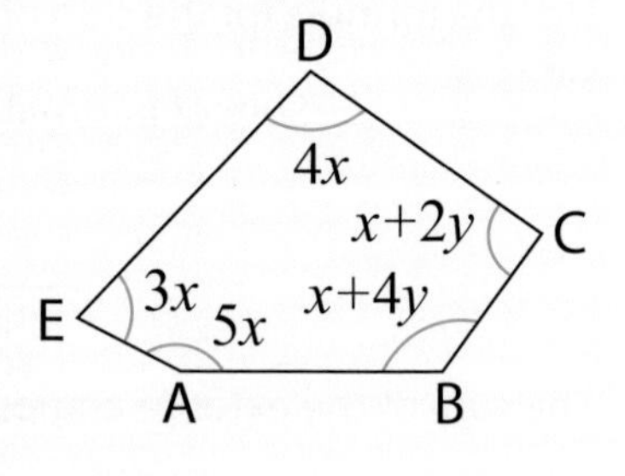

(c) Solve the equations from parts (a) and (b) simultaneously to find the values of x and y.

40 Symmetry and Similarity

Shapes may be symmetrical under reflections or rotations.

The order of reflective symmetry is the number of lines of reflection an object possesses. Not all shapes have a line of symmetry, so the order of reflective symmetry can be 0.

Example 1 – Draw the lines of symmetry onto a copy of the shape below. What is the order of reflective symmetry for this shape?

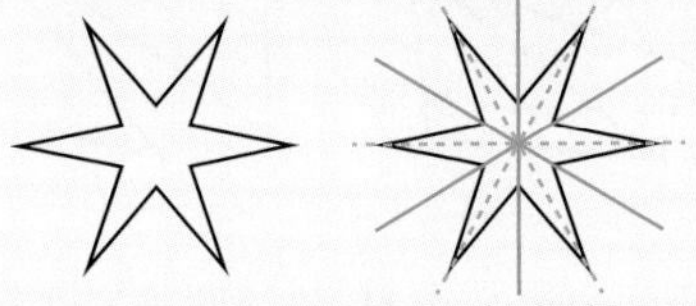

The shape has 6 lines of symmetry.

The order of reflective symmetry is 6.

The order of rotational symmetry is the number of times during a rotation of one full turn ($360°$) that a shape looks exactly the same as before the rotation began. All shapes look the same after being rotated through ($360°$), so the order of rotational symmetry is always at least 1.

Example 2 – What is the order of rotational symmetry of these shapes?

(i) 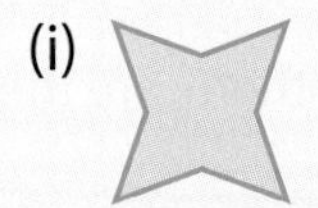 (ii) 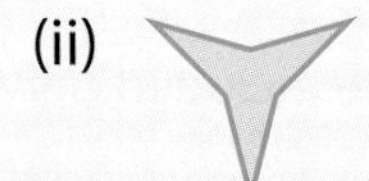 (iii) 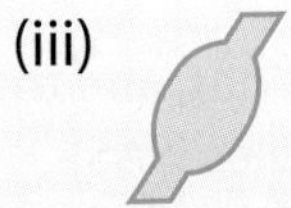

(i) 4: rotations of $90°, 180°, 270°$ and $360°$ leave the shape unchanged
(ii) 3: rotations of $120°, 240°$ and $360°$ leave the shape unchanged
(iii) 2: rotations of $180°$ and $360°$ leave the shape unchanged

Two shapes are similar if all corresponding angles in the two shapes are equal, and the lengths of corresponding sides are all in the same ratio. The second shape may be translated, rotated, reflected, or scaled up or down. The ratio of the lengths of corresponding sides is the linear scale factor. Similar shapes that are also the same size are congruent.

In the diagram on the next page, (i) shows similar shapes (all corresponding angles are equal; all corresponding lengths are twice as large in the larger shape). The shapes in (ii) are congruent (all corresponding angles and lengths are equal). The shapes in (iii) are not similar (A′B′ is the same as AB, but A′D′ is twice AD).

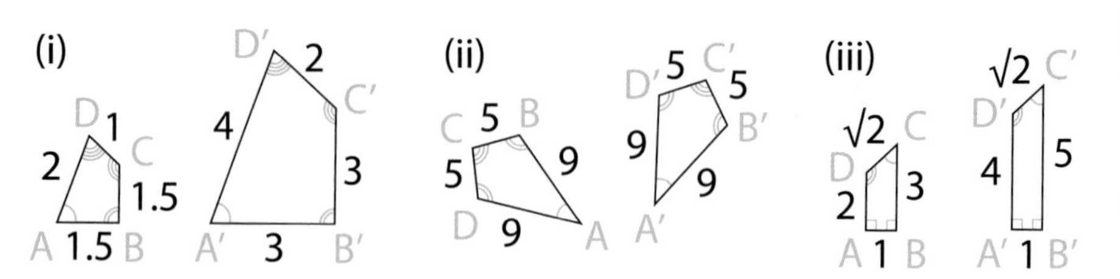

To show that two triangles are congruent, it is necessary to show that they satisfy one of four conditions:

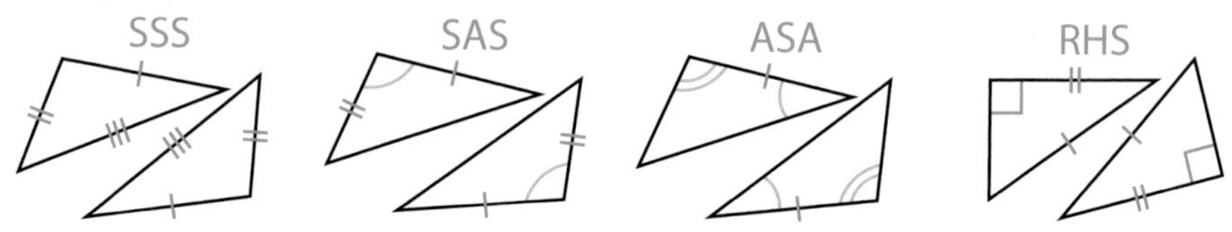

- SSS - three sides are the same
- SAS - two sides and the included angle between them are the same
- ASA - two angles and the included side between them are the same
- RHS - right-angled, the hypotenuse and one other side are the same

Example 3 – Are triangles N and M congruent? Give a reason for your answer.

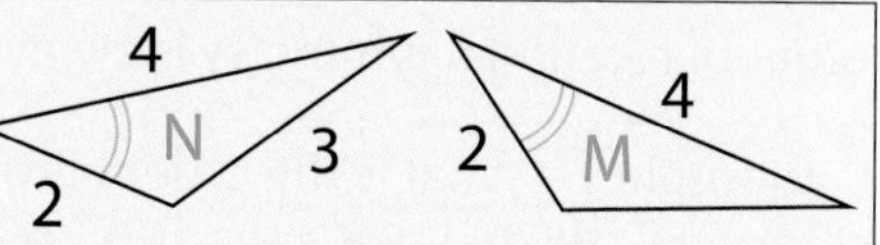

Yes - Two sides, and the angle included between them, are the same in both triangles (SAS).

40.1 (i) (ii) (iii) (iv)

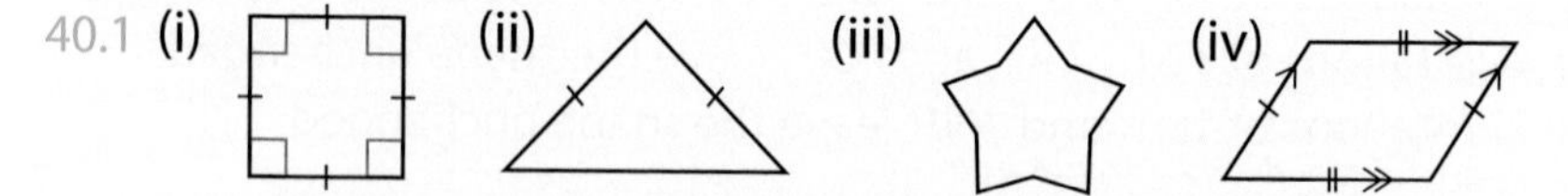

(a) Copy each shape and draw in the lines of reflection.
(b) State the order of reflective symmetry of each shape.
(c) State the order of rotational symmetry of each shape.

40.2 How many similar triangles can be identified in this diagram?

List the triangles that are similar.

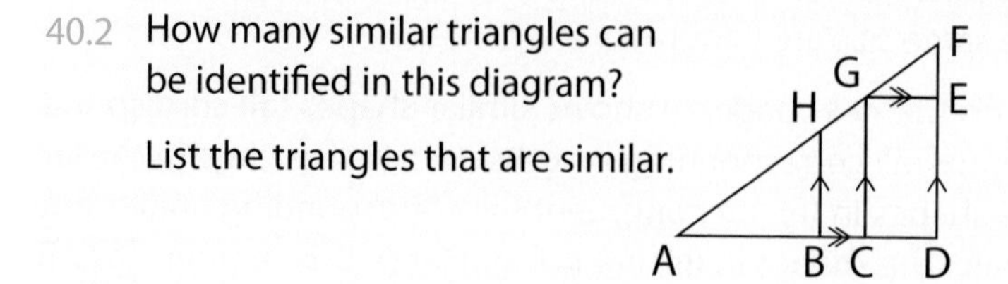

40.3 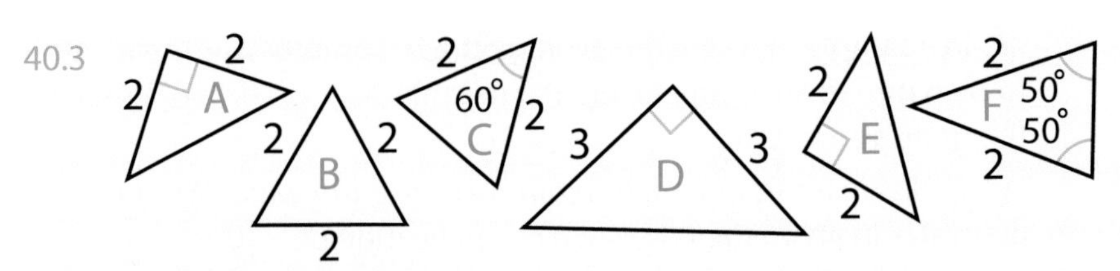

How many triangles are...

(a) Isosceles but not equilateral?
(b) Congruent to triangle A?
(c) Congruent to triangle D?
(d) Similar to triangle E?

40.4 By considering similar triangles, find

(a) s and t (b) x

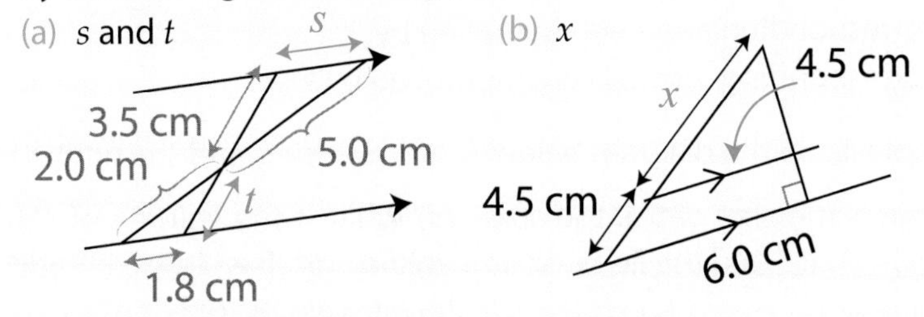

40.5 In each question identify the correct statement.

(a) (i) A parallelogram is a rhombus
(ii) A rhombus is a parallelogram.

(b) If 4 congruent triangles are used to make 1 larger similar triangle, the triangles must be equilateral. (i) True (ii) False.

(c) 4 congruent, scalene triangles can always be re-arranged to make (i) $\leqslant 3$ different parallelograms (ii) $\geqslant 4$ different parallelograms.

40.6 You are shown two similar, right-angled triangles, ABC and DEF.

(a) What is the linear scale factor, f, to create triangle DEF from triangle ABC?

(b) What is angle CÂB ?

(c) What is the exact length of EF?

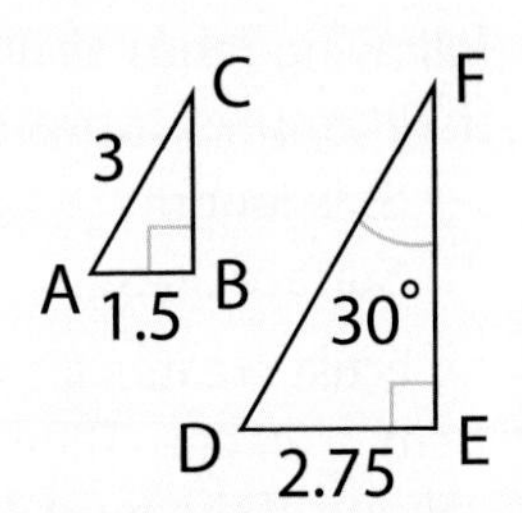

40.7 On the microscopic scale, a metal is divided up into regions called grains. The size of a grain can be measured using a microscope.

(a) In a sample of nickel the average grain diameter was measured to be 6 mm in an image taken at a magnification of $\times 300$. What is the grain size in μm?

(b) Grains in a sample of aluminium are 120 μm wide. What is the grain size in an image taken at a magnification of $\times 100$?

(c) What is the ratio of the grain diameters in the samples of aluminium and nickel?

§ If s is the linear scale factor for a pair of similar shapes,

- corresponding lengths are multiplied by s
- corresponding areas are multiplied by s^2
- corresponding volumes are multiplied by s^3

Example 4 – In the diagram below, S is similar to S′ and T is similar to T′.

(i) What is the area of S′ if the area of S is 14.0 cm^2 and the linear scale factor is $\frac{3}{2}$?

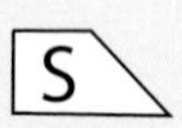

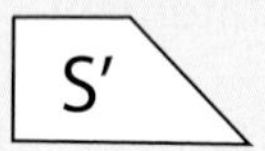

The area of S′ is

$$\left(\frac{3}{2}\right)^2 \times 14.0 = 31.5 \text{ cm}^2$$

(ii) What is the volume of T′ if the volume of T is 125 cm^3 and the linear scale factor is 1.4?

T T′

The volume of T′ is

$$(1.4)^3 \times 125 = 343 \text{ cm}^3$$

40.8 A child has a set of building blocks. There are two sizes of cubes. Give the following ratios as Block A : Block B in their simplest forms.

A B

2.5 cm 5.0 cm

(a) Side lengths (c) Volumes

(b) Surface areas

40.9 An artist creates a small scale-model of a sculpture on a scale of 1 cm : 20 cm. They make a mold and fill it with wax to find the volume of the model. 9.2 cm^3 of wax fills the mold.

(a) Calculate the volume of the sculpture.

(b) The sculpture is made in bronze. If a scale model in bronze has a mass of 81 g, find the mass of the sculpture in kg.

(c) Calculate the density of bronze to 2 sf.

41 Trigonometry

The three trigonometric functions sine, cosine and tangent are related to the lengths of the sides of a right-angled triangle by the following ratios:

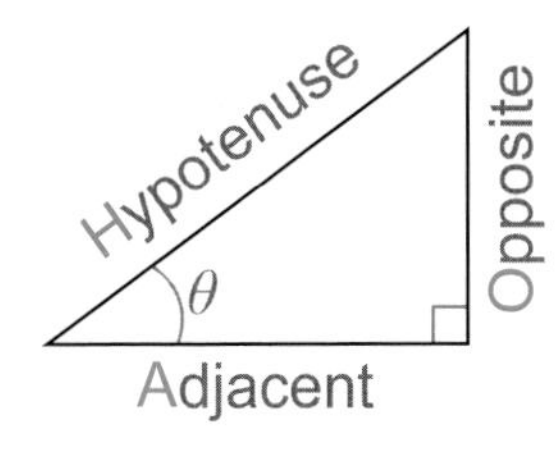

$$\sin\theta = \frac{\text{Opposite}}{\text{Hypotenuse}}$$

$$\cos\theta = \frac{\text{Adjacent}}{\text{Hypotenuse}}$$

$$\tan\theta = \frac{\text{Opposite}}{\text{Adjacent}}$$

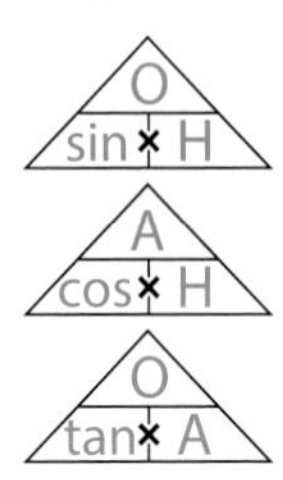

The acronym "SOH CAH TOA" is used as an aid to remember which functions are related to which sides.

In a trigonometry problem first identify the angle you will use or find. Then label the sides as opposite, adjacent and hypotenuse. Finally, decide whether to use sin, cos or tan.

Note: Make sure that your calculator is set to work in degrees!

Example 1 – Find the missing lengths for these two triangles.

(i)

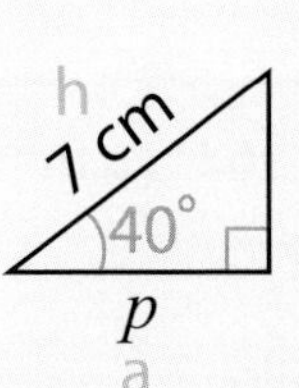

The side labelled p is adjacent to the 40° angle, and the 7 cm is on the hypotenuse, so use $\cos$.

$$\cos 40^\circ = \frac{p}{7} \qquad \downarrow \text{Multiply both sides by 7.}$$

$$\Rightarrow 7\cos 40^\circ = p$$

$$\therefore p = 7\cos 40^\circ = 5.36 \text{ cm, to 3 sf}$$

(ii)

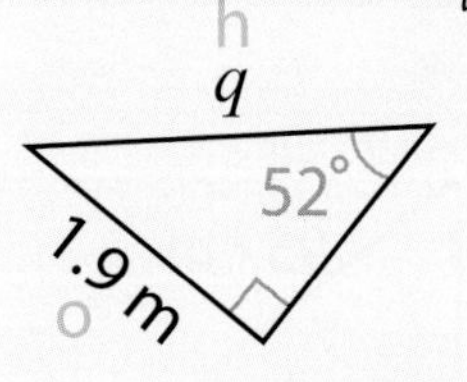

The side labelled 1.9 m is opposite the 52° angle, and q is on the hypotenuse, so use $\sin$.

$$\sin 52^\circ = \frac{1.9}{q} \qquad \downarrow \text{Multiply both sides by } q.$$

$$q\sin 52^\circ = 1.9 \qquad \downarrow \text{Divide both sides by } \sin 52^\circ.$$

$$q = \frac{1.9}{\sin 52^\circ}$$

$$\therefore q = 2.41 \text{ m, to 3 sf}$$

To find angles, you need to use the inverse trigonometric functions $\sin^{-1}\theta$, $\cos^{-1}\theta$ and $\tan^{-1}\theta$. For example:

if $\sin\theta = 0.7$ **then** $\theta = \sin^{-1}(0.7) = 44.4^\circ$ to 3 sf

Using $\sin^{-1}\theta$ effectively "undoes" $\sin\theta$. Likewise, $\cos^{-1}\theta$ undoes $\cos\theta$ and $\tan^{-1}\theta$ undoes $\tan\theta$.

Example 2 – Find the size of angle α.

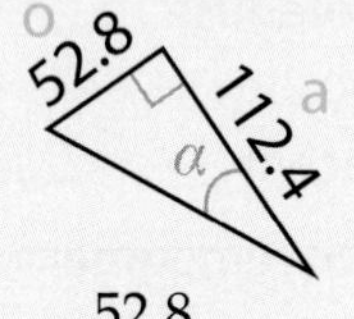

The side labelled 52.8 is opposite angle α, and the side labelled 112.4 is adjacent to angle α, so use tan.

$$\tan\alpha = \frac{52.8}{112.4}$$

↓ Take the inverse tangent of both sides.

$$\alpha = \tan^{-1}\left(\frac{52.8}{112.4}\right)$$

$$\therefore \alpha = 25.2^\circ \text{ to 3 sf}$$

In this exercise give your answers to 3 sf when rounding is required.

41.1 Find the lengths of the indicated sides:

(a)

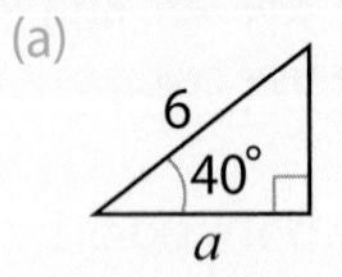

(b)

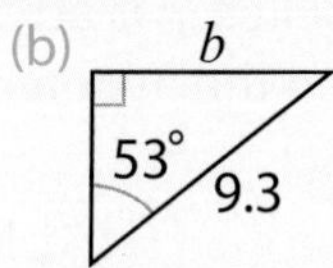

(c)

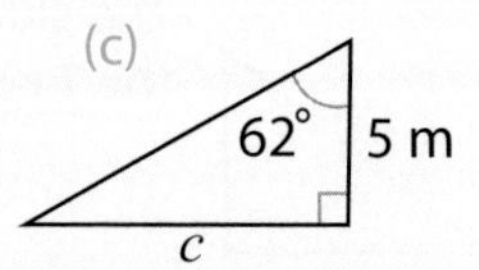

41.2 Find the length of the hypotenuse for each triangle:

(a)

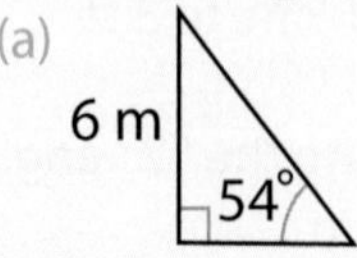

(b)

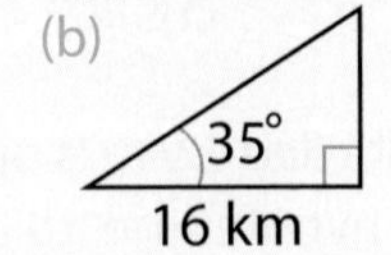

(c)

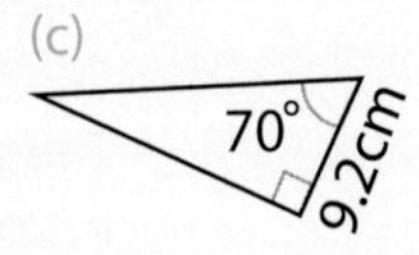

41.3 Find the size of each of the angles indicated:

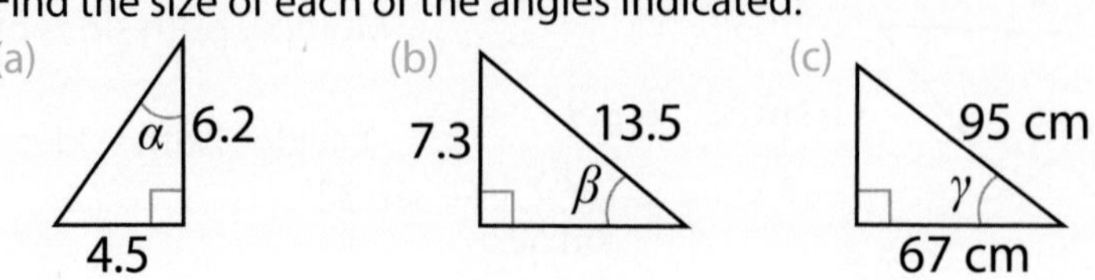

41.4 Find the following angles:

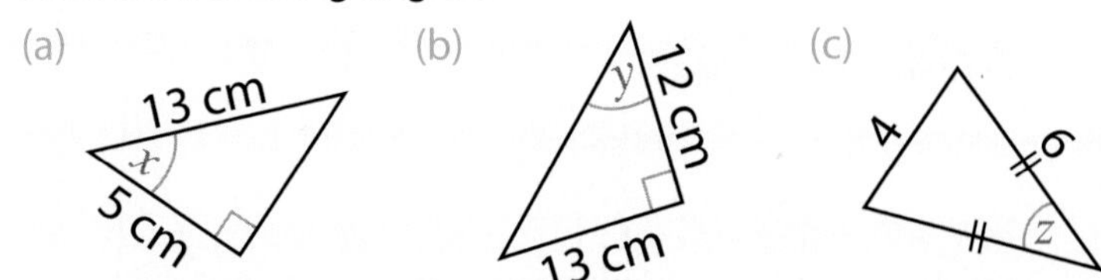

41.5 The base of a ladder is 4 ft from a wall and makes an angle of $70°$ with the ground. How long is the ladder?

There are some exact values of $\sin\theta$, $\cos\theta$ and $\tan\theta$ that it is important to remember. The values for $30°$, $45°$ and $60°$ in the table can be found by applying trigonometry to the triangles shown below, which are halves of an equilateral triangle and a square.

Function	θ				
	$0°$	$30°$	$45°$	$60°$	$90°$
$\sin\theta$	0	$\frac{1}{2}$	$\frac{1}{\sqrt{2}}$	$\frac{\sqrt{3}}{2}$	1
$\cos\theta$	1	$\frac{\sqrt{3}}{2}$	$\frac{1}{\sqrt{2}}$	$\frac{1}{2}$	0
$\tan\theta$	0	$\frac{1}{\sqrt{3}}$	1	$\sqrt{3}$	undefined

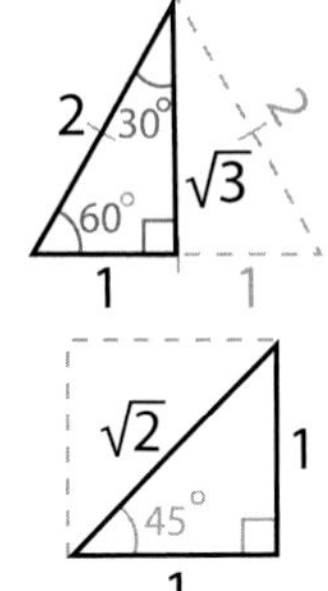

Where it is necessary to give an exact answer, leave your answer in terms of square roots ("in surd form").

One application of trigonometry is finding angles of elevation and depression. An angle of elevation is above the horizontal, and an angle of depression is below the horizontal.

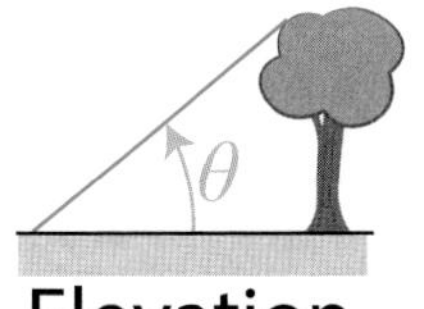

Elevation

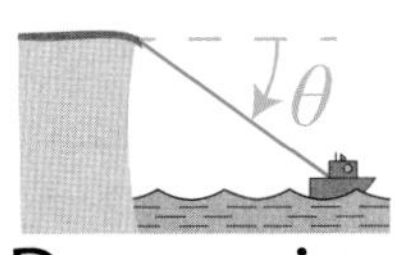

Depression

In this exercise give your answers to 3 sf when rounding is required.

41.6 Find the following angles.

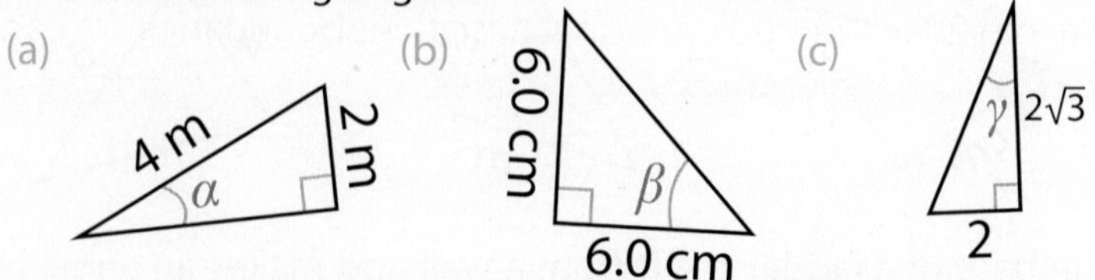

41.7 Find the exact values of the indicated lengths.

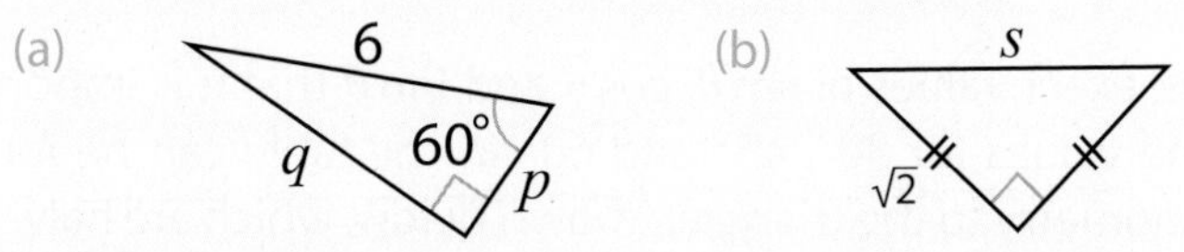

41.8 Find the following angles of elevation and depression.

(a) A surveyor raises the end of a 2 m pole upwards by 65 cm.

(b) A high-jump official lowers one end of a 3.5 m pole by 40 cm.

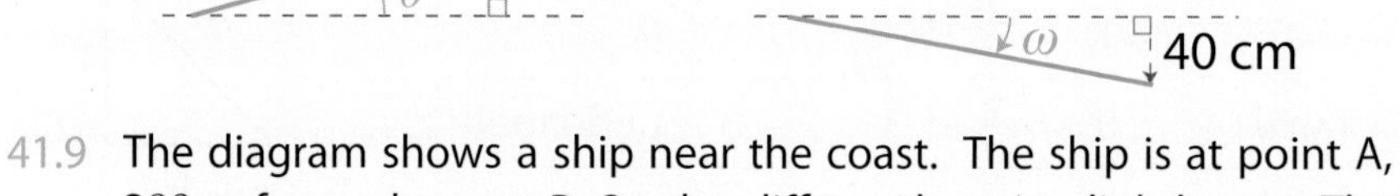

41.9 The diagram shows a ship near the coast. The ship is at point A, 200 m from a buoy at B. On the cliff top there is a lighthouse. The tip of the lighthouse (point C) is a distance y above the level of the sea at D.

The angle of elevation of the top of the lighthouse is $8.5°$ at A and $14.0°$ at B.

What is the value of y?

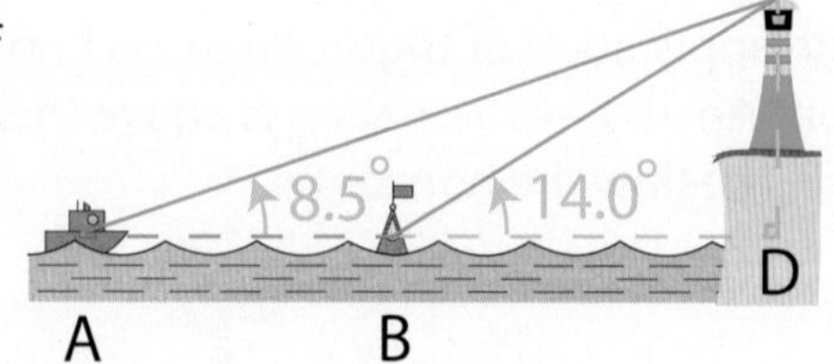

Hint: you may need to set up and solve a pair of simultaneous equations.

41.10 Re-arrange $\frac{\sin i}{\sin r} = n$ to give an expression for

(a) $\sin i$ (b) r

42 Circles and Circle Theorems

Circles are different from polygons because their boundaries are continuous curves rather than made up of straight lines.

The boundary of a circle is called the circumference. The distance between the centre and the circumference is the radius. A straight line from one side of a circle to the other through the centre is a diameter.

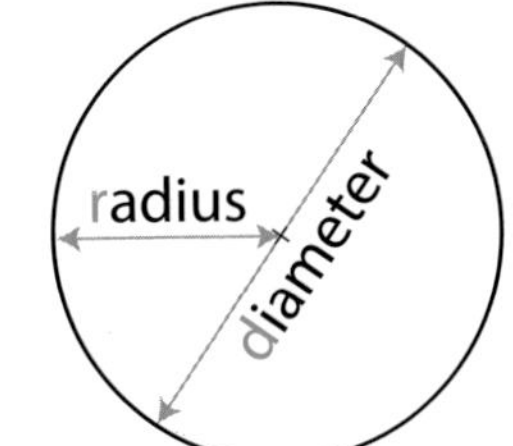

A diameter is twice the length of a radius: $d = 2r$. The length of the circumference, C, and the area of a circle, A, are given by the formulae:

$$C = 2\pi r \text{ or } C = \pi d \qquad A = \pi r^2 \text{ or } A = \frac{\pi d^2}{4}$$

π is an irrational number with the value 3.14159265....

Example 1 – Find the circumference and area of a circle of diameter 120 cm to 3 sf.

120 cm

The radius is half the diameter.

$$r = \frac{d}{2} = \frac{120}{2} = 60 \text{ cm}$$

$\therefore C = 2\pi r$

$\Rightarrow C = 2 \times \pi \times 60$

$\Rightarrow C = 377$ cm to 3sf

and $A = \pi r^2$

$\Rightarrow A = \pi \times 60^2$

$\Rightarrow A = 11\,300$ cm^2 to 3sf

In this exercise give your answers to 3 sf when rounding is required.

42.1 For each shape find

(i) the length of the curved part of the boundary (ii) the area.

(a)

5.0 cm

(b)

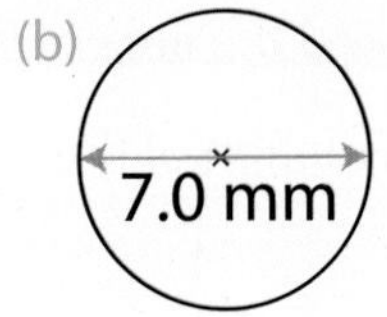

(c)

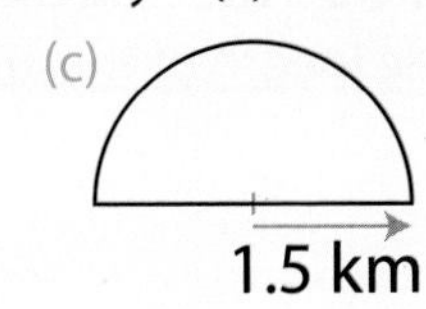

42.2 (a) The circumference of a circle is 82.6 cm. Find the radius.

(b) The area of a circle is 156 cm^2. Find the radius.

(c) The area of a semicircle is 16.4 cm^2. Find the diameter of the circle of which it is a part.

42.3 The diagram shows a "figure-8" consisting of two circles which touch at one point.

The radius of the upper circle, r_1, is 1.2 cm.
The radius of the lower circle, r_2, is 1.6 cm.

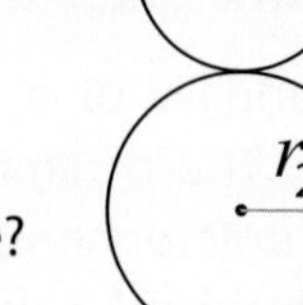

(a) What is the length of the edge of this figure?

(b) What is the area enclosed by the figure?

A chord is a straight line joining two points on the edge of a circle. A chord divides a circle into two segments. The major segment is the larger segment, and the minor segment is the smaller segment.

An arc is a part of the circumference of a circle. The area enclosed by an arc and two radii is a sector.

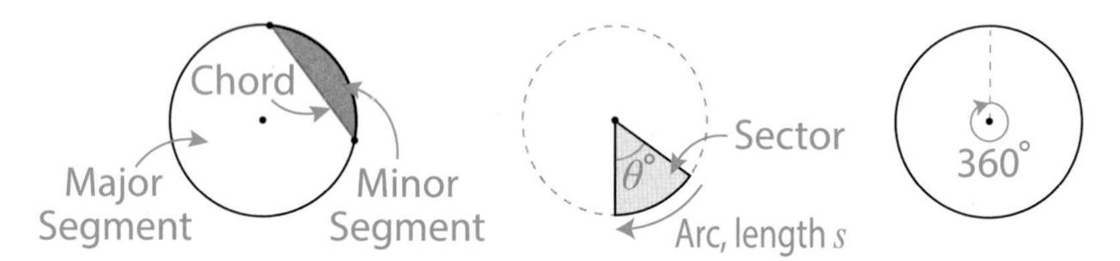

Drawing a full circle with compasses involves rotating 360° about the centre. Turning through $\theta°$ to draw an arc is therefore drawing $\frac{\theta°}{360°}$ of a full circle. Hence, the length of an arc and the area of the corresponding sector are $\frac{\theta°}{360°}$ of the circumference and area of a full circle.

$$\text{Arc length, } s = \frac{\theta°}{360°} \times 2\pi r \qquad \text{Sector area, } A = \frac{\theta°}{360°} \times \pi r^2$$

Example 2 – The diagrams hows a sector cut from a circle of radius 5 cm. Find the length of the arc, s, and the area of the sector, to 3 sf.

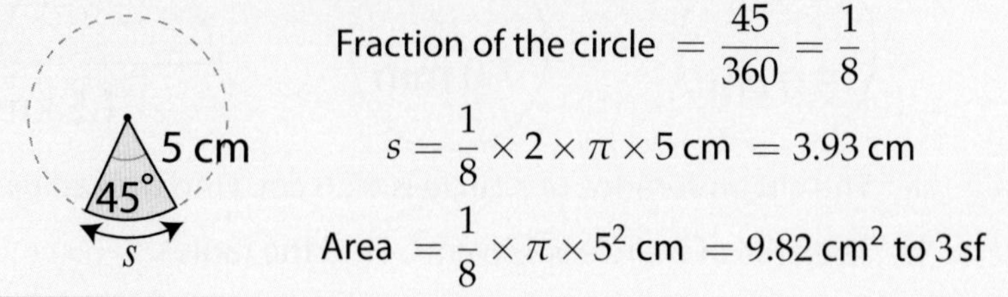

$$\text{Fraction of the circle} = \frac{45}{360} = \frac{1}{8}$$

$$s = \frac{1}{8} \times 2 \times \pi \times 5 \text{ cm} = 3.93 \text{ cm}$$

$$\text{Area} = \frac{1}{8} \times \pi \times 5^2 \text{ cm} = 9.82 \text{ cm}^2 \text{ to 3 sf}$$

42.4 For each sector, find to 3 sf (i) the length of the arc (ii) the area.

(a) 19.5 m 120°   (b) 64.0 cm   (c) 3.4 m 70°

42.5 If A is the area of a circle, what angle would a sector of this circle have if the sector has area:

(a) $\frac{1}{4}A$ (b) $\frac{1}{12}A$ (c) $\frac{1}{72}A$

42.6 The diagram below shows a path made of curved slabs. Each slab is identical, and its geometry is based on a 45° sector of a circle. The gap between adjacent slabs is 2 cm. Find to 3 sf:

(a) The length AB.

(b) The length CD.

1 m 60 cm 45° A B C D

§ There are a number of important circles theorems involving the geometry of tangents and chords.

From any point outside a circle you can draw two tangents to the circle.

- The distance from the point to where it meets the circle is the same for the two tangents: AB $=$ AC.
- A tangent to a circle is perpendicular to the radius at the point of contact: A$\hat{\text{B}}O =$ A$\hat{\text{C}}O = 90^\circ$.

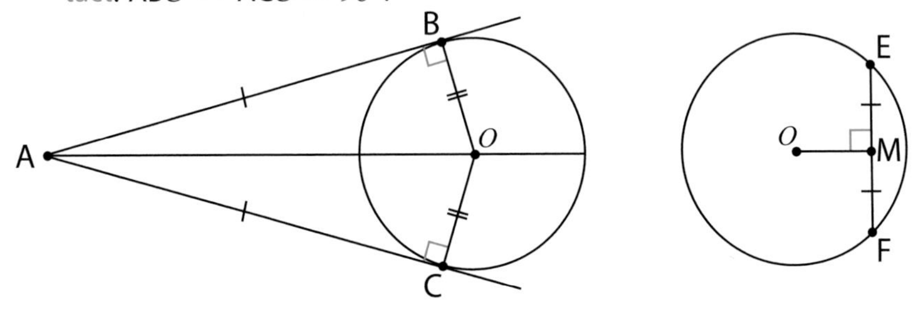

At the mid-point of a chord, the chord makes a right-angle with a line to the centre: E$\hat{\text{M}}O =$ F$\hat{\text{M}}O = 90^\circ$.

The diagram on the left below shows a useful property of circles. Triangle ABO is isosceles as AO and BO are both radii. If $B\hat{A}O = \alpha$, then $A\hat{B}O$ is also α. Hence $A\hat{O}B = 180^\circ - 2\alpha$, and $B\hat{O}C = 2\alpha$. From this property a number of useful results can be derived.

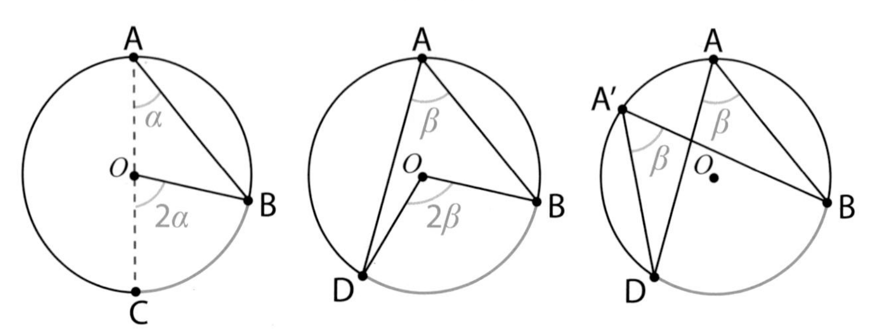

- The angle that an arc subtends at the centre is twice the angle that the arc subtends at a point on the circumference: $B\hat{O}D = 2 \times B\hat{A}D$.
- Angles subtended by an arc in the same segment are equal: $B\hat{A}D = B\hat{A'}D$.

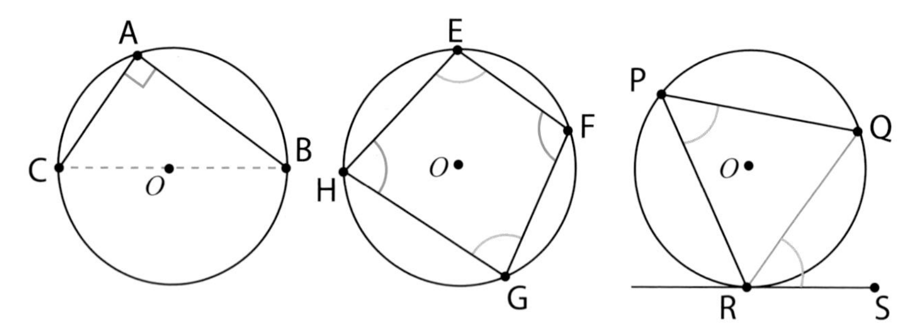

- At a point on the circumference, the angle subtended by a diameter is a right angle: $C\hat{A}B = 90^\circ$.
- A quadrilateral is cyclic if its vertices all lie on a circle. For any cyclic quadrilateral, opposite angles sum to 180°:
  $E\hat{F}G + E\hat{H}G = 180^\circ$ and $F\hat{E}H + F\hat{G}H = 180^\circ$.
- The angle between a tangent and a chord is equal to the angle subtended by the chord in the alternate (opposite) segment: $Q\hat{P}R = Q\hat{R}S$.

42.7 O is the centre of the circle. Find:

(a) α

(b) β

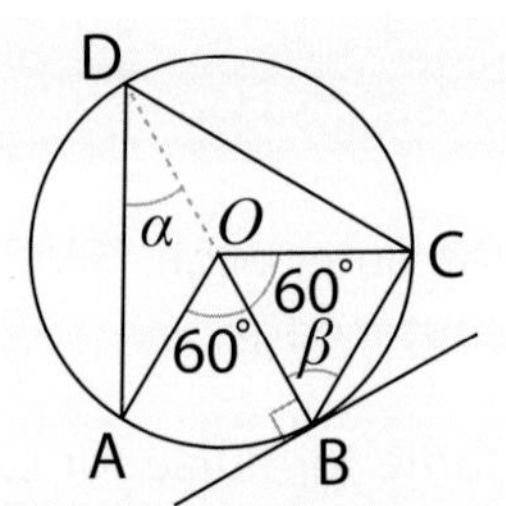

42.8 Point O is the centre of a circle. Find:

(a) α (c) γ

(b) β (d) δ

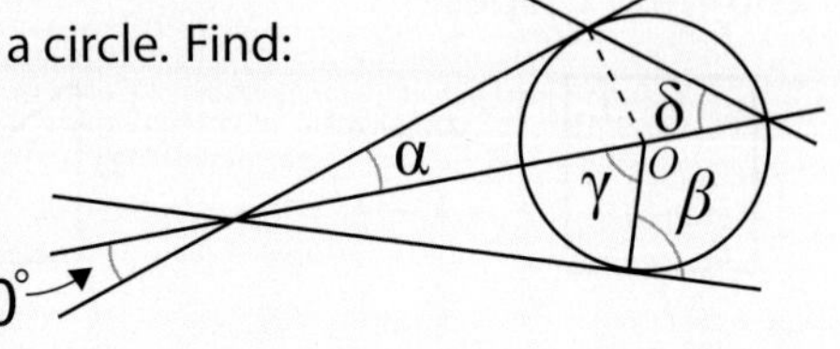

42.9 Point A has coordinates $(3,1)$, and point B has coordinates $(17,1)$.

(a) Work out the position of C, the mid-point of A and B.

(b) Point D is 7 units from C, but not coincident with A or B. What is the value of the angle $A\hat{D}B$?

42.10 Point O is the centre of a circle. What are the values of the following angles in terms of α, β and γ?

(a) OÂC (d) AÔB

(b) OD̂C (e) AÔD

(c) BÔC

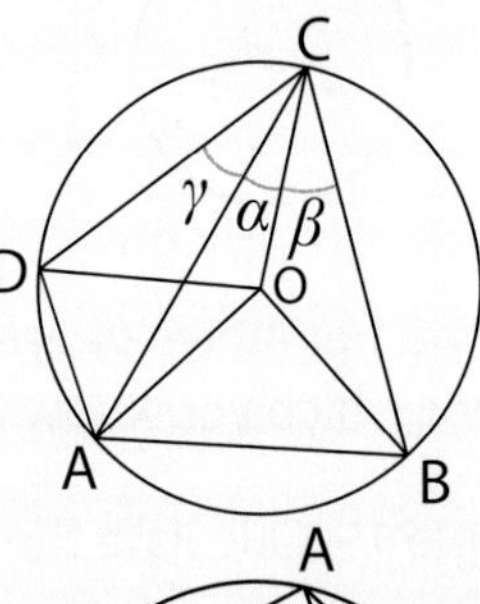

42.11 You are given the following diagram with the added information that AC is a diameter of the circle.
Find the value of the quantity:

$AB^2 + AD^2 + AE^2 + BC^2 + CD^2 + CE^2$

given that $AC = 10$ cm.

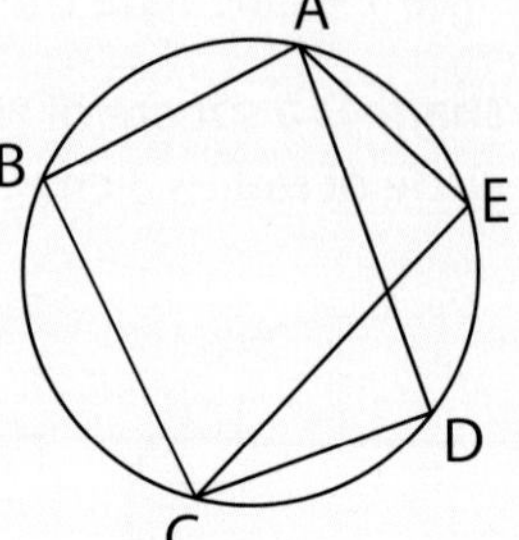

43 Perimeter and Area

The perimeter of a shape is the outer edge. "Finding the perimeter" means calculating the length of the outer edge.

The diagrams below show some formulae for calculating perimeters and areas of common shapes.

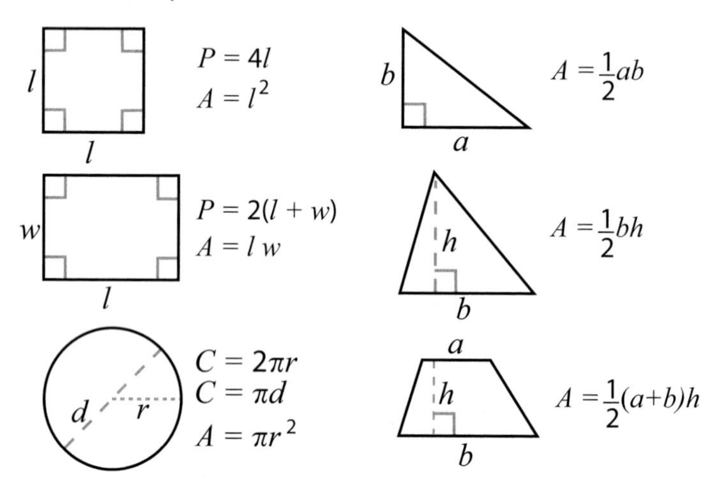

To find the perimeter or area of compound shapes, relate them to simple shapes for which you know formulae.

Example 1 – Calculate the perimeter and area of the shape below.

The shape is a square of side length 3 cm, connected to three-quarters of a circle of radius 3 cm.

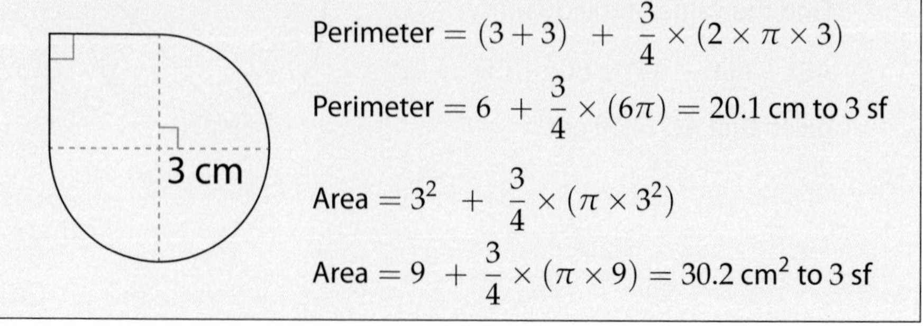

$$\text{Perimeter} = (3+3) + \frac{3}{4} \times (2 \times \pi \times 3)$$

$$\text{Perimeter} = 6 + \frac{3}{4} \times (6\pi) = 20.1 \text{ cm to 3 sf}$$

$$\text{Area} = 3^2 + \frac{3}{4} \times (\pi \times 3^2)$$

$$\text{Area} = 9 + \frac{3}{4} \times (\pi \times 9) = 30.2 \text{ cm}^2 \text{ to 3 sf}$$

In this exercise give your answers to 3 sf where answers are inexact.

43.1 Find the perimeters of the following shapes.

(a)

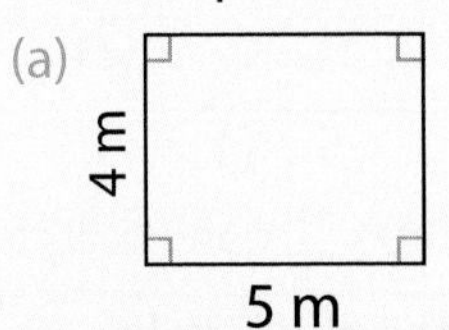

(b)

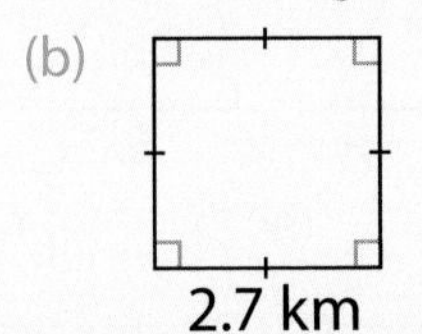

(c)

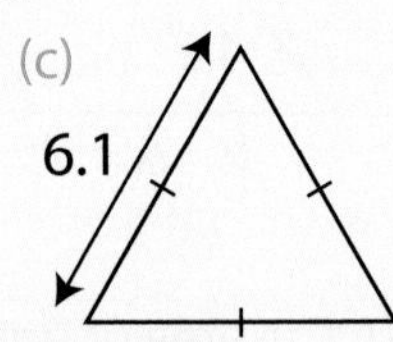

43.2 Find the perimeters of the following shapes.

(a)

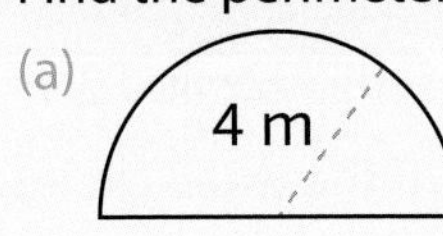

(b)

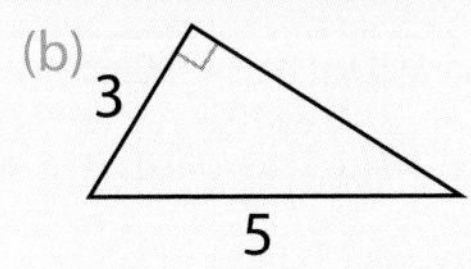

(c)

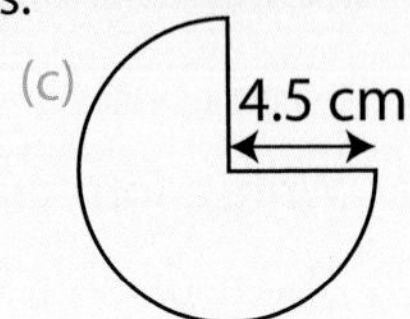

43.3 Find the areas of the following shapes.

(a)

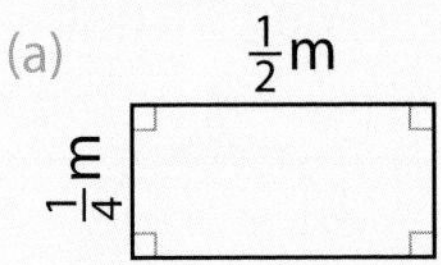

(b)

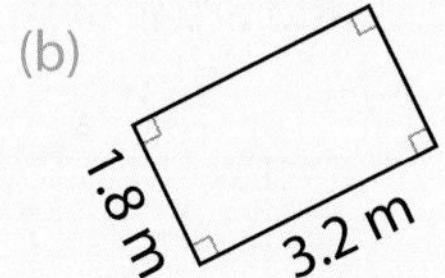

(c)

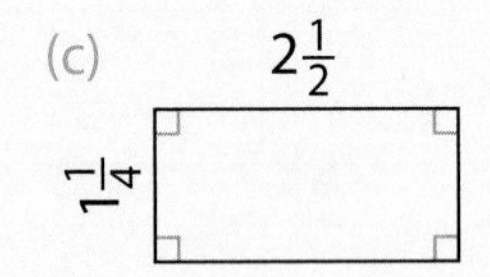

43.4 Find the areas of the following shapes.

(a)

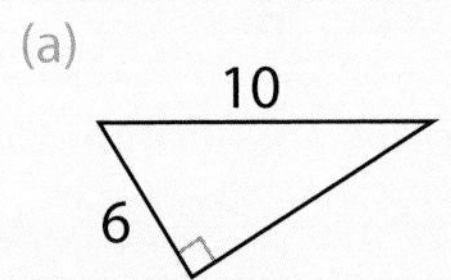

(b)

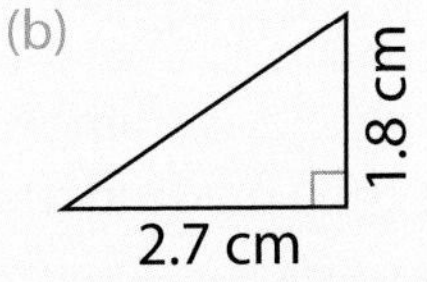

(c)

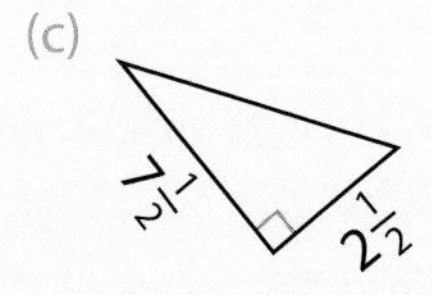

43.5 Find the areas of the following trapezia.

(a) (b)

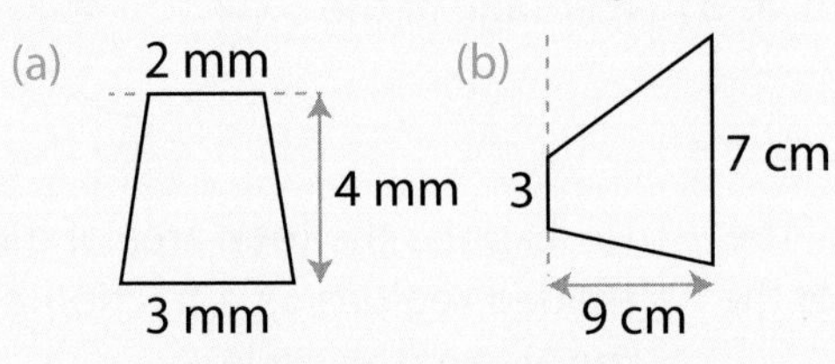

(c)

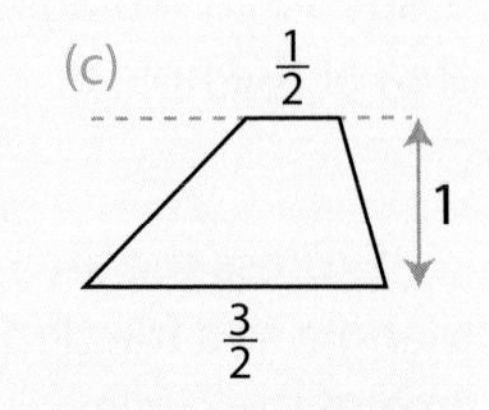

43.6 Calculate the areas of the following shapes based on circles.

(a)

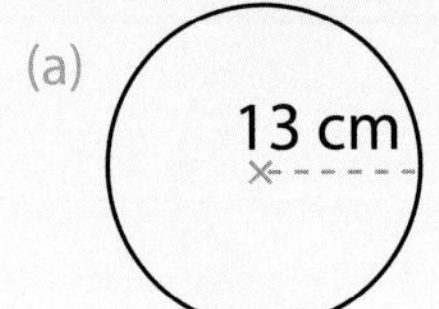

(b)

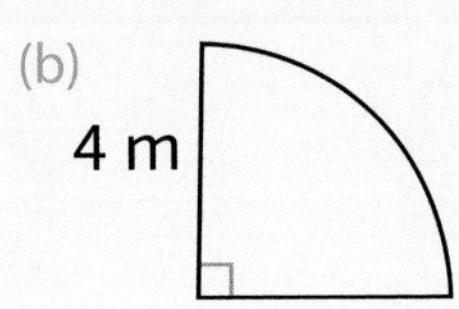

(c)

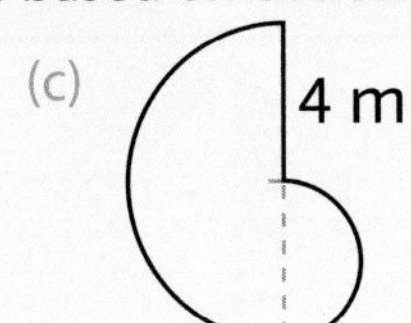

43.7 (a) Which of these trapezia has the largest area?

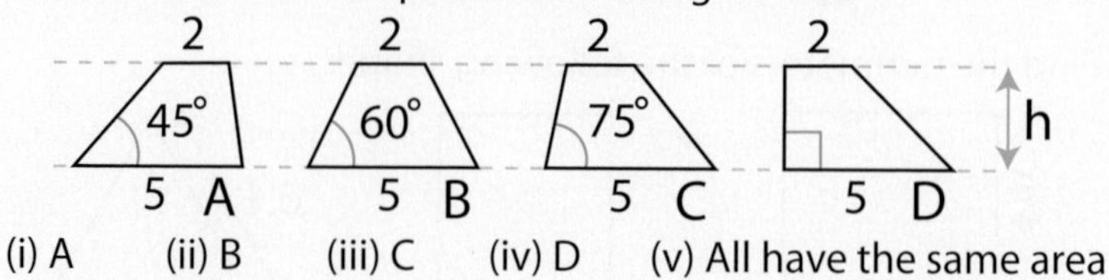

(i) A (ii) B (iii) C (iv) D (v) All have the same area

(b) The area of trapezium D is $28\ \text{cm}^2$. What is the height of the trapezium, h?

43.8 A design consists of 3 separate circles, with radii r, $2r$ and $3r$.

(a) Write a formula to find the total area A of the three circles.

(b) The total area is found to be $90\ \text{cm}^2$. Find the value of r to 1 dp.

43.9 Calculate the perimeters and areas of the following shapes.

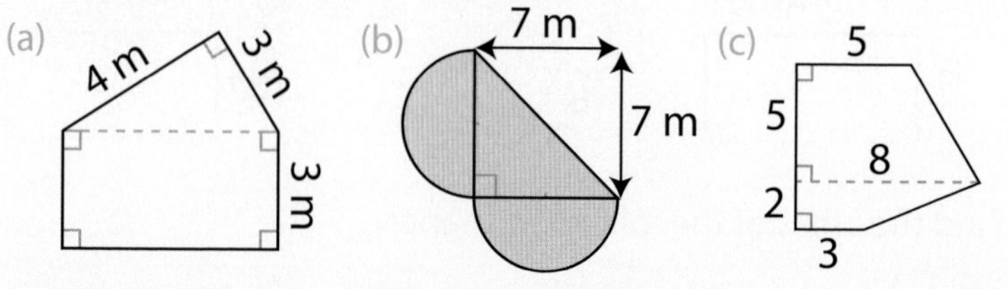

43.10 A circular disc A, of radius $\frac{3}{2}a$, is stamped from a sheet of metal. A hole, B, of radius a is then made in the disc.

Find the area of the remaining metal, shown shaded in the diagram, as a percentage of the area of the hole B.

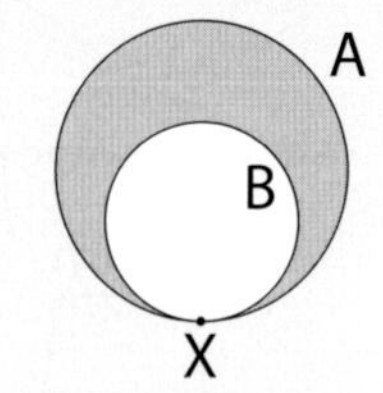

43.11 (a) Express the area of the triangle as a fraction of the area of the circle.

(b) Express the total area of the shaded regions as a fraction of the area of the circle.

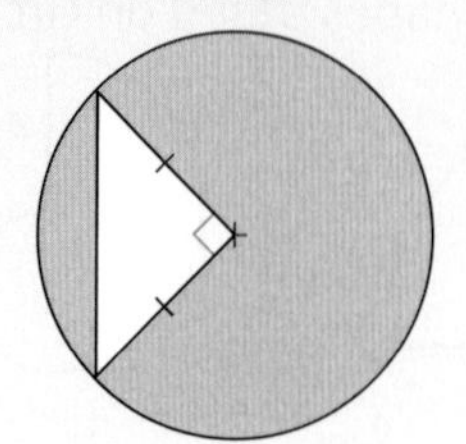

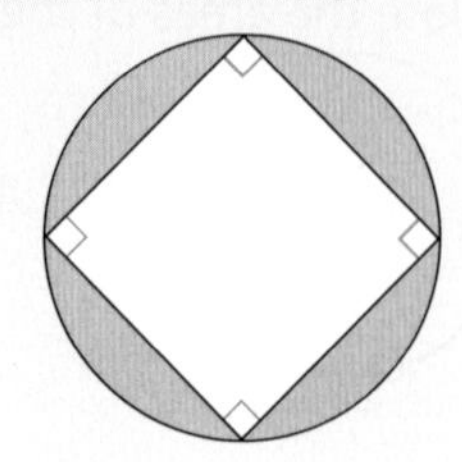

44 Surface Area and Volume

The surface area of a shape is found by adding together the areas of all of the exposed faces of the shape. The units of surface area are the same as the units of area, and are units of length squared: m^2, cm^2, mm^2 etc. The units of volume are units of length cubed: m^3, cm^3, mm^3 etc.

The volumes of a cube and a cuboid are given by the formulae:

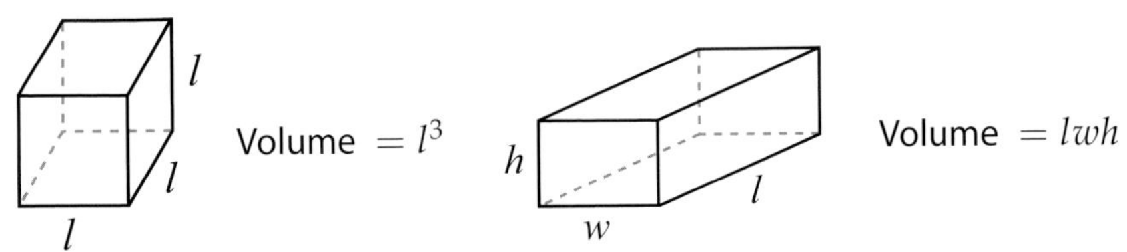

A prism is a 3-D shape with a consistent cross-section down its length.

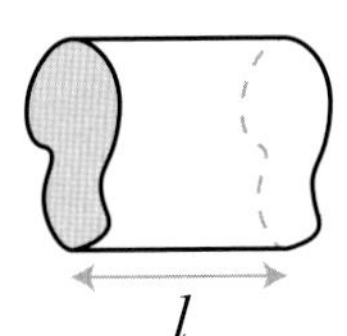

Volume $=$ Area of Cross-section $\times\, l$

A cylinder is a prism with a circular cross-section of radius r.

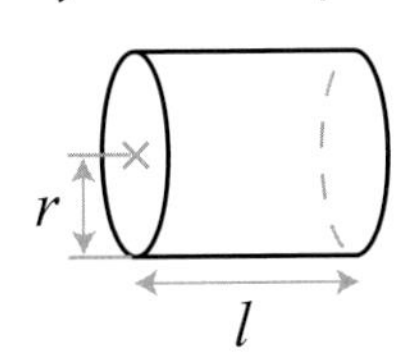

Volume $= \pi r^2 l$

Area of each end $= \pi r^2$

Area of curved surface $= 2\pi r l$

Total surface area $= 2\pi r^2 + 2\pi r l$

A cone has a base of radius r, perpendicular height h and slant height s.

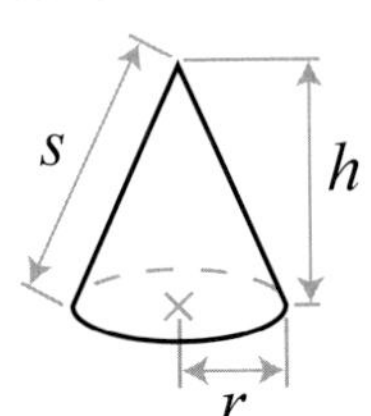

Volume $= \frac{1}{3}\pi r^2 h$

Area of base $= \pi r^2$

Area of curved surface $= \pi r s$

Total surface area $= \pi r^2 + \pi r s$

For a sphere of radius r,

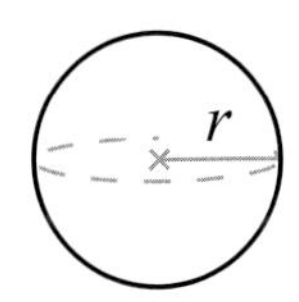

Volume $= \frac{4}{3}\pi r^3$

Surface area $= 4\pi r^2$

Example 1 – Calculate the volume of the shape below, which is made out of a cylinder and a hemisphere.

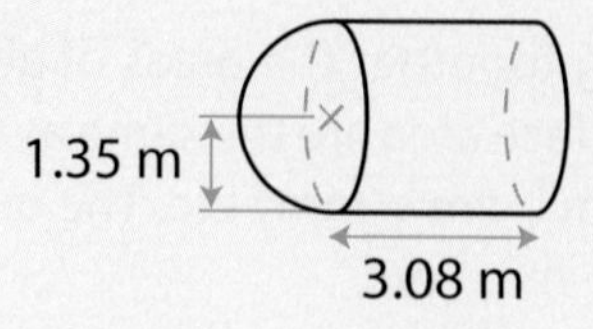

The volume is equal to half the volume of a sphere plus the volume of a cylinder.

$$V_{\text{hemisphere}} = \frac{1}{2} \times (\frac{4}{3}\pi \times 1.35^3) = 5.1529... \text{ m}^3$$

$$V_{\text{cylinder}} = \pi \times 1.35^2 \times 3.08 = 17.634... \text{ m}^3$$

$$V_{\text{Total}} = V_{\text{hemisphere}} + V_{\text{cylinder}} = 5.1529 + 17.634 = 22.8 \text{ m}^3 \text{ to 3 sf}$$

A pyramid has a polygon for a base, triangular sides, and a perpendicular height h.

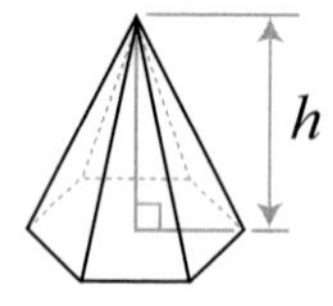

$$\text{Volume} = \tfrac{1}{3} \times \text{Area of base} \times h$$

This formula applies to all pyramids, including ones where the apex is not above the centre of the base.

To find the surface area of a pyramid, find the area of the base and add on the area of each of the triangular sides.

Example 2 – The apex of the square-based pyramid below is vertically above the centre of the base. Find the surface area.

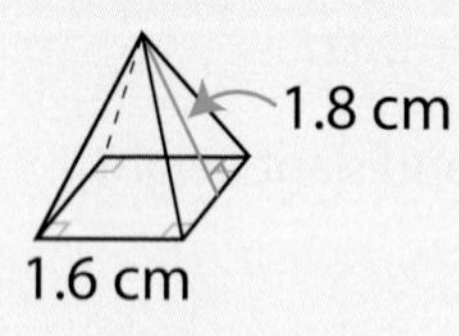

The surface area is the sum of the area of the base and the areas of the four triangular sides.

$$\text{Area of base} = 1.6 \times 1.6 = 2.56 \text{ cm}^2$$

$$\text{Area of one side} = \frac{1}{2} \times 1.6 \times 1.8 = 1.44 \text{ cm}^2$$

$$\therefore \text{Surface area} = 2.56 + 4 \times 1.44$$

$$\Rightarrow \text{Surface area} = 8.32 \text{ cm}^2$$

In this exercise give answers to 3 sf unless otherwise stated.

44.1 For each shape find (i) the surface area and (ii) the volume.

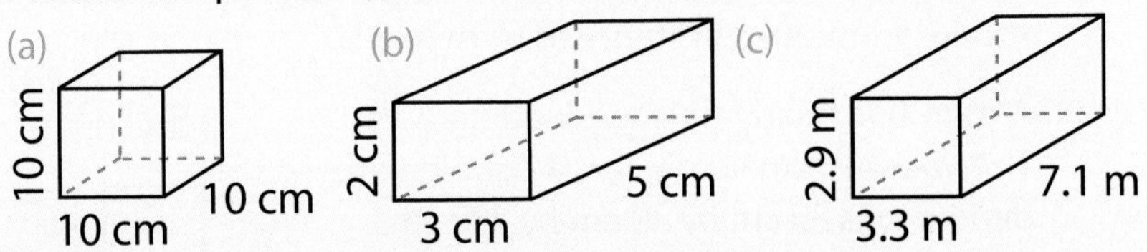

44.2 Find the volumes of these prisms.

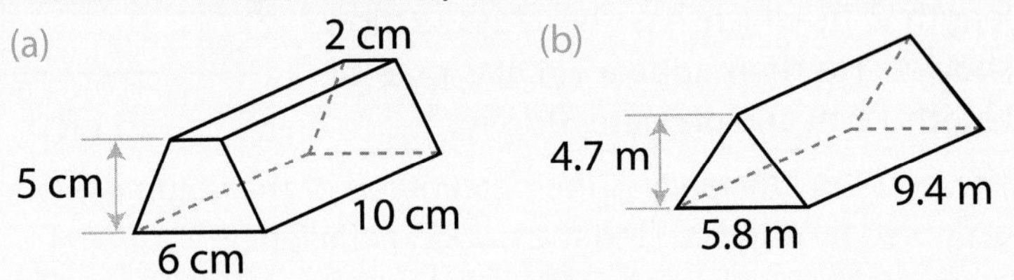

44.3 For these shapes find (i) the surface area and (ii) the volume.

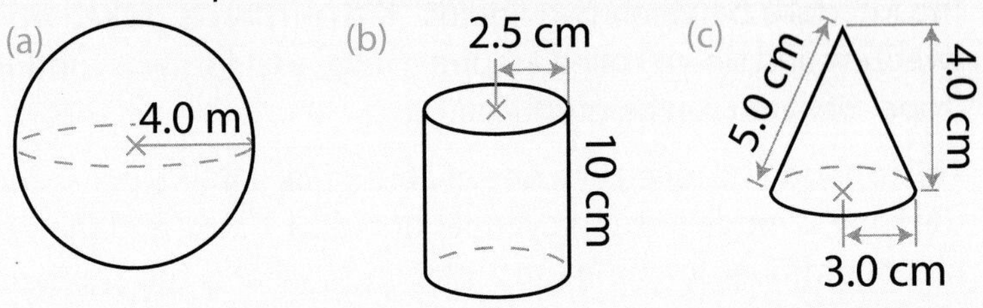

44.4 Jenni wishes to put volume markings onto a cylinder with one closed end. The diameter of the cylinder is 2.0 cm. To the nearest millimetre, what height from the base will contain a volume of 100 ml? (Remember that 1 ml is equal to 1 cm^3.)

44.5 The shape is made up of a cuboid and half a cylinder. Find, giving your answers in terms of π:

(a) The volume.

(b) The surface area.

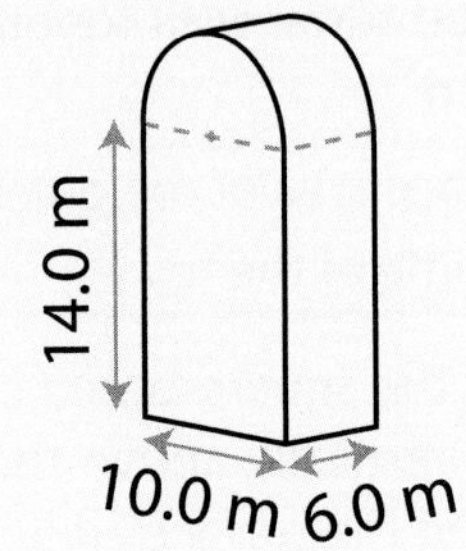

44.6 71 % of the Earth's surface is covered by water. The radius of the Earth is 6 370 km to 3 sf. By modelling the Earth as a sphere, estimate the surface area that is covered by water. Give your answer in square kilometres in standard form to 2 sf.

44.7 A man has nearly finished loading a van. The volume remaining, S, is a cuboid with dimensions 30 cm by 30 cm by 200 cm.

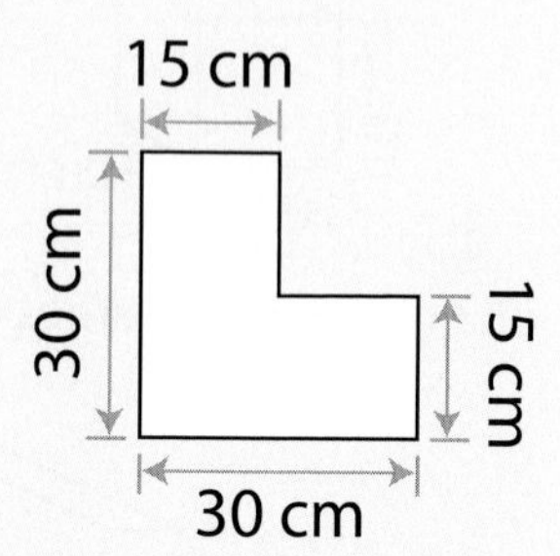

The man pushes in an L-shaped beam of length 2 m which has the cross-section shown. He then adds a circular pole of length 1.5 m and diameter 0.15 m.

The packing efficiency is the percentage of the volume S which is occupied by objects. Find the packing efficiency.

44.8 In a laboratory experiment, a polymer (nylon) can be produced at the interface between two liquids. If the nylon is picked up with tweezers and slowly rolled around a roller as it forms, a continuous "rope" of nylon can be produced.

The rope can be rolled at a rate of about half a metre per second. If the rope is modelled as a cylinder of radius 1 mm, and the experiment continues for 1 minute 25 seconds, what is the approximate volume of polymer produced? Give your answer to 2 sf.

44.9 A toy is made from a hemisphere and a cone stuck together. The radii of the hemisphere and the base of the cone are both 12 cm and the glued surfaces fit together exactly. The height of the cone is 30 cm. Find:

(a) The surface area of the outside of the toy.

(b) The volume of the toy.

44.10 The apex of the square-based pyramid on the right is vertically above the centre of the base. Find the surface area.

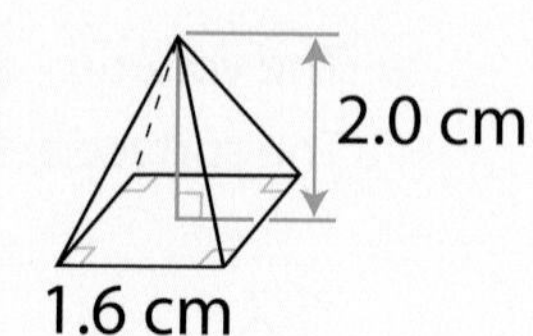

45 Scale Drawings and Bearings

The size and location of 2-D and 3-D objects can be communicated by scale drawing.

3-D objects can be drawn on an isometric grid. These diagrams are useful for visualising what a 3-D object looks like. However, it is difficult to make accurate measurements from a 3-D drawing. 2-D views are used when the ability to measure is important, such as in the building industry. A plan is a 2-D view of a 3-D object from above, and an elevation is a 2-D view of a 3-D object from the front, side, or rear.

Scale drawings must include a statement to indicate what the scale of the drawing is. This may be a scale factor such as "$\times 100$" or a ratio. For example, "1 cm $: 1$ m" indicates that 1 cm on the drawing corresponds to 1 m on the real object. In real-world applications scale is often showing by including an object of known size on the drawing, such as a 1 metre ruler.

Example 1 – An isometric drawing of a building, along with front and side elevations. A labelled arrow to show the scale is included.

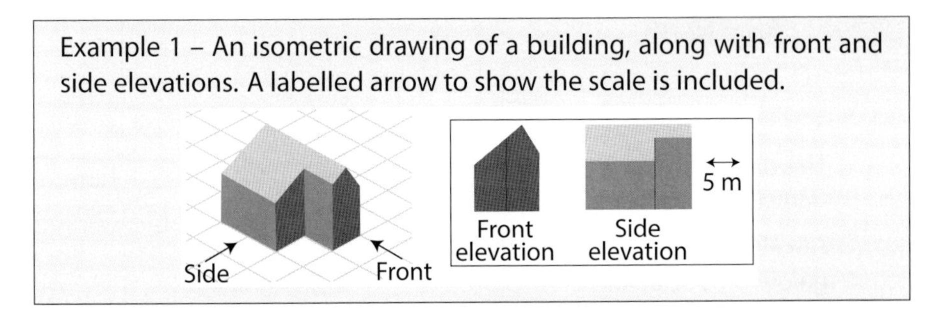

In navigation, directions of travel are stated using bearings. Bearings are angles measured clockwise relative to North. Bearings are always stated as three-figure numbers in degrees. Two-digit angles such as $32°$ are written as bearings with a leading zero, $032°$.

Example 2 – On what bearing is the plane travelling?

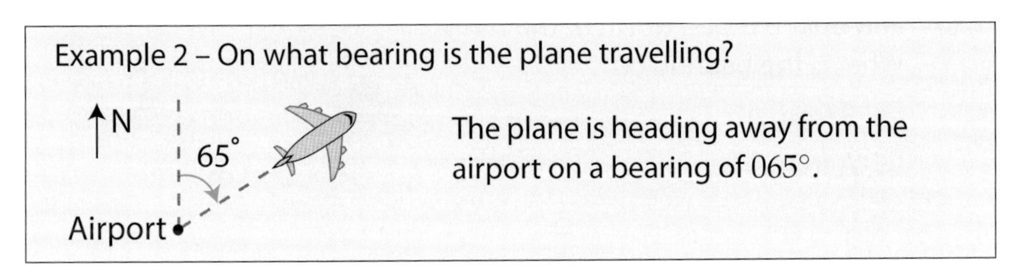

The plane is heading away from the airport on a bearing of $065°$.

45.1 In archaeology objects are often photographed next to rulers to show their size. Estimate the size of each object.

(a) The diameter of a coin

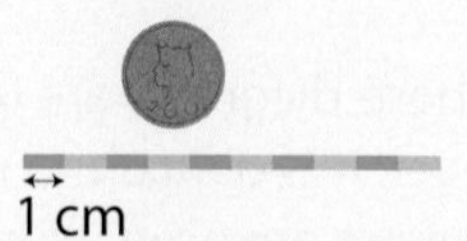

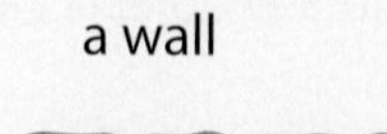
(b) The length of a wall

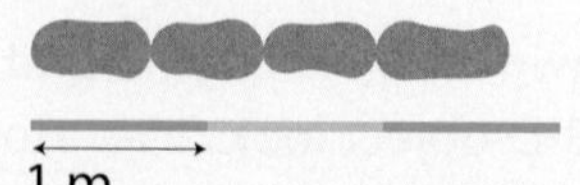

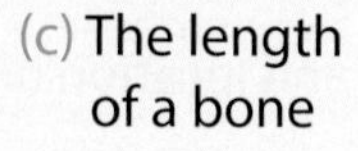
(c) The length of a bone

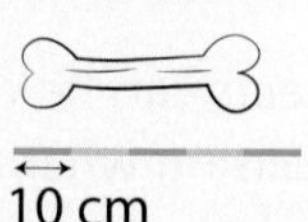

45.2 A scale drawing uses 1 cm on the drawing for 5 m on an object.

(a) Write the scale as a ratio in the form 1 cm : a cm.

(b) What distance on the object is equivalent to 4 cm on the drawing?

(c) Convert 17.8 m on the object to a length on the scale drawing.

45.3 Express the following as bearings:

(a) 9° clockwise from North

(b)

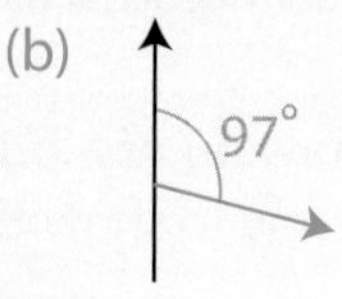

(c)

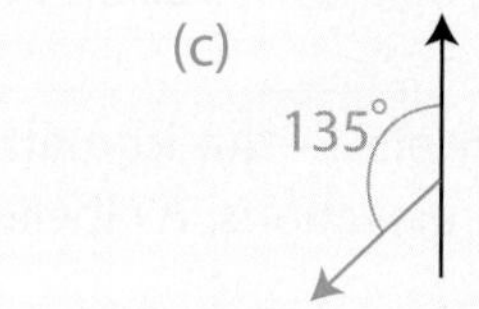

45.4 The diagram shows the front -elevation of a bungalow.

A scale drawing is made of the bungalow on a scale of 1 : 50. State the lengths of (a) to (e) on the drawing, giving your answers in cm.

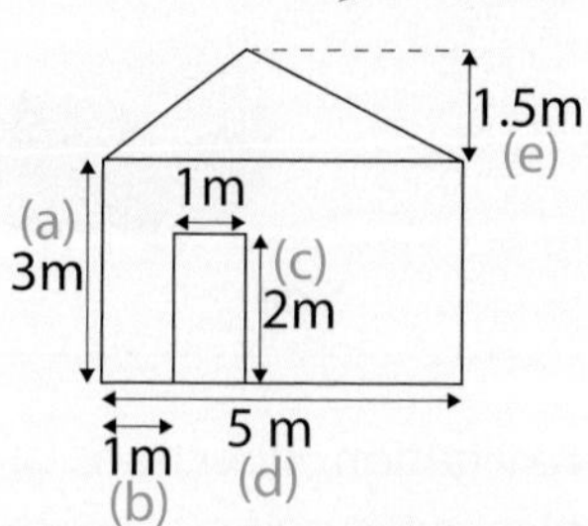

45.5 The diagram shows two boats, A and B. Boat A is due West of a buoy, and boat B is due North of the buoy. What is the bearing of:

(a) B from A?

(b) A from B?

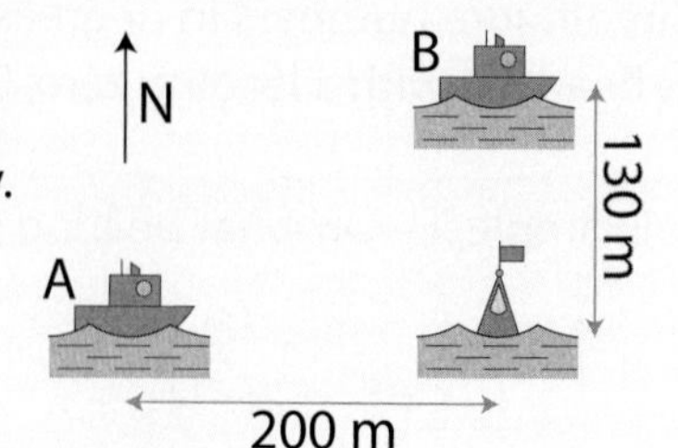

45.6 The diagram shows some measurements that were taken of a buoy.

(a) Using a ruler, a protractor and a pair of compasses, draw a scale diagram of the buoy, using a scale of 1 : 25.

(b) On your scale diagram, what is the total height of the buoy, from the bottom of the base to the top of the flag?

50 cm
40 cm
20 cm
20 cm
200 cm
50 cm
50 cm
30 cm
120 cm

45.7 The map shows the village of Boxthorpe, which is close to a small airport, a fort and a forest.

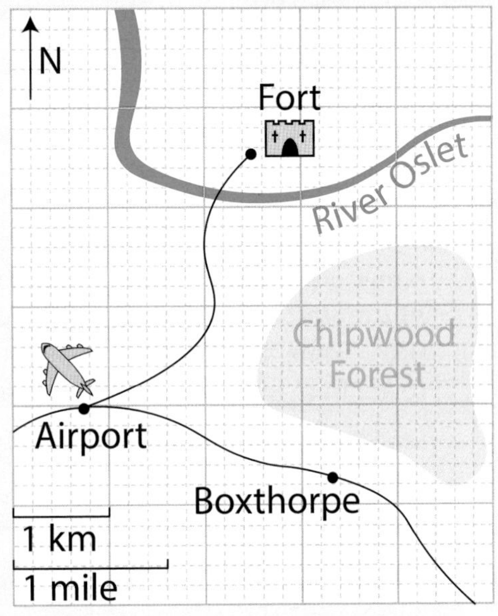

Using a protractor, find the bearing of

(a) The fort from the airport.

(b) The airport from the fort.

(c) What is the shortest distance between Boxthorpe and the Fort in km?

The distance along a curved path can be found with the help of a piece of string.

(d) What is the distance between Boxthorpe and the Fort by road? Give your answer (i) in km (ii) in miles.

(e) Estimate the area of Chipwood Forest in square kilometres.

45.8 An engineer tracks a weather balloon with GPS. The balloon comes to ground on a bearing 045° from his position P. He then travels 50.0 km due East, and at his new position the GPS records the balloon as directly to the North.

(a) How far from the new position is the balloon?

(b) What is the shortest distance from P to the balloon? Give your answer to 3 sf.

45.9 The following formula shows how to find the floor area of a scale drawing of a house:

$$A = r \times s + \frac{1}{2}\pi t^2$$

(a) If $r = 6.0$ cm, $s = 8.3$ cm and $t = 1.5$ cm, find A to 2 sf.

(b) The scale drawing represents the house on a scale of $1{:}100$. What is the floor area of the house? Give your answer in m^2 to 2 sf.

45.10 The diagram shows two planes, A and B, which are at the same altitude. What is the bearing of A from B:

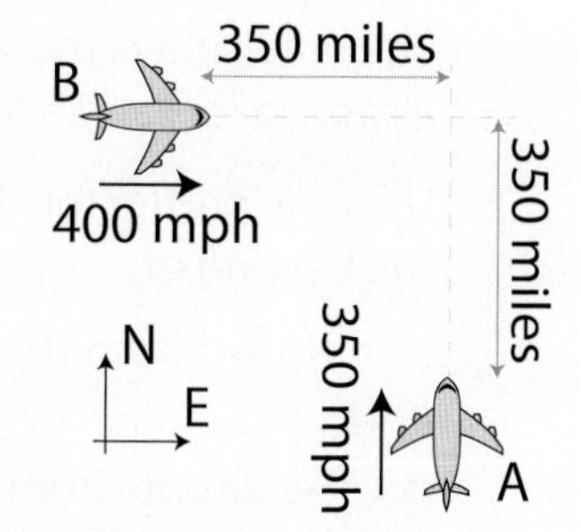

(a) Now?

(b) In one hour?

(c) In 1 hour 15 minutes?

45.11 A man starts a train journey from a station Q and travels due North. At the start of his journey he could see a tower T on a bearing of 030°. Some time later when at point R he looks again and sees the tower from his new position on a bearing of 060°.

(a) Sketch this information on a diagram.

(b) The journey is completed at station S which is due West of the tower. Add S to your sketch.

(c) ST is 4.8 km. Work out the value of the distance QR. Give your answer to 2 sf.

46 Constructions and Loci

Constructions are accurately drawn geometrical shapes, lines and angles. The basic tools needed are a ruler and a pair of compasses.

Many constructions are based on the isosceles triangle, which has two sides the same length and one different. To construct an isosceles triangle,

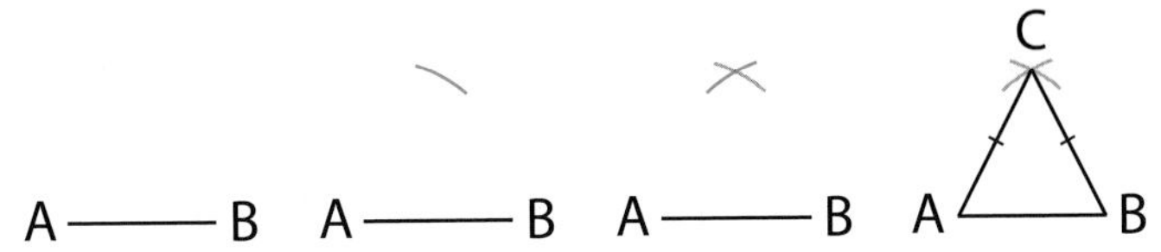

- With a ruler draw the side with a different length, AB.
- Set the width of the compasses to the length of the other two sides. Put the point of the compasses at A and make an arc. Repeat at B.
- With a ruler, draw in AC and BC.

Bisecting means splitting into two equal parts. Both angles and lines can be bisected. To bisect an angle start by setting the width of the compasses. Keeping this width fixed,

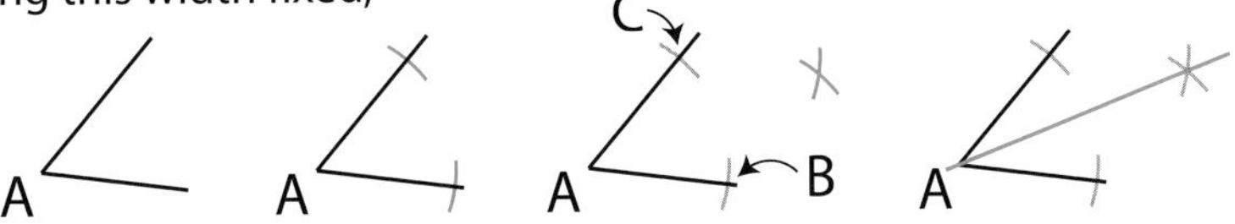

- Put the point of the compasses at A and make two arcs.
- Put the point of the compasses at B and make an arc. Repeat at C.
- With a ruler, draw a line through A and the point where the arcs cross.

A perpendicular bisector of a line is a second line which passes through the midpoint of the first line at a right angle. To construct a perpendicular bisector of a line AB:

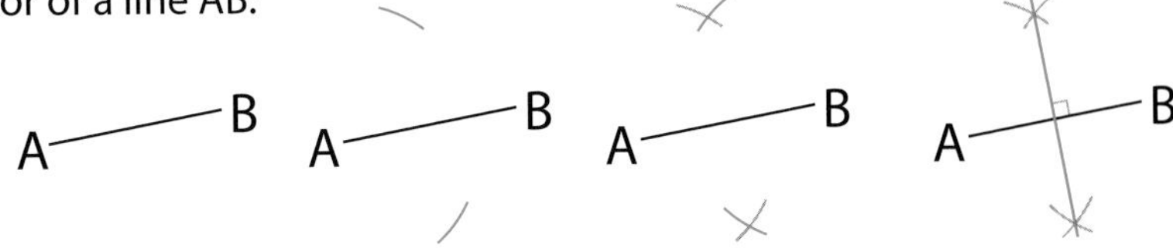

- Set the width of the compasses to be much greater than half of AB.
- Put the point of the compasses at A and make two arcs. Repeat at B.
- With a ruler draw a line through the places where the arcs cross.

To draw the perpendicular to a line at a given point on the line, or from the line to a given point, centre the compasses on A (the point) and make two arcs. Then find the perpendicular bisector of the line segment BC.

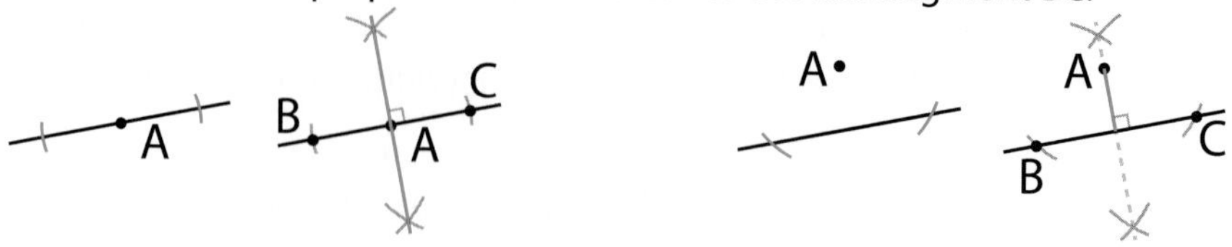

46.1 Construct the perpendicular bisector of a line 8 cm in length.

46.2 Using ruler and compasses only,

(a) Construct an angle of 90°.

(b) Bisect this angle to give an angle of 45°.

46.3 Construct a kite with one pair of sides of length 6 cm, one pair of length 5 cm, and a longest dimension of 8.5 cm.

A locus (plural loci) is the set of points obeying one or more geometric rules. Constructions and loci are closely related. For example, the perpendicular bisector of the line joining two points, A and B, is the locus of points that are equidistant (an equal distance) from A and B.

The diagram below shows the loci of points equidistant from (a) a point (b) a straight line of infinite length (c) a straight line segment and (d) a pair of intersecting straight lines.

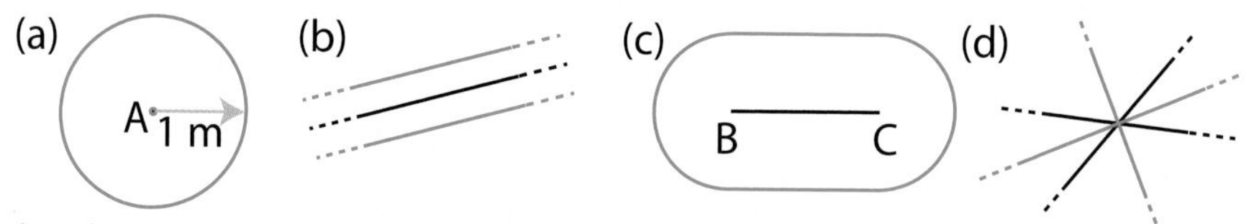

The shapes are (a) a circle, (b) a pair of parallel lines of infinite length at an equal distance on either side of the line, (c) a pair of parallel lines linked with semi-circles at both ends, and (d) a pair of perpendicular lines which bisect the angles at which the straight lines intersect.

A locus can be a line, a single point or an area. Where a locus is an area, a dotted line is used if the boundary is not included in the locus. The diagram shows the loci of points that are (i) exactly 6 cm from A (ii) less than 6 cm from B.

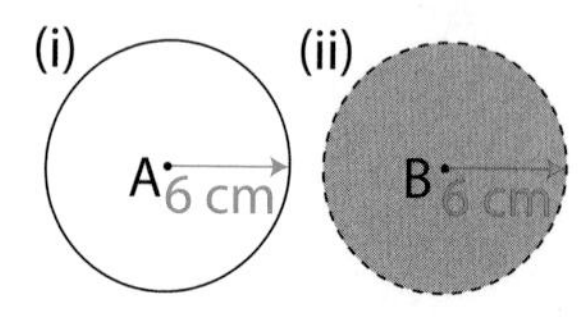

46.4 Construct a line AB which is 6 cm long.

(a) Show the locus of points 4.0 cm from A.

(b) Show the locus of points 4.0 cm from B.

(c) Indicate by shading the locus of points that are 4.0 cm or less from A and 4.0 cm or less from B.

46.5 P is the midpoint of a line ST which is 8.6 cm long.

(a) Show the locus of points 3.5 cm from P.

(b) Add to your diagram the locus of all points 3.0 cm from ST.

(c) Indicate by shading the locus of points that are 3.0 cm or less from ST and also 3.5 cm or more from P.

46.6 Draw a straight line and mark a point C on it. Construct a rhombus which has centre C and at least one 60° angle between a pair of adjacent sides.

46.7 Using a ruler and compasses only, construct a line of length exactly $\sqrt{40}$ cm.

46.8 F, G and H are the vertices of an equilateral triangle with side length 70 cm. Using a ruler and compasses only, construct a scale diagram of the triangle on a scale of 1:10, and show the locus of the points that are within or on the boundary of the triangle, and more than 30 cm from any of the vertices.

46.9 (a) A boat travels between two harbours, A and B. The coast extends directly east from A to B, and B is 1.6 km from A. The boat leaves A and travels 800 m due north to a buoy at C. Draw the coast and the boat's path on a scale diagram where 1 cm : 200 m.

(b) Between the harbours is an area where boats are not permitted due to the presence of rocks close to the surface. Boats are not allowed within 400 m of the shore if they are more than 200 m east of A or 300 m west of B. Add a suitable locus to your diagram.

(c) The boat travels 1.5 km on a bearing of 103°, then travels straight to B. Using a protractor, plot the path of the boat. Did the boat enter the danger zone?

47 Vectors

A vector is a quantity that has both magnitude (size) and direction.

Vectors are written by hand with a line underneath, for example $\underline{b}$. In textbooks vectors are often written in bold instead of underlined, $\boldsymbol{b}$.

Vectors are drawn on diagrams as arrows. The diagram below shows the same vector $\boldsymbol{p}$ in three different locations:

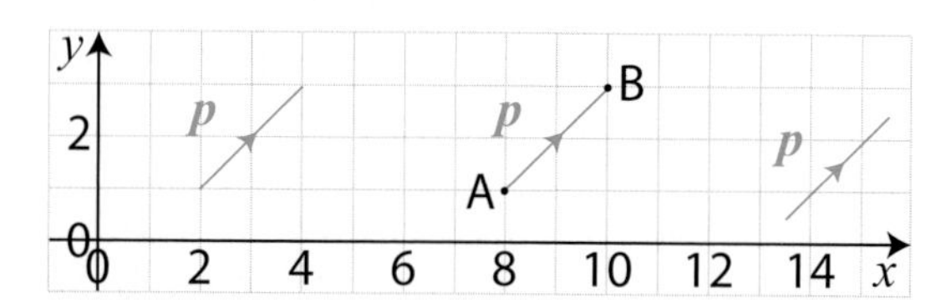

The vector to go from a point A to a second point B is written $\overrightarrow{AB}$. In the diagram above $\overrightarrow{AB} = \boldsymbol{p}$.

When a vector is written in column vector notation, the top number is the component of the vector in the positive x direction, and the bottom number is the component of the vector in the the positive y direction.

Example 1 – Describe the vector v in terms of travelling in the x and y directions, and write v as a column vector.

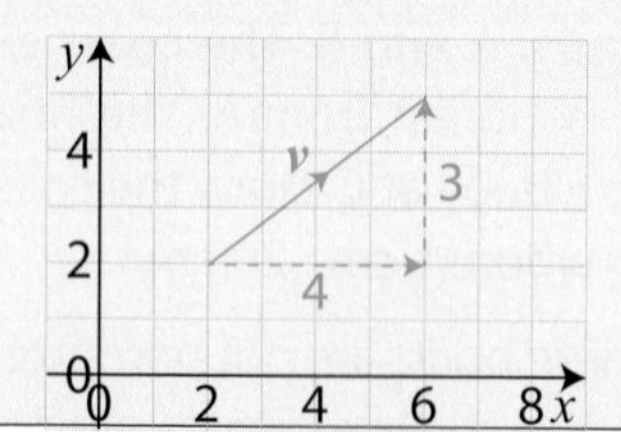

The vector v is "go 4 units in the positive x-direction, plus 3 units in the positive y-direction".

$$v = \begin{pmatrix} 4 \\ 3 \end{pmatrix}$$

Example 2 – Write the vectors shown below as column vectors.

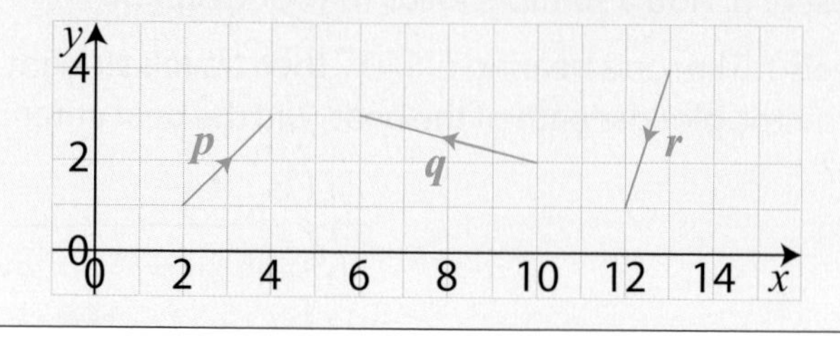

$$\boldsymbol{p} = \begin{pmatrix} 2 \\ 2 \end{pmatrix}$$

$$\boldsymbol{q} = \begin{pmatrix} -4 \\ 1 \end{pmatrix}$$

$$\boldsymbol{r} = \begin{pmatrix} -1 \\ -3 \end{pmatrix}$$

When column vectors are added or subtracted, the top numbers and bottom numbers add or subtract separately.

Numerical constants like 3 and -7 which have a size but not a direction are scalars. When a column vector is multiplied by a scalar, the top and bottom numbers are multiplied separately. Vectors which are scalar multiples of one another have the same direction so they are parallel.

Example 3 –

$p = \begin{pmatrix} 2 \\ 3 \end{pmatrix}$ and $q = \begin{pmatrix} 5 \\ -2 \end{pmatrix}$

Find:

(a) $p + q$ (b) $p - q$ (c) $-7q$

(a) $\begin{pmatrix} 2 \\ 3 \end{pmatrix} + \begin{pmatrix} 5 \\ -2 \end{pmatrix} = \begin{pmatrix} 7 \\ 1 \end{pmatrix}$

(b) $\begin{pmatrix} 2 \\ 3 \end{pmatrix} - \begin{pmatrix} 5 \\ -2 \end{pmatrix} = \begin{pmatrix} -3 \\ 5 \end{pmatrix}$

(c) $-7\begin{pmatrix} 5 \\ -2 \end{pmatrix} = \begin{pmatrix} -35 \\ 14 \end{pmatrix}$

The outcome of a vector sum is the resultant. To display a vector sum visually, connect the vectors tip-to-tail as shown in Example 4. Subtracting a vector r is equivalent to adding the vector $-r$, which has the same size but points in the opposite direction.

Example 4 – $p = \begin{pmatrix} 2 \\ 3 \end{pmatrix}, q = \begin{pmatrix} 4 \\ 1 \end{pmatrix}$ and $r = \begin{pmatrix} -2 \\ 2 \end{pmatrix}$.

$R = p + q - r$. Draw a diagram to show the relationship between R and p, q and r.

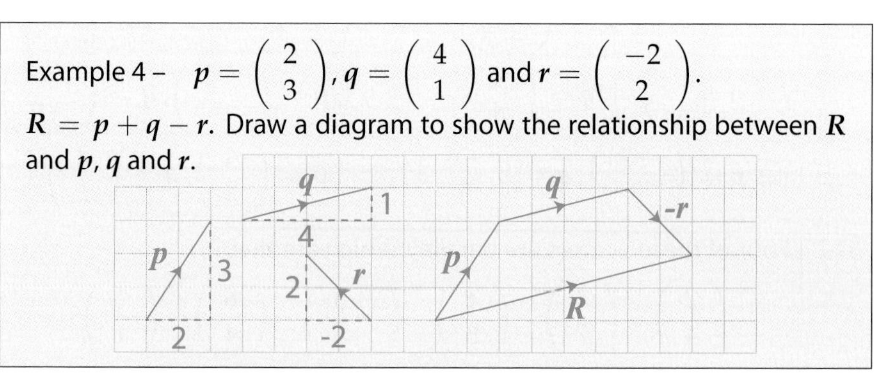

47.1 Write down column vectors for $p, q, r, s,$ and t.

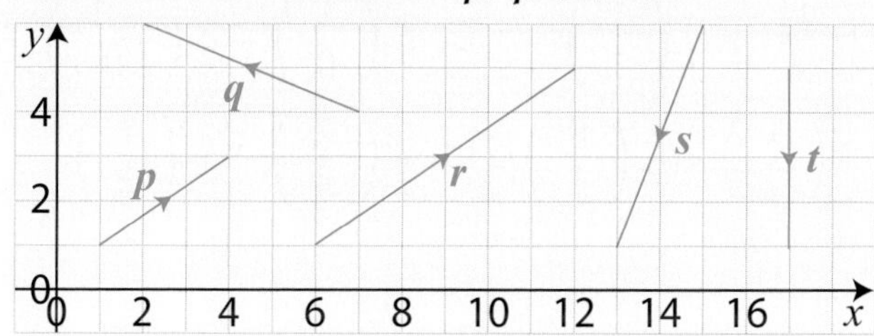

47.2 On a square grid draw the following vectors:

(a) $\begin{pmatrix} 1 \\ 1 \end{pmatrix}$ (b) $\begin{pmatrix} 2 \\ 0 \end{pmatrix}$ (c) $\begin{pmatrix} 0 \\ 3 \end{pmatrix}$ (d) $\begin{pmatrix} -2 \\ -3 \end{pmatrix}$ (e) $\begin{pmatrix} -1 \\ \frac{3}{2} \end{pmatrix}$

47.3 Complete the following vector additions and subtractions.

(a) $\begin{pmatrix} 1 \\ 0 \end{pmatrix} + \begin{pmatrix} 0 \\ 1 \end{pmatrix}$ (c) $\begin{pmatrix} -5 \\ 3 \end{pmatrix} - \begin{pmatrix} 7 \\ 8 \end{pmatrix}$

(b) $\begin{pmatrix} -5 \\ 3 \end{pmatrix} + \begin{pmatrix} 7 \\ 8 \end{pmatrix}$ (d) $\begin{pmatrix} 11 \\ 3 \end{pmatrix} - \begin{pmatrix} -1 \\ -2 \end{pmatrix}$

47.4 $\boldsymbol{a} = \begin{pmatrix} 2 \\ 3 \end{pmatrix}$ and $\boldsymbol{b} = \begin{pmatrix} 5 \\ -2 \end{pmatrix}$. Find

(a) $\boldsymbol{a} + \boldsymbol{b}$ (b) $2\boldsymbol{b}$ (c) $5\boldsymbol{a} - 3\boldsymbol{b}$

47.5 $\boldsymbol{a} = \begin{pmatrix} -6 \\ 1 \end{pmatrix}$ and $\boldsymbol{b} = \begin{pmatrix} 2 \\ -2 \end{pmatrix}$. Find

(a) $2\boldsymbol{a} + 3\boldsymbol{b}$ (b) $-3\boldsymbol{a} - 4\boldsymbol{b}$ (c) $2\boldsymbol{a} - \frac{1}{2}\boldsymbol{b}$

47.6 In each case write $\boldsymbol{q}$ as a scalar multiple of $\boldsymbol{p}$.

For example, if $\boldsymbol{p} = \begin{pmatrix} 3 \\ 2 \end{pmatrix}$ and $\boldsymbol{q} = \begin{pmatrix} 9 \\ 6 \end{pmatrix}$, then $\boldsymbol{q} = 3\boldsymbol{p}$.

(a) $\boldsymbol{p} = \begin{pmatrix} 1 \\ 2 \end{pmatrix}, \boldsymbol{q} = \begin{pmatrix} 4 \\ 8 \end{pmatrix}$ (c) $\boldsymbol{p} = \begin{pmatrix} -2 \\ 3 \end{pmatrix}, \boldsymbol{q} = \begin{pmatrix} 6 \\ -9 \end{pmatrix}$

(b) $\boldsymbol{p} = \begin{pmatrix} -2 \\ 3 \end{pmatrix}, \boldsymbol{q} = \begin{pmatrix} -6 \\ 9 \end{pmatrix}$ (d) $\boldsymbol{p} = \begin{pmatrix} 4 \\ 2 \end{pmatrix}, \boldsymbol{q} = \begin{pmatrix} 2 \\ 1 \end{pmatrix}$

47.7 Four of these vectors are parallel. Which are they?

$$\begin{pmatrix} 2 \\ 4 \end{pmatrix} \begin{pmatrix} 3 \\ 7 \end{pmatrix} \begin{pmatrix} 4 \\ 8 \end{pmatrix} \begin{pmatrix} -3 \\ -6 \end{pmatrix} \begin{pmatrix} 8 \\ 4 \end{pmatrix} \begin{pmatrix} \frac{1}{2} \\ 1 \end{pmatrix}$$

47.8 Complete the following vector additions and subtractions.

(a) $2\begin{pmatrix} 4\frac{1}{2} \\ 6 \end{pmatrix} + \begin{pmatrix} 1 \\ 1 \end{pmatrix}$ (c) $\frac{1}{2}\begin{pmatrix} 1 \\ 0 \end{pmatrix} - \frac{1}{2}\begin{pmatrix} -1 \\ 0 \end{pmatrix}$

(b) $-5\begin{pmatrix} 1 \\ 2 \end{pmatrix} + \frac{7}{2}\begin{pmatrix} 0 \\ 1 \end{pmatrix}$ (d) $\frac{3}{2}\begin{pmatrix} \frac{1}{2} \\ \frac{5}{2} \end{pmatrix} + \frac{1}{3}\begin{pmatrix} 1 \\ 2 \end{pmatrix}$

47.9 If $\boldsymbol{a} = \begin{pmatrix} 3 \\ 0 \end{pmatrix}$ and $\boldsymbol{b} = \begin{pmatrix} 0 \\ 2 \end{pmatrix}$,

(a) What is $\boldsymbol{q}$ if $\boldsymbol{q} = \boldsymbol{a} + \boldsymbol{b}$?

(b) Let $\boldsymbol{p} = 2\boldsymbol{q}$. Write down the value of $\boldsymbol{p}$.

(c) Find $\boldsymbol{r}$ if $\boldsymbol{r} = \boldsymbol{p} + \boldsymbol{a}$.

(d) Sketch a diagram showing the relationship between $\boldsymbol{a}$, $\boldsymbol{p}$ and $\boldsymbol{r}$.

47.10 Solve the equation $\begin{pmatrix} 6 \\ 7 \end{pmatrix} + p \begin{pmatrix} x \\ 4 \end{pmatrix} = \begin{pmatrix} 2 \\ 23 \end{pmatrix}$ to find the values of the variables p and x.

47.11 A man walks 120 m due East and then 50 m due North.

(a) If the x-axis points east and the y-axis points north, write the two parts of his journey as column vectors.

(b) Write a single column vector that describes his overall change in position.

(c) On what bearing is his end point from his start point?

(d) What is the shortest distance between his start and end points?

A position vector gives the position of a point with respect to the origin, $(0,0)$, of the x-y grid. When the letter O is used for "Origin", the position vector of the point A is $\overrightarrow{OA}$.

§ Example 5 shows an application of vectors to geometry.

Example 5 – Find $\overrightarrow{OM}$, where M is the mid-point of AB.

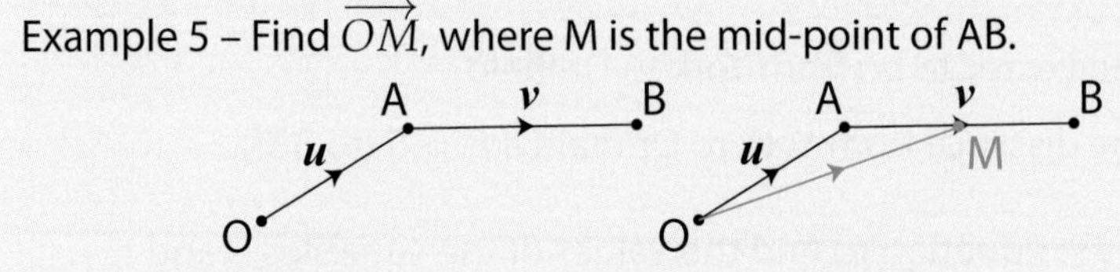

To go from O to M directly is equivalent to going from O to A, then from A to M.

$$\overrightarrow{OM} = \overrightarrow{OA} + \overrightarrow{AM} = \overrightarrow{OA} + \frac{1}{2}\overrightarrow{AB} = \boldsymbol{u} + \frac{1}{2}\boldsymbol{v}$$

47.12 Find the following vectors in terms of $\boldsymbol{p}$ and $\boldsymbol{q}$:

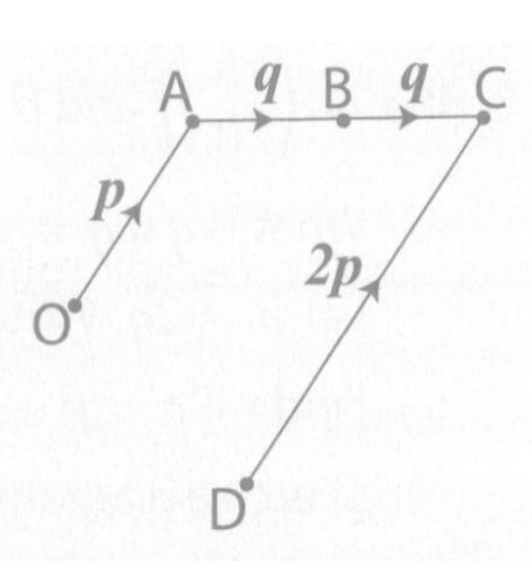

(a) $\overrightarrow{OB}$.

(b) $\overrightarrow{OC}$.

(c) $\overrightarrow{OD}$.

(d) $\overrightarrow{OM}$, where M is the mid-point of BC.

47.13 The diagram shows a regular hexagon. Find, in terms of $\boldsymbol{s}$ and $\boldsymbol{t}$,

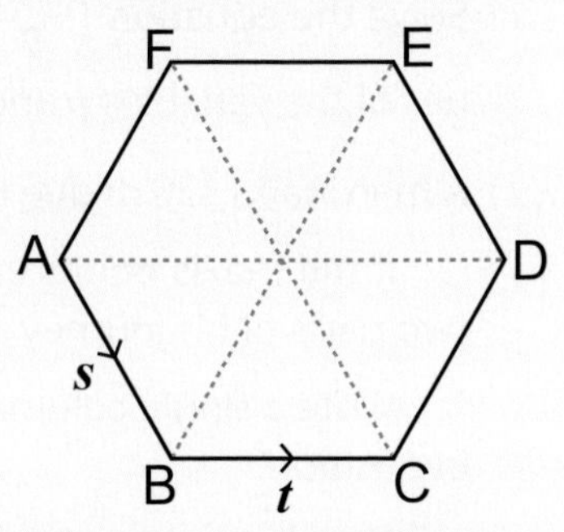

(a) $\overrightarrow{AC}$.

(b) $\overrightarrow{AD}$.

(c) $\overrightarrow{AF}$.

(d) $\overrightarrow{AM}$, where M is the mid-point of $\overrightarrow{DE}$.

(e) $\overrightarrow{EN}$, where N is two-thirds of the way from E to F.

(f)  $\overrightarrow{MN}$.

47.14 The roads which connect York, Market Weighton, and Driffield, form a triangle. Using a coordinate system where the x-axis runs west to east, and the y axis south to north, the vector for travelling from Market Weighton to Driffield is $k\begin{pmatrix} 2 \\ 2 \end{pmatrix}$ miles, where k is a positive integer. The route from Market Weighton to York is given by $k\begin{pmatrix} -2 \\ 1 \end{pmatrix}$. Make a sketch showing the relative positions of the three locations, and find

(a) The vector to go from York to Driffield.

(b) The distance from York to Driffield if $k = 5$ (to 3 sf).

47.15 Solve the equation to find the values of the variables, s and t.

$$s\begin{pmatrix} 1 \\ -2 \end{pmatrix} + t\begin{pmatrix} 3 \\ 5 \end{pmatrix} = \begin{pmatrix} 10 \\ 2 \end{pmatrix}$$

48 Shape Transformations

Shapes can be reflected, rotated, translated and enlarged. These are all types of transformation.

A reflection occurs in a mirror line (line of reflection). The mirror image has the same size as the original shape (they are congruent).

To construct a reflection, draw a perpendicular to the mirror line for each vertex on the shape. Vertices in the original and mirror images are the same distance from the line of reflection, but on opposite sides.

Points that start on the mirror line are unchanged by the reflection. They are invariant.

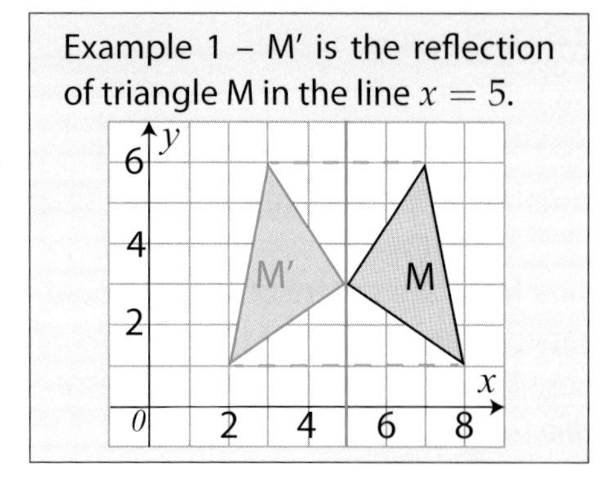

Example 1 – M′ is the reflection of triangle M in the line $x = 5$.

A description of a rotation needs three facts: the centre of rotation (the point about which the rotation occurs), the direction of rotation (clockwise or anti-clockwise), and the size of the rotation (an angle in degrees). A point at the centre of rotation is invariant.

Example 2 – Rotate triangle N 90° clockwise about the point $(0, 0)$ to make triangle N′.

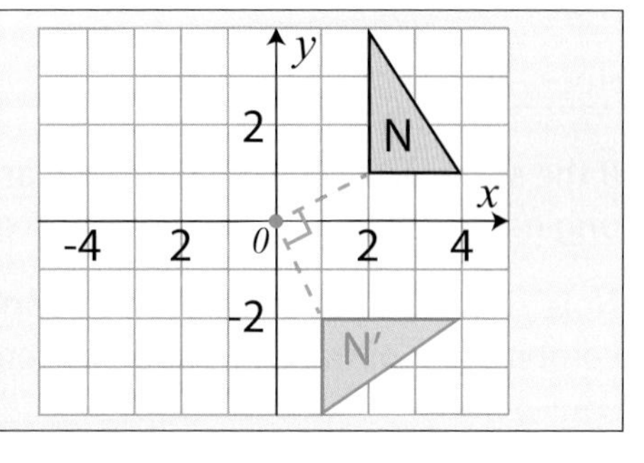

A translation moves a shape around without rotating it or changing its size. To describe a translation it is necessary to state how far the object is moved and in which direction. Translations are often written as column vectors, such as $\begin{pmatrix} 4 \\ -2 \end{pmatrix}$. The top number gives the distance the object is moved in the positive x direction, and the bottom number gives the distance moved in the positive y direction.

Example 3 – Translate shape P by the vector $\begin{pmatrix} 4 \\ -2 \end{pmatrix}$ to make shape P′.

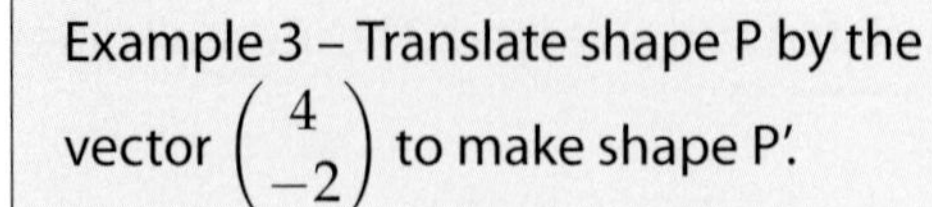

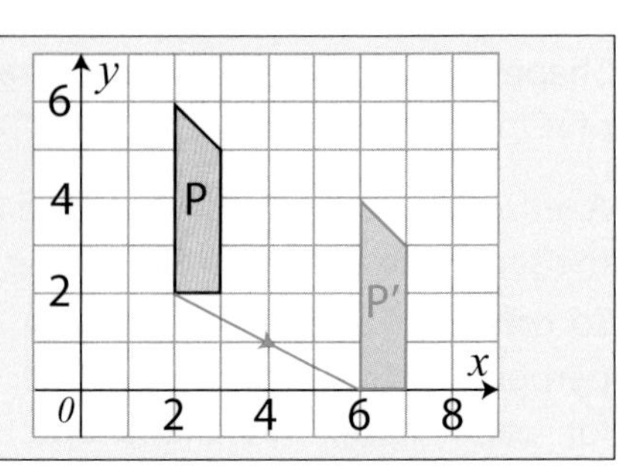

An enlargement creates a similar shape. An enlargement has a centre of enlargement and a linear scale factor. To construct an enlargement, draw a line from the centre of enlargement through each vertex on the original shape. The positions of the vertices of the enlarged shape lie on the same lines. Their distances from the centre of enlargement are multiplied by the scale factor.

Example 4 – Enlarge triangle Q by a scale factor of 3 with centre of enlargement (2,4) to make triangle Q′.

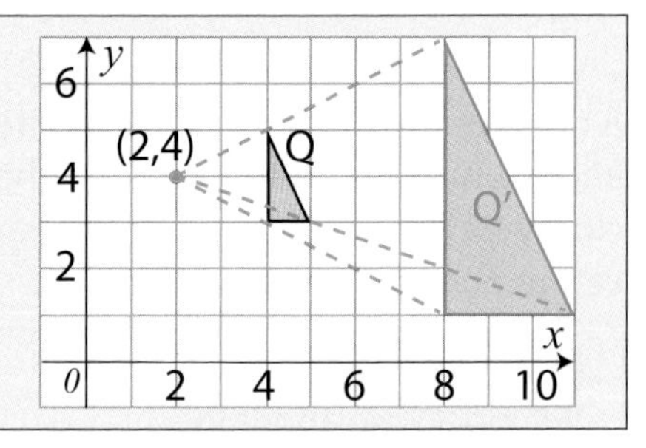

If the scale factor is a fraction such as $\frac{1}{2}$, the image will be smaller than the original shape. A point at the centre of enlargement is invariant.

Note: Transformations are often applied successively, and more than one combination of transformations often achieves the same result.

48.1 The shape shown is reflected in the x-axis. List the points which are invariant under the transformation.

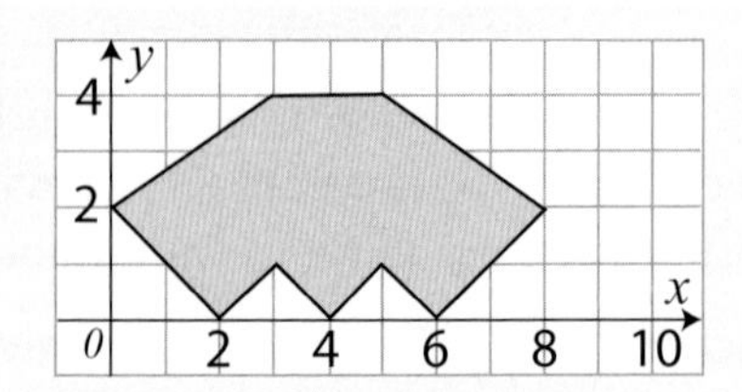

48.2 The sketch shows a triangle. Copy the shape onto a large set of axes and add the following to your drawing:

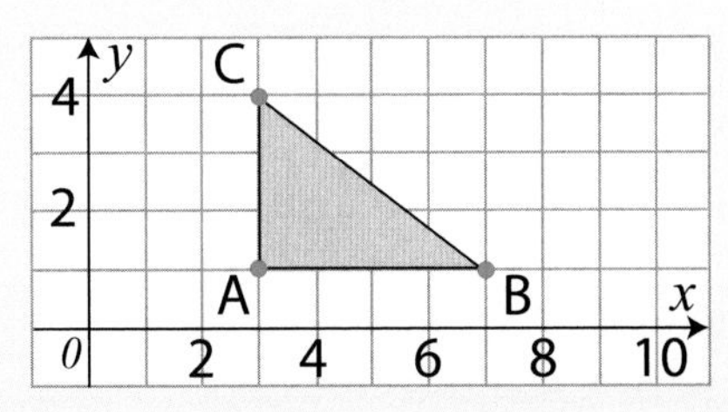

(a) A′B′C′, which is the reflection of ABC in the line $x = 0$.

(b) DEF, which is the result of translating ABC by $\begin{pmatrix} 2 \\ 3 \end{pmatrix}$.

(c) JKL, which is the result of rotating ABC 90° clockwise about $(0, 0)$.

48.3 (a) Give the angle of rotation anticlockwise about the origin to rotate shape T onto (i) A (ii) B.

(b) What is the vector that translates shape T to give C ?

(c) T is reflected in a line of symmetry to make D. What is the equation of the line of symmetry?

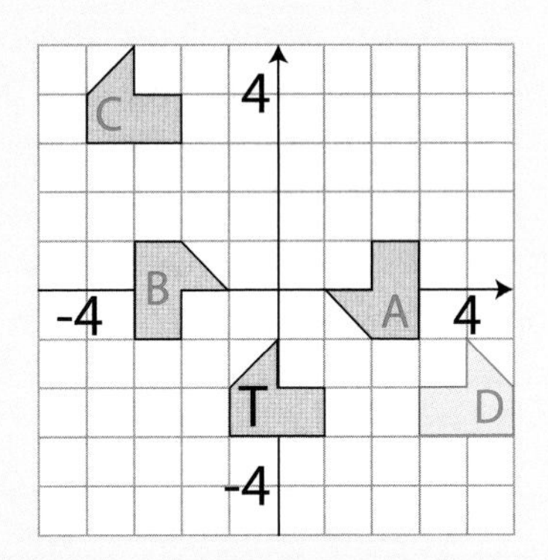

48.4 (a) On a square grid draw a quadrilateral with vertices at $(2, 2)$, $(2, 4)$, $(4, 2)$, and $(4, 4)$. Label this shape P.

(b) Enlarge shape P using a scale factor of 2, with the origin as the centre of enlargement. Label this shape Q.

(c) Shade in shape P and shape Q. Consider the two shapes together as a composite shape R. Reflect R in the line $x = 0$.

48.5 The coordinates of a shape A drawn on x-y axes are $(4, 3)$, $(5, 3)$, $(6, 4)$ and $(6, 5)$.

(a) Draw shape A on a diagram. What type of quadrilateral is A?

(b) Add the line $y = x$ to your diagram.

(c) Shape B is the reflection of A in $y = x$. Draw B, and list the coordinates of the vertices.

(d) Rotate shape B by 90° anticlockwise about the origin to create shape C. List the coordinates of the vertices of C.

(e) What single transformation would map A onto C?

48.6 Shape R is enlarged by a linear scale factor. Which of A, B, C and D are enlargements of R?

For those shapes which are enlargements of R, find the centre of enlargement.

Hint: draw lines through corresponding vertices and find where the lines intersect.

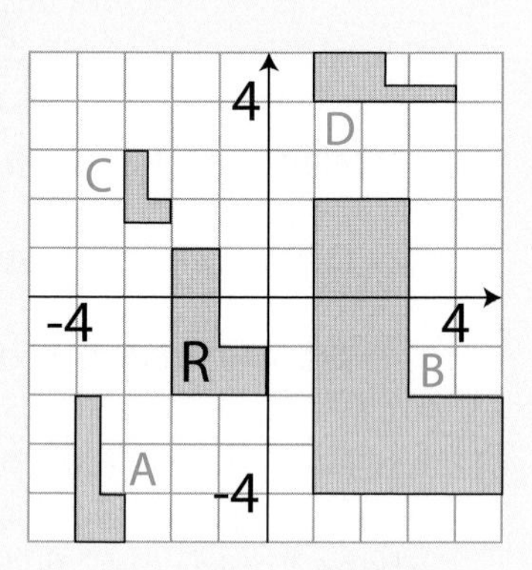

§ When a shape is enlarged by a negative scale factor, the enlarged shape is on the opposite side of the centre of enlargement from the original shape.

Example 5 – Enlarge triangle R by a scale factor of -2 with centre of enlargement (4,3) to make triangle R′.

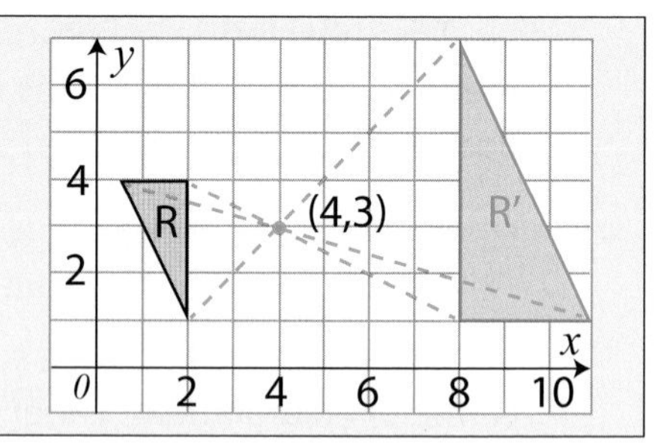

48.7 On separate copies of the diagram, enlarge M by:

(a) A scale factor of 3, with the transformation centred on the origin.

(b) A scale factor of $\frac{1}{2}$, with the transformation centred on $(1,4)$.

(c) A scale factor of $-\frac{1}{4}$, with the transformation centred on $(0,0)$.

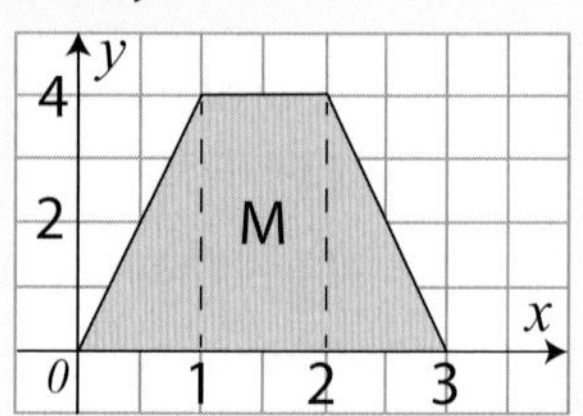

48.8 (a) Calculate the area of shape N.

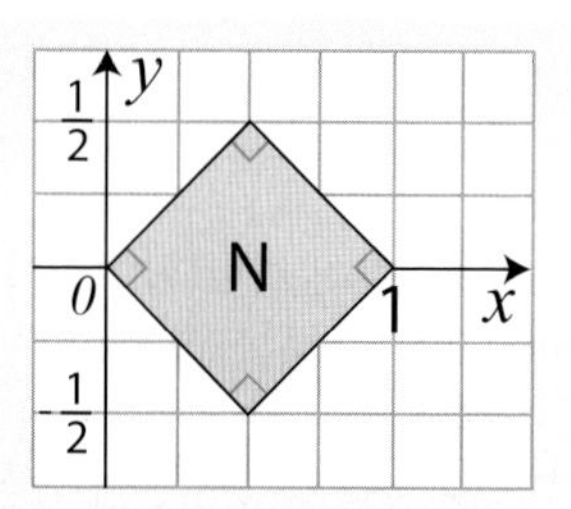

(b) On a copy of the diagram, enlarge N by a linear scale factor of $-\frac{1}{2}$, with centre of enlargement $(-1,0)$, to give shape N′.

(c) What is the area of N′?

48.9 Which of the following transformations are equivalent? There are four pairs.

(a) Translation by $\begin{pmatrix} 0 \\ 3 \end{pmatrix}$ and then $\begin{pmatrix} 6 \\ 1 \end{pmatrix}$.

(b) Enlargement: scale factor $-\frac{1}{2}$, centre of enlargement $\begin{pmatrix} 0 \\ 0 \end{pmatrix}$.

(c) Reflection in the y-axis, followed by reflection in the x-axis.

(d) Reflection in the y-axis, followed by rotation by 180° about the origin.

(e) Enlargement by scale factor $\frac{1}{2}$, with centre of enlargement $\begin{pmatrix} 0 \\ 0 \end{pmatrix}$, followed by rotation by 180° about the origin.

(f) Translation by $\begin{pmatrix} 3 \\ 2 \end{pmatrix}$, then translation by $\begin{pmatrix} 3 \\ 2 \end{pmatrix}$ again.

(g) Reflection in the x-axis.

(h) Rotation by 180° about the origin.

48.10 A shape has area A. What would the area be if:

(a) The original shape is reflected in the y-axis?

(b) The original shape is enlarged by a linear scale factor of 2, with centre of enlargement $(0,0)$?

(c) The original shape is translated by 3 units in the positive x-direction, followed by 5 units in the negative y-direction?

(d) The original shape is enlarged by a linear scale factor of $-k$, with centre of enlargement $(2,-5)$?

49 § Graphs of Trigonometric Functions

The graphs of the functions $\sin x$, $\cos x$ and $\tan x$ all show periodicity - a pattern that repeats.

The graphs of $\sin x$ and $\cos x$ both oscillate between $+1$ and -1 and repeat after $360°$. $\sin x$ is $\cos x$ translated by $90°$ in the direction of positive x, and it is sometimes said that $\sin x$ and $\cos x$ are "$90°$ out of phase."

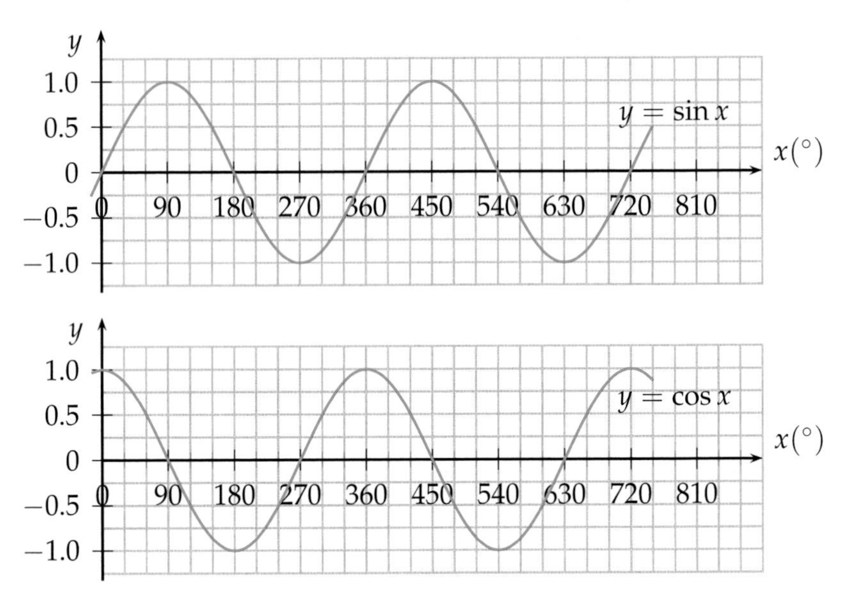

$\tan x$ repeats after $180°$. At $x = 90°$, $\tan x$ is undefined, and the line $x = 90°$ is an asymptote to the curve $y = \tan x$.

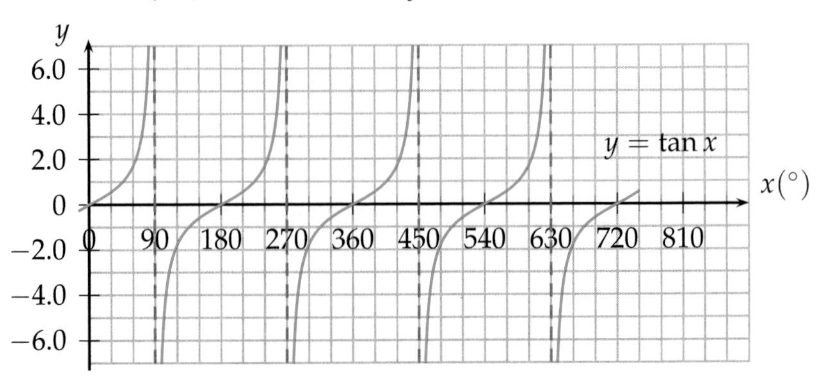

In this exercise you may need to refer back to the table of exact values of $\sin\theta°$, $\cos\theta°$ and $\tan\theta°$ in chapter 41.

49.1 (a) Sketch the graph of $y = \sin x$ for $-360° \leqslant x \leqslant 360°$.
(b) List the values of x for which $\sin x = 0$.
(c) List the values of x for which $\sin x = 1$.
(d) List the values of x for which $\sin x = -1$.

49.2 (a) Sketch the graph of $y = \cos x$ for $-90° \leqslant x \leqslant 630°$.
(b) List the values of x for which $\cos x = 0$.
(c) List the values of x for which $\cos x = 1$.
(d) List the values of x for which $\cos x = -1$.

49.3 (a) Sketch the graph of $y = \tan x$ for $-360° \leqslant x \leqslant 360°$.
(b) Add to your graph the line $y = 1$.
(c) List all the values of x for which $\tan x = 1$.

49.4 By sketching graphs, solve the following pairs of simultaneous equations for x values in the interval $0° \leqslant x \leqslant 720°$:
(a) $y = \sin x$ and $y = 1$. (b) $y = 2\cos x$ and $y = 1$.

49.5 By sketching graphs, find the solutions to the simultaneous equations $y = 2\sin x + 1$ and $y = 1 + \sqrt{3}$ for $0° \leqslant x \leqslant 720°$.

49.6 By sketching graphs, find the solutions to the equation $\sqrt{2}\sin x = 1$ for $-360° \leqslant x \leqslant 360°$.

49.7 Sketch the following functions for $0° \leqslant x \leqslant 720°$.
(a) $y = \cos\frac{1}{2}x$. (b) $y = \cos 2x$.

49.8 Sketch the following functions for $0° \leqslant x \leqslant 720°$.
(a) $y = \cos(x - 90°)$. (b) $y = -\sin(x - 90°)$.

49.9 By sketching the curves $y = \sin x$ and $y = -\cos x$ on the same axes, find the coordinates at which these curves meet for $-360° \leqslant x \leqslant 360°$.

49.10 By sketching graphs, find all the solutions to the simultaneous equations $y = \cos x$ and $y = \frac{1}{\sqrt{2}}(\frac{x}{45°})^2$.

50 § Applications of Trigonometry to Geometry

Three formulae which are useful in geometry are the sine rule, the cosine rule and the formula for the area of a triangle. As the names suggest, they make use of the sine and cosine functions.

The sides of a triangle are labelled a, b and c, and the angles are labelled A, B and C. It does not matter which sides and angles receive which letter, as long as a is opposite A, b opposite B and c opposite C.

The sine rule is

$$\frac{a}{\sin A} = \frac{b}{\sin B} = \frac{c}{\sin C}$$

The cosine rule is

$$a^2 = b^2 + c^2 - 2bc\cos A$$

The area of a triangle is

$$\text{Area} = \frac{1}{2}ab\sin C$$

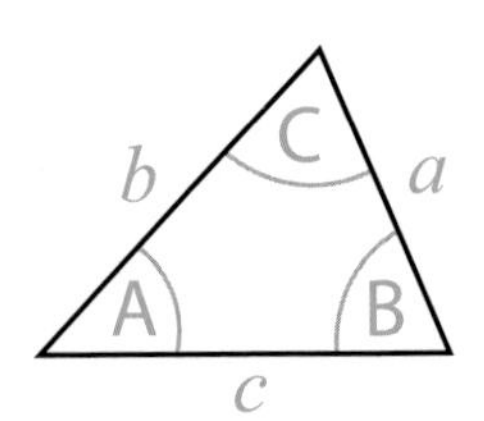

These formulae apply to all triangles, including ones where one of the angles is obtuse.

Example 1 – Use the sine rule to find the length x and the angle α.

(i) Triangle with vertices A, B, C; side $b = x$, side $a = 8.03$, side c; angle A = 70°, angle B = 30°.

$$\frac{x}{\sin 30^\circ} = \frac{8.03}{\sin 70^\circ}$$

↓ Multiply both sides by sin 30°.

$$\Rightarrow x = \frac{8.03}{\sin 70^\circ} \times \sin 30^\circ$$

$$\therefore x = 4.27 \text{ m to 3 sf}$$

(ii) Triangle with vertices A, B, C; side $b = 4.21$, side $a = 4.97$, side c; angle A = 50°, angle B = α.

$$\frac{4.21}{\sin\alpha} = \frac{4.97}{\sin 50^\circ}$$

↓ Multiply both sides by sin 50°.

$$\frac{4.21}{\sin\alpha} \times \sin 50^\circ = 4.97$$

↓ Multiply both sides by sin α.

$$4.21 \times \sin 50^\circ = 4.97 \times \sin\alpha$$

↓ Divide both sides by 4.97.

$$\frac{4.21 \times \sin 50^\circ}{4.97} = \sin\alpha$$

$$\therefore \alpha = \sin^{-1}\left(\frac{4.21 \times \sin 50^\circ}{4.97}\right) = 40.5^\circ \text{ to 3 sf}$$

Example 2 illustrates the ambiguous case of the sine rule.

Example 2 – A triangle ABC has angle $A = 30°$ and side lengths $a = 2.20$, $c = 3.74$. Find the possible sizes of angle C, and hence draw sketches of the triangle.

$$\frac{a}{\sin A} = \frac{c}{\sin C} \qquad \Rightarrow \frac{2.20}{\sin 30°} = \frac{3.74}{\sin C}$$

This re-arranges as in Example 1 (ii) to give:

$$\therefore C = \sin^{-1}\left(\frac{3.74 \times \sin 30°}{2.20}\right) = 58.2116...° = 58.2° \text{ to 1 dp}$$

Using $\sin^{-1}$ on a calculator always gives an acute angle, but as the diagram below left shows there is an obtuse angle with the same value of $\sin\alpha$. The value of the obtuse angle is

$$\text{Obtuse angle} = 180° - C = 121.788... = 121.8° \text{ to 1 dp}$$

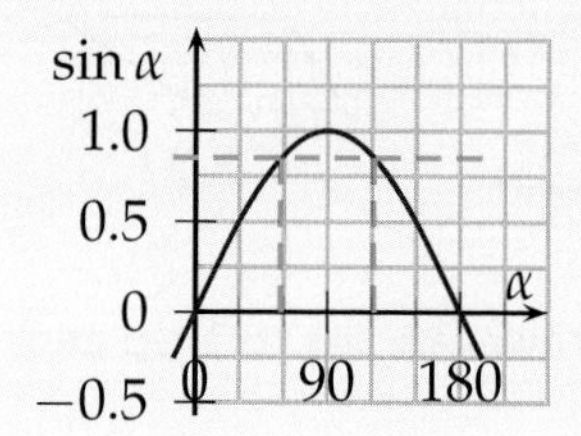

The two possible triangles are:

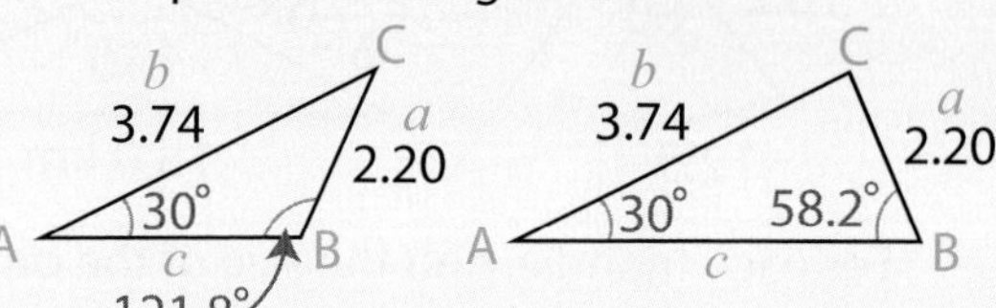

Example 3 – Use the cosine rule to find the missing lengths and angles.

(i)

C
b
3.14 m
a
x
35°
A
B
2.91 m
c

$$x^2 = 3.14^2 + 2.91^2 - 2 \times 3.14 \times 2.91 \cos 35°$$

$$\Rightarrow x^2 = 3.35786...$$

$$\therefore x = 1.83 \text{ m to 3 sf}$$

(ii)

C
b
7.80
α
a
7.50
A
B
8.90
c

$$8.90^2 = 7.80^2 + 7.50^2 - 2 \times 7.80 \times 7.50 \cos\alpha$$

This rearranges to:

$$\cos\alpha = \frac{7.80^2 + 7.50^2 - 8.90^2}{2 \times 7.80 \times 7.50}$$

$$\Rightarrow \cos\alpha = 0.3237606...$$

$$\therefore \alpha = 71.1° \text{ to 3 sf}$$

Example 4 – Find the area of the triangle by using the area formula.

$$\text{Area} = \frac{1}{2} \times 37.2 \times 41.1 \times \sin 82.4^\circ$$

$$\Rightarrow \text{Area} = 758\ \text{m}^2 \text{ to 3 sf}$$

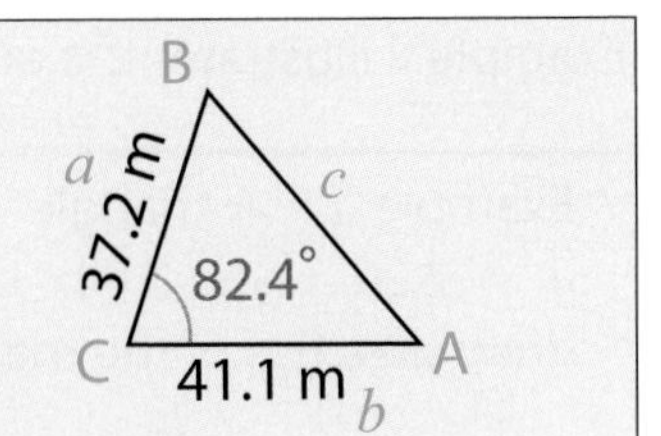

In this exercise give your answers to 3 sf unless instructed otherwise.

50.1 Use the sine rule to find the indicated lengths.

(a)

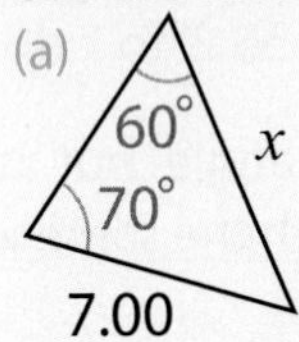

(b)

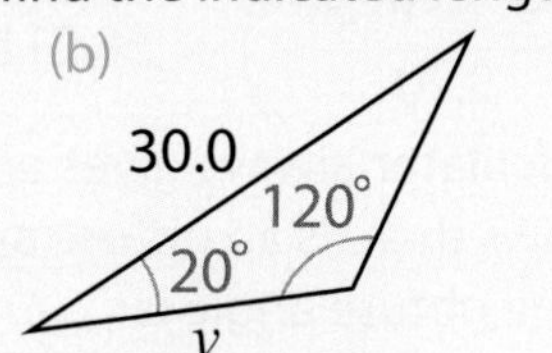

(c)

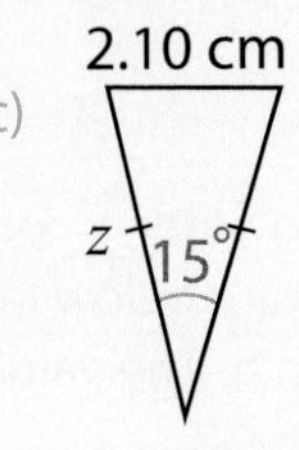

50.2 Find the values of the indicated angles.

(a)

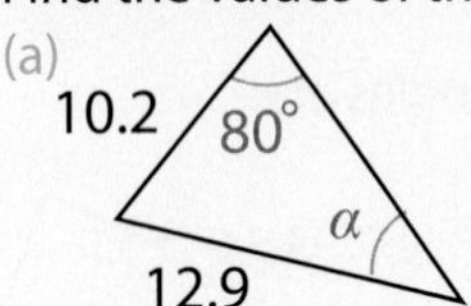

(b)

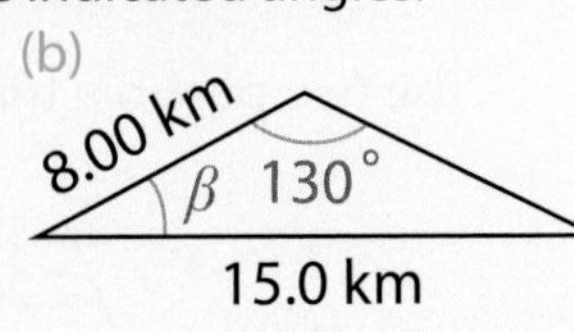

(c)

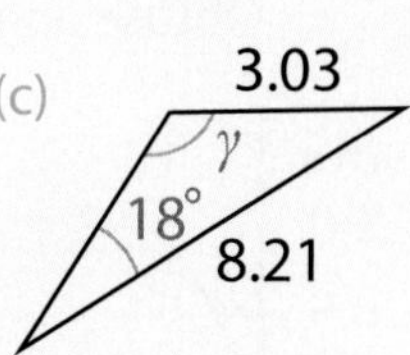

50.3 For each triangle, find the size of the other two angles to 1 dp and sketch the possible triangle or triangles.

(a) $A = 150^\circ, a = 305$ cm, $c = 175$ cm.

(b) $A = 40^\circ, a = 75.0, c = 101.$

(c) $B = 60^\circ, a = 90.0$ km, $b = 120$ km.

50.4 Find the missing lengths:

(a)

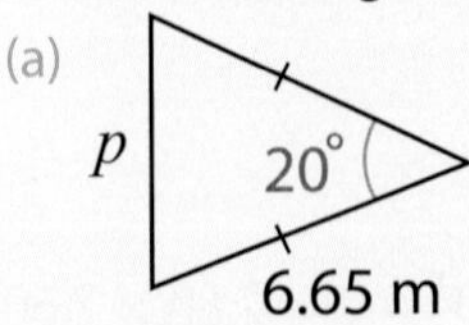

(b)

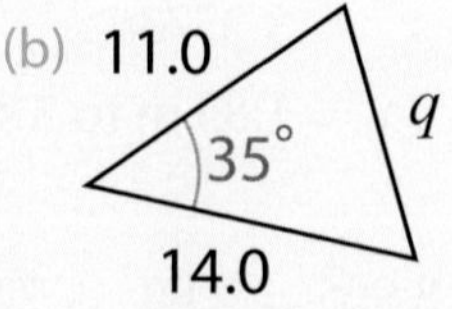

(c)

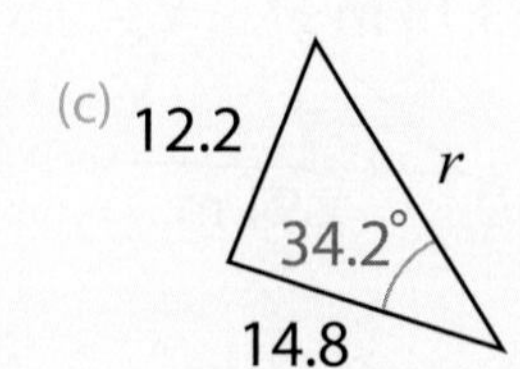

50.5 Find the size of the three angles:

(a)

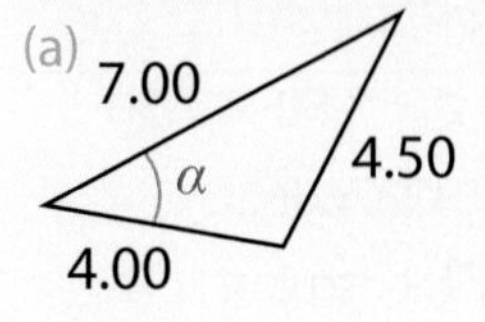

(b)

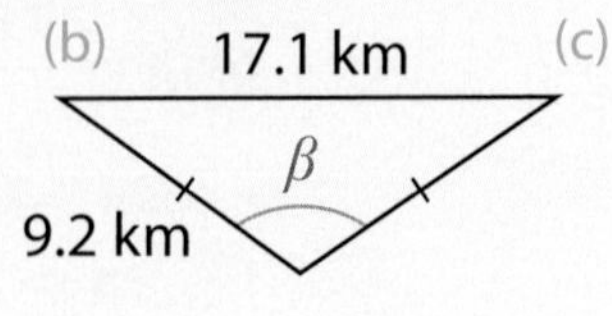

(c)

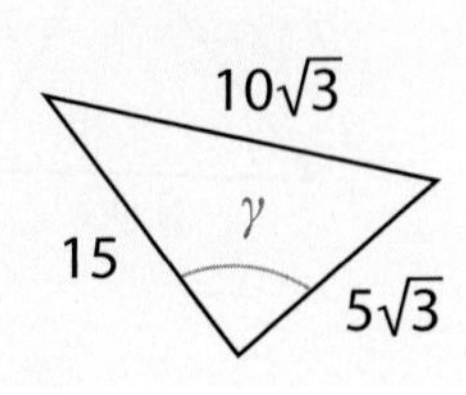

50.6 Find the area of these triangles:

(a)

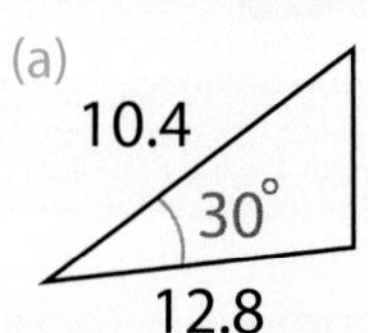

(b)

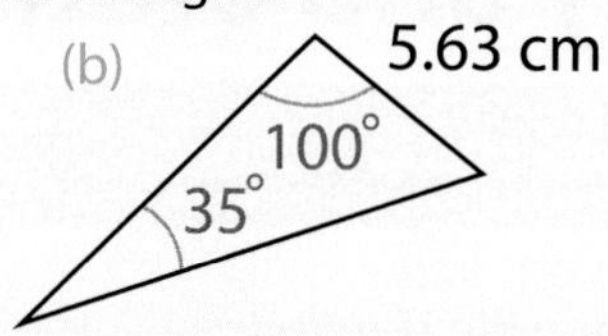

(c)

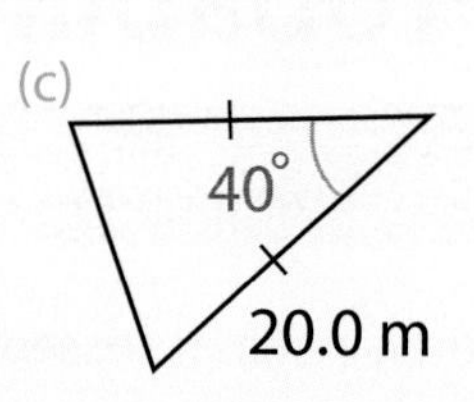

50.7 A garden designer is planning to build a semi-circular patio on one side of a triangular lawn.

The plans are shown in the diagram.

(a) What will the area of the lawn be?

(b) What will the area of the patio be?

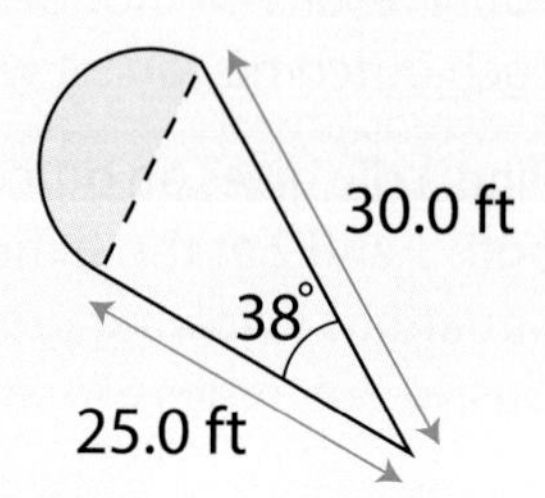

50.8 A drone is to be flown between different locations:

(a) From F to H.

(b) From H to G.

(c) From G back to F.

For each part of the journey, give the bearing on which the drone flies and the distance the drone travels.

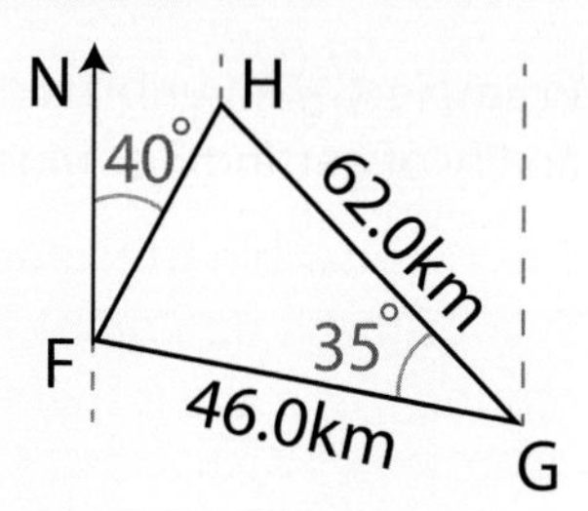

50.9 A landowner has a triangular piece of land. They are planning to build a path along the boundary of the land, and plant trees in the centre. Each tree will need 50 m^2 of land when it is mature. The landowner knows that some trees will not survive to maturity. They plant 30% more trees than the maximum suggested by an area calculation.

(a) How long is the path?

(b) Assuming that the landowner plants as many trees as possible, how many trees will be planted? Round your answer to the nearest whole tree.

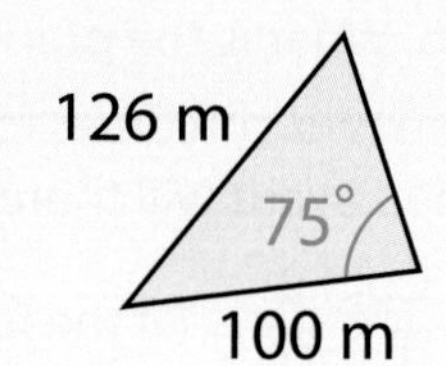

Probability and Statistics

51 Probability Laws and Outcomes

When a coin is tossed or a die is rolled fairly, the outcomes are random. Individual results cannot be predicted. However, the theoretical probabilities of each outcome can be worked out.

Rolling a die gives an outcome of $1, 2, 3, 4, 5$ or 6. It cannot give an outcome of both 1 and 2 at the same time. These outcomes are mutually exclusive. In all situations involving probability, the probabilities of all possible mutually exclusive outcomes always add up to 1.

If a die is unbiased, each of the 6 possible outcomes from 1 to 6 is equally likely; therefore, the probability of each outcome is exactly 1 out of 6, or $\frac{1}{6}$. For example, using P notation, the probability of rolling a 5 is $\mathrm{P}(5) = \frac{1}{6}$.

> Example 1 – An unbiased 6-sided die is rolled once. What is the probability of getting 5 of more?
>
> The six possible outcomes when rolling the die are $1, 2, 3, 4, 5$ and 6. Two of these outcomes have scores of 5 or more. The probability of scoring 5 or more is therefore 2 out of 6. $\mathrm{P}(5 \text{ or more}) = \frac{2}{6} = \frac{1}{3}$

Rolling a die is an example of an event. The sample space of an event is a list of the possible outcomes. When two events are combined, a sample space diagram or grid can be used to list all the possible outcomes. The number of outcomes of the combined event is found by multiplying the numbers of outcomes of the two individual events.

> Example 2 – A mathematician tosses two coins. Draw a sample space diagram. What is the probability of getting one Head and one Tail?
>
> There are two outcomes for each of the coins. The sample space for the combined event will therefore contain $2 \times 2 = 4$ outcomes.
>
> | | | Coin 2 | |
> |---|---|---|---|
> | | | T | H |
> | Coin 1 | T | TT | TH |
> | | H | HT | HH |
>
> Of the four outcomes in the grid, two have one Head and one Tail. The probability of getting one Head and one Tail is $\mathrm{P(HT)} = \frac{2}{4} = \frac{1}{2}$.

If two outcomes are mutually exclusive, the probability of getting the first outcome or the second outcome is equal to the sum of their individual probabilities.

For mutually exclusive outcomes, $P(A \text{ or } B) = P(A) + P(B)$

Example 3 – An unbiased 8-sided die is rolled once. What is the probability of getting 1 or 2?

The probability of getting a 1 is $\frac{1}{8}$. The probability of getting a 2 is $\frac{1}{8}$.
The probability of scoring 1 or 2 is $P(1 \text{ or } 2) = \frac{1}{8} + \frac{1}{8} = \frac{2}{8} = \frac{1}{4}$.

The probability of getting a particular outcome and the probability of not getting that outcome always add up to 1. If the outcome is A, "not A" is written as A'. A' is the complement of A.

$$P(A) + P(A') = 1 \qquad \Rightarrow P(A') = 1 - P(A)$$

When two events happen in succession, the events are independent if the probabilities for the second event are unaffected by the outcome of the first event; otherwise the events are dependent.

For independent events, the probability of a sequence of outcomes is found by multiplying the probabilities of the outcomes of the individual events. Writing the probability of getting outcome A from the first event followed by outcome B from the second event as P(AB),

For independent events, $P(AB) = P(A) \times P(B)$

Example 4 – An unbiased 6-sided die is rolled twice. What is the probability of rolling a 6 twice in succession?

The probability of getting a 6 on the first roll is $\frac{1}{6}$.
The probability of getting a 6 on the second roll is $\frac{1}{6}$.
The probability of getting 6 twice in succession is $P(6\ 6) = \frac{1}{6} \times \frac{1}{6} = \frac{1}{36}$.

When an event is repeated, the number of repeats is the number of trials. The expected frequency of getting a particular outcome is equal to the theoretical probability of that outcome multiplied by the number of trials.

When an experiment is done, the experimental probability (relative frequency) of an outcome is equal to the number of times the outcome occurred, divided by the number of trials. As the number of trials increases, experimental probability is expected to become closer to theoretical probability.

Example 5 – An unbiased 6-sided die is rolled 120 times.

(i) What is the expected frequency of scoring a 6?

The theoretical probability of getting a 6 is $\frac{1}{6}$ on every roll. The expected number of 6's from an experiment involving 120 trials is $\frac{1}{6} \times 120 = 20$.

(ii) In the experiment a 6 was scored 24 times. What is the relative frequency of scoring a 6?

The relative frequency of scoring a 6 is $\frac{24}{120} = \frac{1}{5}$.

51.1 A baker makes two kinds of muffin: plain and chocolate. Each muffin is iced with one of three types of icing: vanilla, orange, or chocolate.

(a) How many different combinations of muffin and icing are there?

(b) The baker makes equal numbers of each combination. What is the probability that a muffin chosen at random has orange icing?

51.2 An unbiased 6-sided die is rolled once. Calculate the probability that the outcome is:

(a) 6 (b) 4 or more (c) Not 5 (d) 1 or 6 (e) Neither 2 nor 3

51.3 A regular, unbiased octahedron has the integers from 1 to 8 printed on its faces. When it is rolled, calculate the probability of getting:

(a) 7 (b) An odd number (c) Neither 3 nor 4 (d) Greater than 2

51.4 Two children each have three cards. They have the numbers 1, 2, and 3 printed on them. Both children put their cards into a bag, draw one at random and place it on the table.

(a) Fill in the table to show the possible combinations of cards.

Child 1 \ Child 2	1	2	3
1	1,1		
2			
3			

What is the probability that:

(b) Both cards show the same number?

(c) The cards on the table sum to less than 5?

(d) The product of the two numbers is a square number?

51.5 A biased 6-sided die is rolled. The probability of rolling 4 or less is $\frac{17}{24}$. The probability of a 6 is $\frac{1}{4}$. What is the probability of rolling a 5?

51.6 Two unbiased, four-sided dice with faces showing the numbers 1 to 4 are rolled, and the numbers on the faces added together.

(a) Fill in the table to show the sums of the values on the dice.

		Die 2			
		1	2	3	4
Die 1	1				
	2				
	3				
	4				

What is the probability of getting a score of

(b) 2? (c) 5? (d) Greater than 4?

51.7 A tub of sweets contains 12 toffees and 8 mint creams. Sweets are taken out of the tub one at a time at random and eaten.

(a) What is the probability that the first sweet taken out is a toffee?

(b) If the first sweet taken out is a toffee, what is the probability that the next sweet taken out is also a toffee?

(c) If the first two sweets are both toffees, what is the probability that the third sweet taken out is a mint cream?

51.8 A number generator can produce the numbers $1, 2, 3, 4, 5$ and 6. The probabilities of producing $1, 2, 5$ and 6 are the same. The probability of producing 3 is twice the probability of producing 5, and the probability of producing 4 is four times the probability of producing 1. What are the probabilities of producing each number?

51.9 A bag contains marshmallows in two sizes, large and small, and two colours, pink and white. The numbers of each size and colour are shown in the table.

	Large	**Small**
Pink	3	8
White	7	12

(a) If a marshmallow is chosen at random, what is the probability it is large and pink?

If two marshmallows are taken out at random and put into a mug of hot chocolate, what is the probability that:

(b) Both of them are pink? (c) Neither of them is pink?

51.10 Two 6-sided dice are rolled and the numbers added together.

(a) The pair of dice are rolled 360 times. Out of these 360 trials 95 give a score of 7. What is the relative frequency of scoring 7?

(b) What is the theoretical probability of scoring 7?

(c) Out of the 360 trials, how many are expected to score 7?

(d) Do you think the dice are biased or unbiased? State a reason.

52 Tree Diagrams and Venn Diagrams

Tree diagrams are used to display probabilities for short sequences of events, each of which has a small number of possible outcomes. Each branching of the tree represents a new event, and the probabilities of the outcomes are marked on the branches as fractions or decimals.

When drawing tree diagrams, it is important to decide whether events are independent or dependent. For example, consider a bag containing 2 red and 3 blue balls. Two balls are chosen at random, one after the other. If the first ball is not replaced, there is one fewer ball in the bag when the second ball is drawn; the ratio of the colours, and hence the probabilities of drawing each colour, depend on which colour was drawn first.

Example 1 – A bag contains 3 red balls (R) and 2 blue balls (B). Amit takes out two balls at random, one after the other, and looks at their colour. Draw tree diagrams for the following cases:

(i) The first ball is replaced before the second ball is drawn.

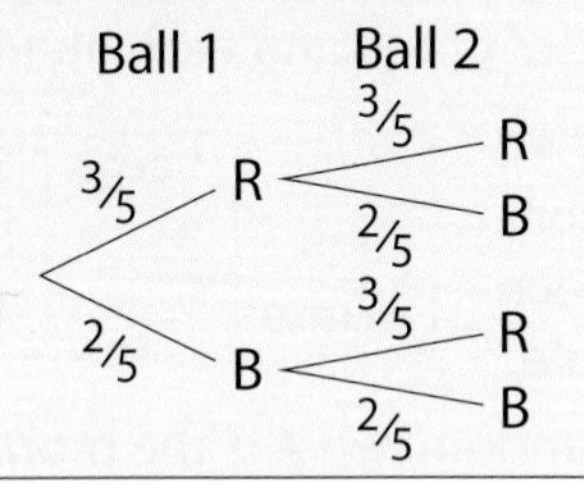

(ii) The first ball is not replaced before the second ball is drawn.

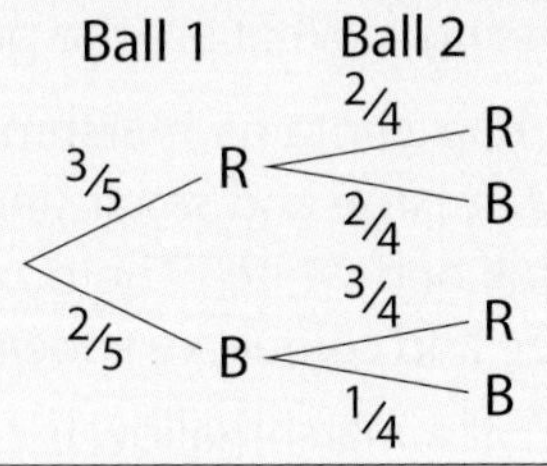

To find the probability of a sequence of outcomes, work through a probability tree from left to right, multiplying the probabilities on the branches.

Example 2 – A bag contains mint and strawberry chocolates. Sue takes out two at random and eats them. Find the probability that:

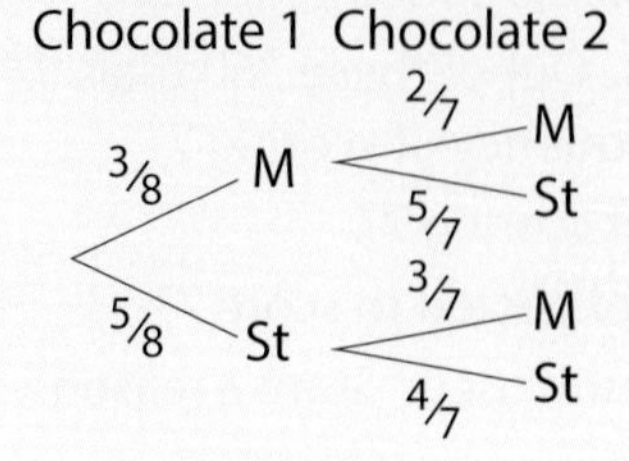

(i) Sue gets two mint chocolates.

P(M M) $= \frac{3}{8} \times \frac{2}{7} = \frac{6}{56} = \frac{3}{28}$

(ii) Sue gets two of the same type.

P(Two the same) $=$ P(M M) $+$ P(St St)

P(Two the same) $= \frac{3}{8} \times \frac{2}{7} + \frac{5}{8} \times \frac{4}{7} = \frac{13}{28}$

Venn diagrams are used to display the results of surveys. A Venn diagram always has an outer rectangle labelled ε. This represents the "universal set", which includes all survey respondents. Answers to survey questions are represented by circles, and the total number within a circle is the number of positive responses. Where two circles overlap, respondents gave positive responses to both questions. For example, in the Venn diagram in Example 3 below, 8 respondents went to the beach and also had ice cream.

Example 3 – On a hot day a survey asked 24 people if they had gone to the beach, and if they had ice cream. If one of those surveyed is chosen at random, what is the probability that they:

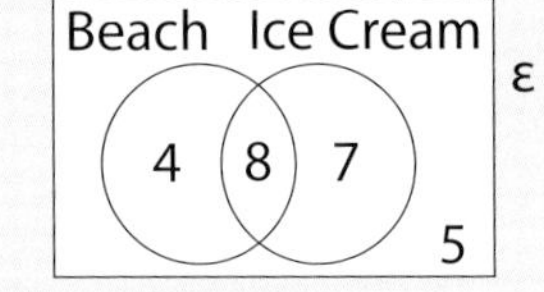

(i) Went to the beach and had ice cream?

8 out of 24 people went to the beach and had ice cream. The probability is $\frac{8}{24} = \frac{1}{3}$.

(ii) Went to the beach but did not have ice cream?

The probability is $\frac{4}{24} = \frac{1}{6}$.

(iii) Did not go to the beach or have ice cream?

The probability is $\frac{5}{24}$.

A second use of Venn diagrams is to display the overlap between sets. In set notation the elements (members) of a set are written inside curly brackets.

$A = \{1, 2, 3, 4\}$
The members of set A are $1, 2, 3$ and 4.

$B = \{x : 3 \leqslant x \leqslant 8\}$, x is an integer.
The members of set B are $3, 4, 5, 6, 7$ and 8.

Example 4 – $A = \{1, 2, 3, 4\}$ and $B = \{x : 3 \leqslant x \leqslant 8\}$, where x is an integer. Display sets A and B on a Venn diagram.

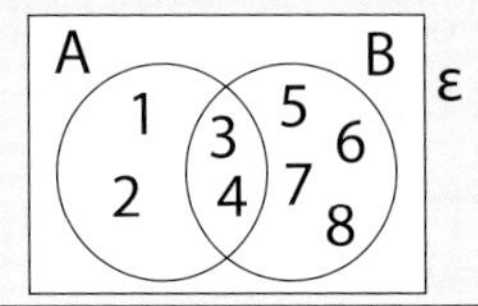

1 and 2 are in set A but not set B.
3 and 4 are in set A and set B.
5, 6, 7 and 8 are in set B but not set A.

When calculating probabilities from Venn diagrams,

- P(A ∪ B) ("A union B") is the probability of A or B or both A and B.
- P(A ∩ B) ("A intersection B") is the probability of both A and B.
- P(A′) is the probability of not A. A′ is the complement of A.

Example 5 – 50 children on a camping trip are asked if they remembered to bring a map (M) and compass (C). If one child from the group is chosen at random, what is the probability:

(i) $P(M \cup C)$

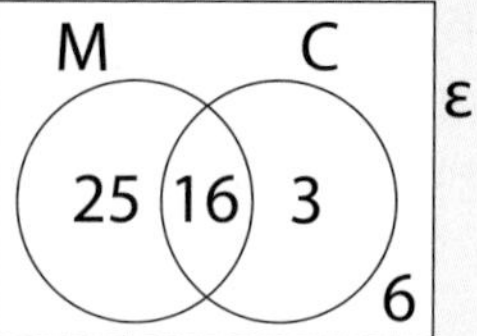

$25 + 16 + 3 = 44$ out of 50 children have a map, or a compass, or both.

$P(M \cup C) = \frac{44}{50} = \frac{22}{25}$.

(ii) $P(M \cap C)$

16 out of 50 children have a map and a compass.

$P(M \cap C) = \frac{16}{50} = \frac{8}{25}$.

(iii) $P(M')$

$3 + 6 = 9$ out of 50 children do not have a map.

$P(M') = \frac{9}{50}$.

52.1 A boy travels to school by bus. Each morning, two buses arrive at at about the same time, the school bus (S) and the town bus (T). On any day, the probability the school bus arrives first is 0.6.

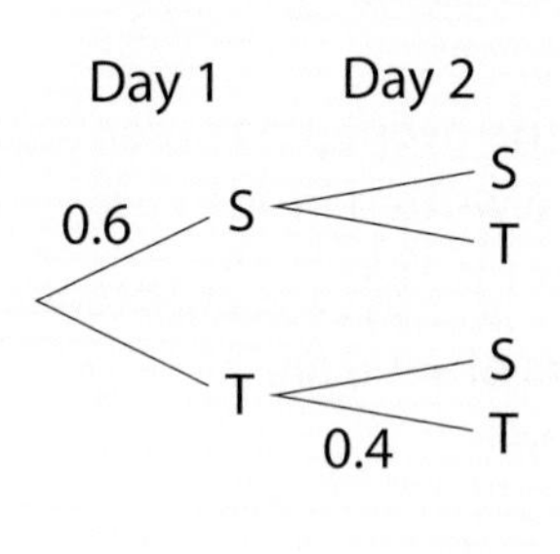

(a) Complete the tree diagram to show the probabilities for two consecutive days.

(b) What is the probability the school bus arrives second on both days?

(c) What is the probability that the school bus arrives first on one of the days and second on the other?

52.2 A bag contains 3 yellow balls and 5 green balls. Two balls are taken out of the bag at random, one after the other. The first ball is put back in the bag before the second ball is taken out.

(a) Draw a probability tree for this situation.

(b) Find the probability of getting a yellow ball twice.

(c) Find the probability of drawing one yellow and one green ball.

(d) What is the probability of not taking out a yellow ball?

52.3 A survey into the use of public facilities in a town centre asked visitors if they had visited the library or used the public toilets.

(a) How many people were questioned?

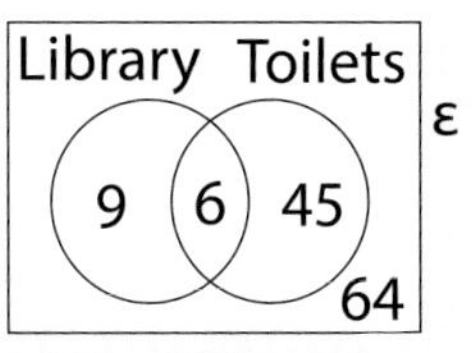

If one of the people surveyed was chosen at random, what would be the probability that they had:

(b) Visited the library? (c) Used the library and the toilets?

(d) Used neither the library nor the toilets?

52.4 60 people in a town are surveyed about where they work and how they get to work. Of these people, a total of 40 drive to work, 32 work in an office, and 26 drive to work and work in an office.

(a) show this data on a Venn diagram.

If one person from the survey is chosen at random, calculate the probability that:

(b) They work in an office.

(c) They drive to work but don't work in an office.

(d) They neither drive to work nor work in an office.

52.5 Consider the numbers 1 to 10. Set M is the multiples of 2. Set N is the multiples of 3.

(a) Write the members of the two sets in set notation in the form $M = \{...\}$ and $N = \{...\}$.

(b) Put the numbers 1 to 10 on the Venn diagram. Three numbers have been done for you.

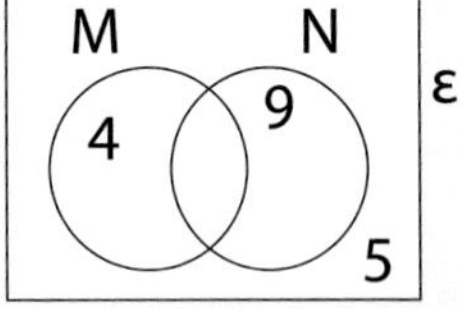

Cards labelled 1 to 10 are put into a bag and one is drawn at random. What is the probability that the number on the card is:

(c) In set M? (d) In M and N? (e) In M or N but not both?

52.6 A person has forty-eight socks. They have 32 identical white socks and 16 identical black socks. One morning the socks are all jumbled up in a drawer. The person pulls out two socks at random to wear, one after the other.

(a) Draw a probability tree for the two socks the person picks.

Calculate the following probabilities:

(b) P(a pair of white socks)

(c) P(a matched pair of socks)

(d) P(a mis-matched pair of socks)

52.7 An unbiased coin with sides Heads and Tails is tossed three times.

(a) Draw a probability tree for this situation.

(b) Find the probability of getting Tails three times in a row.

(c) Calculate the probability of getting Heads at least twice.

(d) What is the probability of getting Tails exactly once?

(e) What is the probability of getting Tails either 0, 2 or 3 times?

52.8 An unbiased 6-sided die is rolled twice.

(a) Put the missing probabilities on the diagram.

(b) What is the probability of rolling 5 or 6 twice in a row?

(c) What is the probability of rolling a 5 or 6 exactly once?

(d) What is the probability of rolling a 5 or 6 at least once?

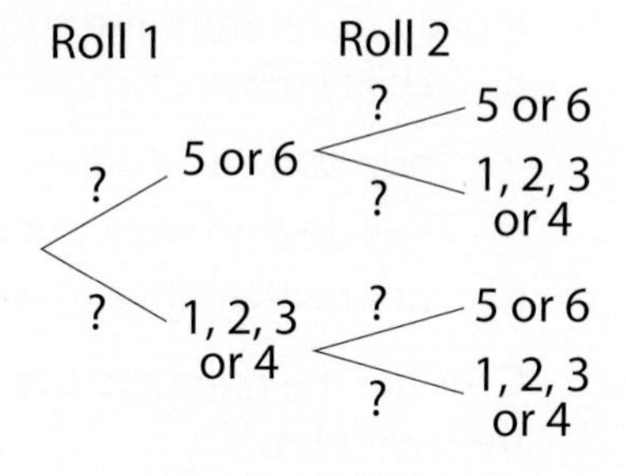

52.9 The 70 children in a school year-group are asked if they had a hot breakfast (B) or a hot lunch (L) the previous day. If one student from this year-group is chosen at random, find the probability:

(a) P(L′)

(b) P(B ∩ L)

(c) P(B ∪ L)

(d) P(B ∩ L′)

B L ε

5 8 45

12

52.10 The diagram shows a probability tree for two events, A and B, along with the probabilities of their outcomes. All the possible outcomes of the two events are shown. Find the values of x and y.

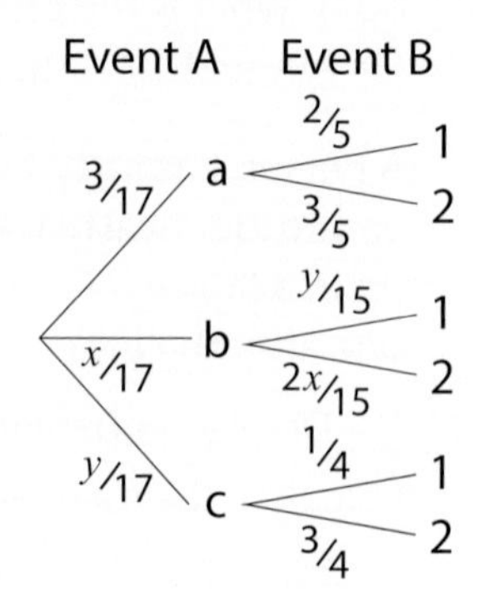

53 § Conditional Probability

When two events are dependent, the probabilities for the second event are determined by the outcome of the first event. The conditional probability $P(B \mid A)$ is the probability that the outcome of the second event is B given that the outcome of the first event is A.

Example 1 – A bag contains 1 white ball and 3 red balls. Two balls are taken out at random, one after another, and the first ball is not replaced before the second ball is taken out. What is:

(i) The probability the second ball is white, given that the first is red.

After the first ball is drawn there are 1 white and 2 red balls in the bag. Therefore, $P(W \mid R) = \frac{1}{3}$.

(ii) The probability the second ball is white, given that the first is white.

The probability that the second ball is white is zero because there are no white balls left in the bag. $P(W \mid W) = 0$

The sample space of an event is the list of possible outcomes. Imposing a condition such as "people who drink coffee" defines a new sample space, containing only those outcomes which obey the condition.

Example 2 – 48 people in an office were surveyed to find out who drinks coffee or tea. If one of the survey participants is chosen at random, what is the probability that they drink tea, given that they drink coffee?

Of the 48 people in the office, 35 drink coffee.

Of these 35 people, 7 also drink tea.
Therefore, $P(\text{Tea} \mid \text{Coffee}) = \frac{7}{35} = \frac{1}{5}$

The probability of one event having outcome A and a second event having outcome B is given by $P(A \text{ and } B) = P(A) \times P(B \mid A)$. This rearranges to:

$$\Rightarrow P(B \mid A) = \frac{P(A \text{ and } B)}{P(A)} \qquad \text{or} \qquad P(B \mid A) = \frac{P(A \cap B)}{P(A)}$$

If the two events are independent, the probability of outcome B from the second event has the same value for all possible outcomes of the first event, and we can simply write $P(B \mid A)$ as $P(B)$.

53.1 38 economists are asked to predict whether there will be a recession in the following two years, "Year 1" and "Year 2". 14 predict a recession in Year 1, 28 predict a recession in Year 2, and 1 predicts there will not be a recession in either year.

(a) Display this data on a Venn diagram.

If one of the economists is chosen at random, calculate the probability that:

(b) They predict a recession in Year 2.

(c) They do not predict a recession in either year.

(d) They predict a recession in both years, given that they predict a recession in Year 1.

(e) They predict a recession in Year 2, given that they predict a recession in both years.

53.2 The tree diagram shows the results of a survey of exercise habits. People were asked if they went running (R) or not (R′) and if they went to the gym (G) or not (G′).

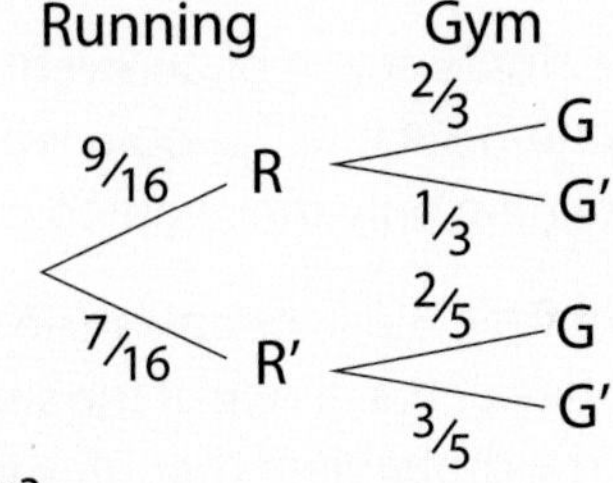

(a) Write down the probability that someone goes to the gym, given that they go running.

What is the probability that someone:

(b) Goes to the gym and goes running?

(c) Goes to the gym?

(d) Goes running, given that they go to the gym?

53.3 Kyla has two unbiased dice. One has 6 faces, marked with the numbers 1 to 6. The other has 8 faces, marked with the numbers 1 to 8. Kyla rolls both dice and adds the numbers together.

(a) What is the probability that the total is 2?

(b) What is the probability that the total is greater than 12?

(c) If the total of the two dice is less than or equal to five, what is the probability that at least one of the dice scored a two?

54 Sampling and Representations of Data

A data set that includes all individual values that could be gathered (the population) can be very large, so statistical analyses usually employ samples.

Samples should represent an entire population fairly, so if certain groups can be identified in the population (men, women, the elderly, the young, etc) then these groups should appear in the sample in the same ratio as they appear in the population. This is called stratified sampling. The selection of individuals within each group should be random to avoid bias in the results.

Example 1 – A transport survey collected data from 2000 people about how they get to work:

Walk	Bike or Car	Public Transport
375	1280	345

The surveyors ask follow-up questions from 400 people. How many must be randomly selected from each category to give a stratified sample?

The fraction of people who walk to work is $\frac{375}{2000} = \frac{3}{16}$. Therefore, the follow-up survey should include $\frac{3}{16} \times 400 = 75$ people who walk.

Doing similar calculations, the follow-up survey should include 256 who use a bike or car and 69 who use public transport.

Data collected about a quantity that can only take certain specific values is discrete. For example, the number of goats in a field can only be an integer. Data collected about quantities that can take an uninterrupted range of values, such as height or weight, is continuous.

Sometimes a data set contains an outlier. This is a value very different from all the others.

The number of times a value appears in a data set is called the frequency of that value. For example, if a survey about food preference finds that 3 choose pizza, the frequency of pizza is 3. Frequency information is often recorded in a frequency table.

Food	Frequency
Curry	6
Roast	5
Chilli	5
Pizza	3

Bar charts are used to represent frequency data visually. There are several types which are shown in Example 2. Multiple bar charts and composite bar charts must include a key to indicate what the different bar types represent.

Example 2 – A bar chart, composite bar chart, and multiple bar chart.

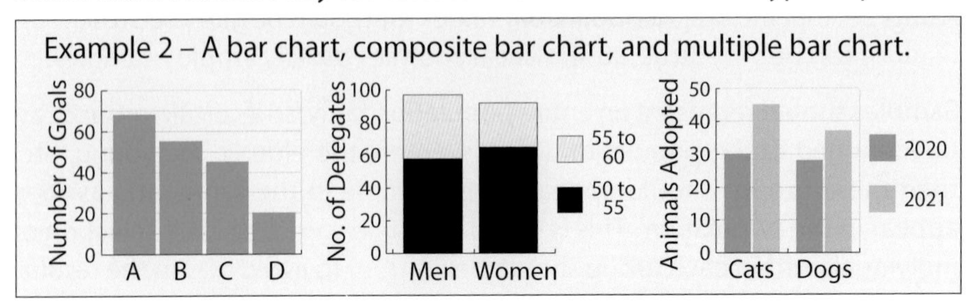

Tally charts are used to record frequency data quickly by hand. One stroke is made per piece of data, and every 5th stroke is drawn diagonally across the previous four to help with counting.

Vertical line charts are similar to bar charts, except vertical lines are used instead of bars. Pictograms use images for interesting visual presentations of data. They must be accompanied by a key to communicate what numerical value an image represents.

Example 3 – A study monitors where cars travel to after arriving at a roundabout from a motorway exit.

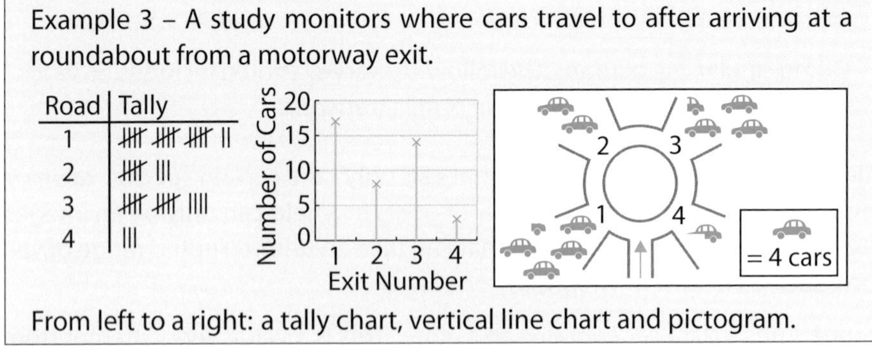

Road	Tally
1	卌 卌 卌 II
2	卌 III
3	卌 卌 IIII
4	III

From left to a right: a tally chart, vertical line chart and pictogram.

Time series are used when data is collected at intervals over a period of time. For example, a weather station may record the number of millimetres of rain to fall each month. Data points are positioned in the centre of each time interval and connected by straight lines.

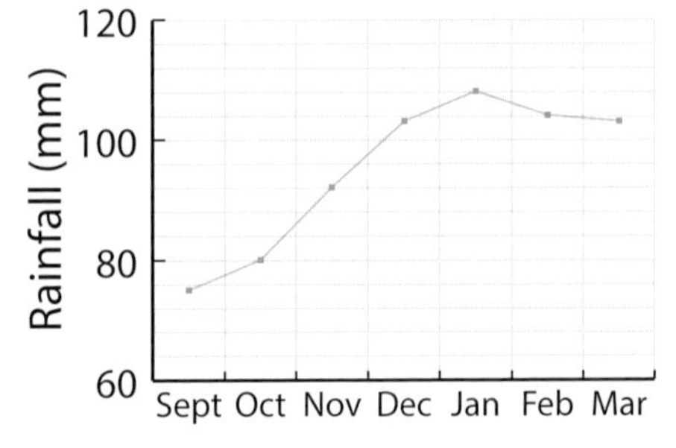

Pie charts are used to plot data that is in categories. Each category is shown as a sector of a circle. To find the angle of the sector, work out the fraction of the total that the category represents, then multiply this fraction by $360°$.

$$\text{Angle of sector} = \frac{\text{Number in category}}{\text{Total number}} \times 360°$$

Example 4 – A pie chart showing sales of ice cream on a summer day.

Flavour	No. Sold	Degrees / °
Chocolate	54	$162°$
Vanilla	36	$108°$
Mint	24	$72°$
Other	6	$18°$

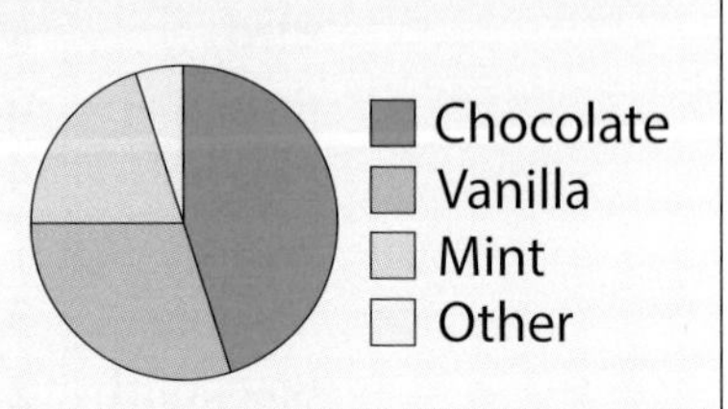

120 ice creams were sold in total. The angle of the sector for chocolate is $\frac{54}{120} \times 360° = 162°$.

54.1 A hospital has a total of 9760 employees. They are divided into 4 categories:

Doctors	Nurses	Scientists	Administrators
1 240	5 020	1 080	?

(a) How many administrators work for the hospital?

A stratified sample is required for a survey of employees' opinions. 5% of the employees will be surveyed.

(b) How many employees will be included in the survey?

(c) Work out how many people must be randomly selected from each of the four employee categories to give a stratified sample.

54.2 A train company carried out a large survey on their passengers to learn about their reasons for travelling. The responses were:

Going on holiday 4%
Going shopping 27%
Visiting friends and family 7%
Travelling for work ? %
Other reasons 15%

(a) What percentage of the passengers were travelling for work?

(b) The number of people who answered the survey with "going shopping" was 540. How many people answered the survey with "visiting friends and family"?

(c) How many people were surveyed in total?

54.3 The birds visiting a garden were observed for 5 days. Draw a composite bar chart to display this data, with one column for each day of the week.

Bird	**Mon**	**Tue**	**Wed**	**Thur**	**Fri**
Robin	0	1	1	0	1
Pigeon	4	3	5	0	4
Wren	1	1	1	1	1
Magpie	3	3	2	0	3
Blackbird	2	0	2	0	2

54.4 The following sales of spring bulbs were recorded at a garden centre. 1 box contains 10 packets.

Flower	**Year 1 / boxes**	**Year 2 / boxes**
Snowdrops	150	120
Crocuses	110	98
Daffodils	340	370
Hyacinths	75	54
Tulips	270	310

(a) Show the data on a labelled multiple bar chart.

(b) What is the difference between the two years in the total number of packets of bulbs sold?

(c) Which type of bulb showed the smallest percentage change in packets sold?

54.5 The tally chart shows the number of burgers sold in a restaurant on five weekdays.

(a) Display the results on a suitable pictogram using the image of a burger.

Day	Tally
Mon	𝍸 IIII
Tues	𝍸 II
Wed	𝍸 𝍸 I
Thur	𝍸 I
Fri	𝍸 𝍸 𝍸 IIII

(b) If the price of each burger sold was £5.20, what was the restaurant's total sales income from burgers during these five days?

54.6 (a) The maximum and minimum daily temperatures reached on a patio were recorded for a week. Plot the data below as two time series on the same axes.

Day	**Mon**	**Tue**	**Wed**	**Thur**	**Fri**	**Sat**	**Sun**
Max. / °C	14	16	18	22	25	27	19
Min. / °C	3	2	5	8	9	7	6

(b) Which day had the smallest difference in maximum and minimum temperature?

(c) What was the greatest difference between maximum and minimum temperatures on one day?

54.7 (a) A survey is taken of the sales of meals at a food court in a shopping centre. Create a pie chart to display these results:

Stall	Pizza	Noodles	Curry	Salad	Burgers	Nachos
Meals	121	144	97	156	74	128

(b) What percentage of customers bought noodles?

(c) What fraction of purchases were pizzas?

54.8 A charity published the following figures for their sources of income:-

Government grants and fees 60%   Donations 15%
Trading in shops 20%   Other sources 5%

(a) Show these values on a pie chart.

(b) The sector for donations had an annual value of £390 000. What is the total annual income for the charity?

54.9 An ecologist uses capture and recapture sampling to estimate the total number of terrapins, T, in a large pond.

(a) She captures 30 terrapins, marks their shells, then returns them to the pond. What fraction of the total did she capture?

(b) The terrapins disperse. Four days later, she captures 40 terrapins. 5 have her mark. What fraction of this sample are marked?

(c) The answer to (b) is an estimate of the fraction of turtles in the pond that are marked. Equate answers to (a) and (b) to estimate T.

55 Summary Statistics

An average is a measure of the "central value" in a set of data. Three different types of average are the mode, median and mean.

The mode is the most common value in a data set (or values, if there is a tie).

Example 1 – Find the mode for these data sets:

(i) $1, 4, 2, 4, 3, 4, 5, 3, 4, 4$

4 appears more than any other number, so the mode is 4.

(ii) Blue, Yellow, Red, Yellow, Red, Blue, Blue, Green, Green, Yellow

Blue and Yellow are tied for most common, so the modes are Blue and Yellow.

The median is the middle value in a set of data when the data is arranged in order of increasing size. To find the median, first order the data. Then, if the number of data values is odd, the median is the value in the centre of the list. If the number of data values is even, the median is half-way between the two values in the centre of the list.

Example 2 – Find the median for these data sets:

(i) $2, 5, 10, 6, 5, 8, 5, 7, 12$

First, order the data.

$$2 \quad 5 \quad 5 \quad 5 \quad \underset{\uparrow}{6} \quad 7 \quad 8 \quad 10 \quad 12$$

There are 9 data values, which is an odd number. The median is the central value, which is 6.

(ii) $10, 4, 4, 3, 9, 5, 8, 7$

First, order the data.

$$3 \quad 4 \quad 4 \quad 5 \quad \underset{\uparrow}{} \quad 7 \quad 8 \quad 9 \quad 10$$

There are 8 data values, which is an even number. The median is half-way between the two central values of 5 and 7. The median is 6.

To find the mean of a data set, sum all the values and then divide by the number of values.

$$\text{Mean} = \frac{\text{Sum of data values}}{\text{Number of data values}}$$

Example 3 – Calculate the mean for this data set:

$$2 \quad 6 \quad 12 \quad 14 \quad 13 \quad 4 \quad 7 \quad 8 \quad 9 \quad 5$$

To find the mean, sum the values and divide by the number of values.

$$\text{mean} = \frac{2+6+12+14+13+4+7+8+9+5}{10} = \frac{80}{10} = 8$$

Example 4 shows how to calculate the mean when data about a numerical quantity is presented in a frequency table. Start by adding an extra column to the table in which the numerical quantity is multiplied by the frequency. Then divide the total of the new column by the total of the frequency column.

Example 4 – The number of books visitors to a library check out at one time is monitored for a day. The results are shown in the table.

Number of Books	Frequency	Number of Books × Frequency
1	47	47
2	33	66
3	9	27
4	1	4
Totals:	90	144

The mean number of books checked out at one time is $\frac{144}{90} = 1.6$.

It is often important to measure the spread of values in a data set. One way is to find the range. This is equal to the largest value minus the smallest value.

The three types of average have different advantages and disadvantages, and this affects when it is appropriate to use them:

- The mode, median and mean can all be used for numerical data, but only the mode can be used when data is collected about non-numerical categories (for example, favourite colour).
- Half the values in a data set are smaller than the median, and half are larger. The median is not strongly affected by very large outlier values. However, calculating the median doesn't make full use of all the data: data is listed in order of size, but the numerical values of most of the data are not used.
- The mean makes use of all the data in a data set, but can be strongly influenced by very large outlying values.

Note: In other subjects, you may come across a formula for the mean written in algebraic notation. If n is used for the number of data values, and the data values are written as x_1, x_2, and so on up to x_n, the mean value $\bar{x}$ is given by

$$\bar{x} = \frac{x_1 + x_2 + ... + x_n}{n} \quad \text{or} \quad \bar{x} = \frac{\Sigma_{i=1}^{n} x_i}{n}$$

On the right the formula is written in Sigma notation, with the Greek letter Σ used as a shorthand for "sum of".

55.1 A biologist monitors a cat living on a farm for one month in the spring to see what kinds of prey the cat catches. The results for the whole month are shown in the table below.

(a) Draw a bar chart to illustrate this data.

(b) What is the type of prey that the cat catches most often?

(c) Which animal is the mode?

Type of Prey	Number Caught
Mice	15
Voles	8
Shrews	9
Rabbits	3
Birds	1

(d) What is the mean number of prey creatures that the cat catches each day? You may assume that the month has 30 days.

55.2 For these data sets find the median, mean and range:

(a) 1 3 4 6 7 10 11

(b)
$-1.5 \quad 1.0 \quad -0.6 \quad -0.4 \quad 0.3$
$0.8 \quad -0.7 \quad 1.2 \quad 1.0 \quad -0.1$

(c)
2.45 mm 2.58 mm 3.01 mm 3.02 mm
2.67 mm 2.79 mm 2.04 mm 3.12 mm

55.3 For the data set, find:

(a) The mode(s).

(b) The median.

(c) The mean.

5 4 9 6 3 7 8 5 1
6 8 6 4 4 3 6 5 6
5 2 1 6 5 8 1 4 8
4 7 6 4 2 9 6 4 2

55.4 20 packets of biscuits were chosen at random. The number of biscuits in each packet was counted. The results are shown below.

$$\begin{array}{cccccccccc} 20 & 20 & 20 & 19 & 20 & 20 & 17 & 22 & 22 & 20 \\ 20 & 18 & 19 & 20 & 19 & 20 & 20 & 20 & 21 & 20 \end{array}$$

(a) Put this information into a frequency table.

(b) Draw a bar chart to illustrate the data.

(c) What are the mode, median and mean numbers of biscuits?

(d) What is the range of the data?

55.5 Below are listed the salaries for the 9 people in a small company.

$$\begin{array}{ccccc} £22\,500 & £23\,000 & £23\,000 & £26\,000 & £22\,500 \\ £26\,000 & £22\,500 & £30\,000 & £47\,500 & \end{array}$$

(a) Find the mode, median and mean salaries.

(b) Why is the mean not the best measure of the average salary of a person in this company?

(c) Which average would be the best measure of the average salary of a person?

55.6 The following data set has one missing value:

$$0.7 \quad -1.0 \quad 1.3 \quad 0.8 \quad 0.4 \quad -0.5 \quad -3.7 \quad 0.2 \quad 0.3$$

(a) The mean for the complete data set is -0.2. What is the missing value?

For the complete data set,

(b) What is the median?

(c) Which value would you consider to be an outlier?

(d) What is the mode?

55.7 During one particular cricket season, a bowler takes $1, 2, 3$ or 4 wickets in each of his matches. Find the mean number of wickets he takes per match.

Wickets	Frequency
1	5
2	6
3	8
4	2

§ The value of the range can be strongly affected by the presence of a single outlier value. An alternative measure of spread is Inter-Quartile Range (IQR), which measures the spread of the central 50% of a data set.

The lower quartile, median, and upper quartile are positioned one quarter, one half (two-quarters), and three-quarters of the way through a data set. They are given the labels Q_1, Q_2 and Q_3.

To find the quartiles, first put a data set into ascending order and find the median (Q_2). This divides the data set into two halves. Next, find the median of each half. The lower quartile is the median of the lower half, and the upper quartile is the median of the higher half. When the number of data values is odd, omit the median value (Q_2) from the quartile calculations.

The inter-quartile range is given by the formula

$$\text{Inter-quartile range} = Q_3 - Q_1$$

Example 5 – Find the quartiles and inter-quartile range for this data set:

$$2 \quad 4 \quad 6 \quad 7 \quad 8 \quad 9 \quad 12 \quad 13 \quad 14$$

The data is already ordered. The median is 8. There are 9 data values, an odd number, so omit the median value (8) from quartile calculations.

The half of the data on the lower-value side is $2 \quad 4 \quad 6 \quad 7$. The median for this half is 5, so $Q_1 = 5$.

The half of the data on the higher-value side is $9 \quad 12 \quad 13 \quad 14$. The median for this half is 12.5, so $Q_3 = 12.5$.

The inter-quartile range is $Q_3 - Q_1 = 12.5 - 5 = 7.5$.

A box plot or box-and-whisker diagram shows at a glance the median, inter-quartile range and range. Five values are marked on the plot in total: the lowest data value, lower quartile, median, upper quartile and highest data value. The lower and upper quartiles are connected to make a box.

Example 6 – The heights of 40 rose bushes are measured. The median is 65 cm; the shortest is 48 cm; the tallest is 92 cm; and the quartiles are at 56 cm and 77 cm. Construct a box plot to display this information.

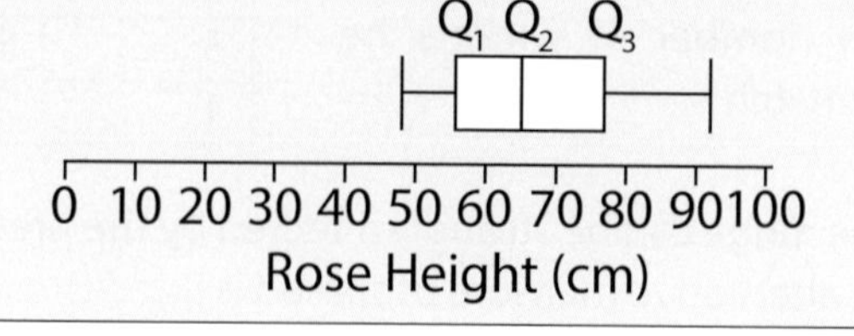

55.8 Construct box and whisker plots for the following sets of data.

(a) 4 5 6 8 8 10 11 15

(b) 1 3 3 1 7 3 1 2 5 6 6 8 3

55.9 The ages of the children in a small youth group are

$$4, 5, 6, 7, 7, 8, 8, 8, 9, 9, 10, 11, 11, 15$$

(a) Construct a box plot (box and whisker diagram) for this data.

(b) What is the range of the data?

(c) What fraction of the children are older than 7?

55.10 Some members of a jogging club were asked to do a test to see how quickly they could run 400 m. 12 men and 12 women were chosen, and their times to the nearest second were:

Men: 56, 59, 58, 61, 61, 65, 64, 62, 60, 67, 61, 58

Women: 66, 67, 72, 60, 62, 59, 71, 71, 66, 64, 65, 69

(a) For both the men and the women find
(i) the mean time (ii) the range (iii) the IQR.

(b) On the same diagram, construct separate box plots for the men and the women.

(c) Is the spread of times smaller for the men or the women? Explain your answer.

55.11 A technician is given a list of measurements in cm, correct to the nearest 0.1 cm. He is told that the mean of the values is 3.3 cm, but when he checks the calculation he finds a different value. Here is the list:

$$3.6, 3.4, 3.2, 2.9, 3.8, 3.4, 3.6, 3.2, 3.3, 3.6$$

(a) What is the mean of these values?

(b) To find the source of the discrepancy, the technician checks the list he was given against the original data for the experiment, and finds two identical numbers are missing. What is the value of these numbers?

56 Grouped Data and Diagrams

Statistics can be collected about variables (discrete and continuous) by grouping the data into classes. For example, a survey could record the number of people attending a concert in different age groups.

Classes for continuous data must be defined with no gaps between them. When the width of every class is the same, a frequency plot looks like a bar chart with no gaps between the bars.

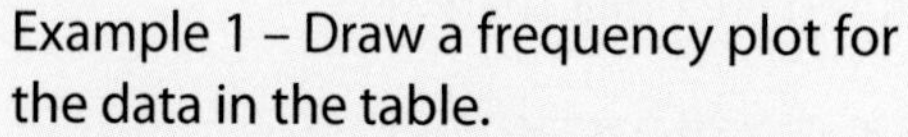
Example 1 – Draw a frequency plot for the data in the table.

Age in years, t	Frequency, f
$0 \leqslant t < 20$	40
$20 \leqslant t < 40$	80
$40 \leqslant t < 60$	55
$60 \leqslant t < 80$	25

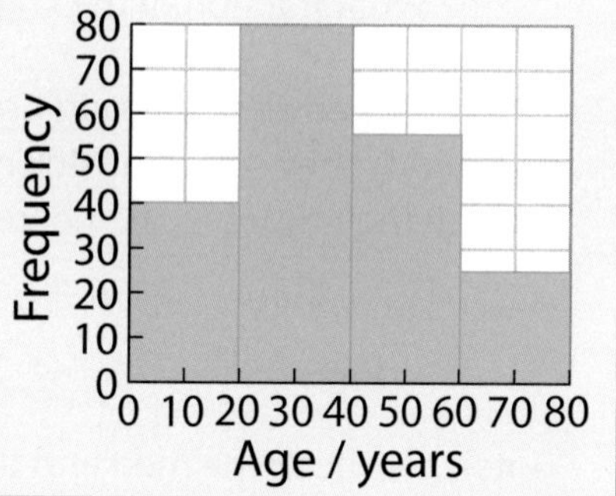

When working from tables care must be taken to identify boundaries correctly. For example, if heights are rounded to the nearest cm, the boundaries of a "$160 - 169$ cm" class will be at 159.5 cm and 169.5 cm.

Finding averages from grouped frequency data is similar to finding averages from un-grouped data. The modal class is the class with the highest frequency, and the class containing the median is the class containing the central value of the data set.

Example 2 – Find the modal class and the class containing the median.

Mass in kg, m	Frequency
$40 \leqslant m < 60$	48
$60 \leqslant m < 80$	33
$80 \leqslant m < 100$	19
Total:	100

The modal class is $40 \leqslant m < 60$ as this class has the highest frequency.

The size of the data set is 100. The median is between the 50th and 51st data values. There are 48 values in the lowest class ($40 \leqslant m < 60$), and a total of 81 in the first two classes ($48 + 33$). The class containing the median is therefore $60 \leqslant m < 80$.

When data is grouped the mean can only be estimated as individual numerical values are not recorded. To estimate the mean, treat each data point as if it were at the mid-point of its group. This is equivalent to assuming that the data is evenly spread out within the group.

Starting with a frequency table with two columns, add a third column for the mid-point of each class. Then add a fourth column for the product of the frequency of each class and its mid-point. The estimate for the mean is then given by

$$\text{Estimate of the mean} = \frac{\text{Total of (Mid-point} \times \text{Frequency) column}}{\text{Total of Frequency Column}}$$

Example 3 – Find the mean for the data in the table.

Age in years, t	Frequency	Class midpoint / years	Frequency × Midpoint
$0 \leqslant t < 10$	17	5	85
$10 \leqslant t < 20$	20	15	300
$20 \leqslant t < 30$	13	25	325
Totals:	50		710

The estimate for the mean is $\frac{710}{50} = 14.2$ years.

56.1 A geographer measures the depth of water in 75 rock pools.

(a) What is the modal class?

(b) In which class is the median value?

(c) Estimate the mean depth of water. Give your answer to 3 sf.

Depth in mm, d	Frequency
$0 \leqslant d < 100$	31
$100 \leqslant d < 200$	22
$200 \leqslant d < 300$	14
$300 \leqslant d < 400$	2
$400 \leqslant d < 500$	6

(d) Plot a frequency graph for this data.

56.2 In a vegetable growing competition the judges measure the lengths of vegetables to the nearest cm. Three of the classes are given as

$40 - 49$ cm $\quad 50 - 59$ cm $\quad 60 - 69$ cm

(a) What is the midpoint of the $50 - 59$ cm class?

(i) 50.4 cm (ii) 54.5 cm (iii) 55.0 cm

(b) What are the boundaries of the $50-59$ cm class?
(i) 50 and 59 cm (ii) 49 and 60 cm (iii) 49.5 and 59.5 cm

56.3 A plant nursery prices fruit trees according to their height above the level of the soil, h. The trees available on one day were:

Height in m, h	Frequency
$1.00 \leqslant h < 1.20$	12
$1.20 \leqslant h < 1.40$	22
$1.40 \leqslant h < 1.60$	18
$1.60 \leqslant h < 1.80$	14
$1.80 \leqslant h < 2.00$	7
$2.00 \leqslant h < 2.20$	8

(a) What is the modal class?

(b) In which class is the median value?

(c) Estimate the mean height of the trees. Give your answer to 3 sf.

(d) A tree in the class $1.00 \leqslant h < 1.20$ costs £35. The price per tree for each of the other classes is found by adding £10 to the price of the previous class. What would the nursery make in sales if they sold all of the trees?

§ Plotting a frequency graph is visually misleading when grouped data does not have the same width for every class. In the graph on the right there are 80 people in both the $20 \leqslant t < 25$ and $60 \leqslant t < 80$ age groups, so the bars are the same height. However, the bar for the $60 \leqslant t < 80$ age group has a much larger area.

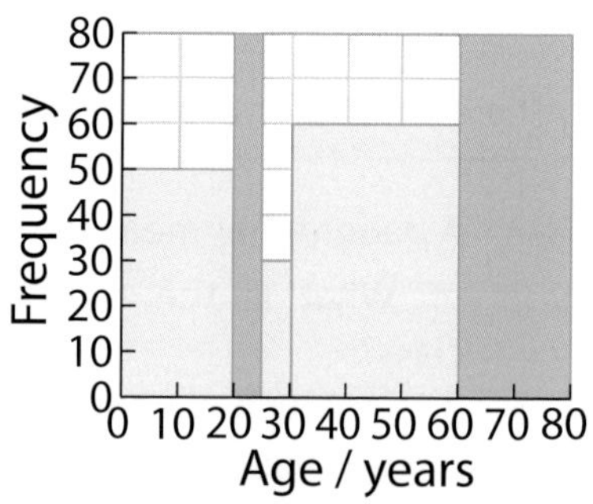

A better quantity to plot is frequency density. This is equal to the frequency of the class divided by the class width. In a frequency density graph, bars of equal frequency have the same area. A frequency density plot for the same data as the graph above is shown in Example 4.

$$\text{Frequency density, f.d.} = \frac{\text{frequency}}{\text{class width}}$$

A histogram is a plot where the area of the bars is proportional to the frequency. Where all classes have the same width a frequency plot is also a histogram. Where class width varies a frequency density plot is a histogram.

Example 4 – Plot a histogram for the given age-group data.

Age in years, t	Frequency	f.d. / per year
$0 \leqslant t < 20$	50	2.5
$20 \leqslant t < 25$	80	16
$25 \leqslant t < 30$	30	6
$30 \leqslant t < 60$	60	2
$60 \leqslant t < 80$	80	4

The frequency table below has a column for cumulative frequency. The cumulative frequency for a particular value of M is the total number of data values with a weight less than this value of M. For example, for $M = 50$ the cumulative frequency is $13 + 26 + 48 = 77$.

The cumulative frequency is always 0 at the lower boundary of the first class, and equal to the total frequency at the upper boundary of the final class. For the data in the table, the cumulative frequency is 0 for $M = 30$ and 120 for $M = 70$.

Mass in kg, M	Frequency	Cumulative Frequency
$30 \leqslant M < 40$	13	13
$40 \leqslant M < 45$	16	29
$45 \leqslant M < 50$	48	77
$50 \leqslant M < 55$	35	112
$55 \leqslant M < 70$	8	120
Total	120	

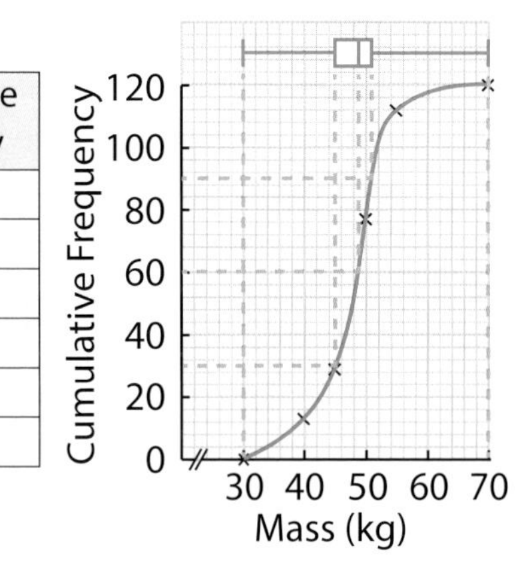

On the right above is a cumulative frequency diagram, together with a box plot. The points on the cumulative frequency diagram are plotted at the boundaries of the classes, and a smooth curve is drawn through them.

For the box plot, the lowest value is at the lower boundary of the first class and the highest value is at the upper boundary of the last class. The quartiles and the median are estimated by drawing lines across the diagram at one quarter, one half and three quarters of the total frequency.

In the example, drawing a line at half the total frequency to find the median effectively puts the median equal to the 60th data value, rather than half-way between the 60th and 61st values. Cumulative frequency is often used when the total frequency of a data set is large, and the difference in making this approximation is small.

56.4 The table shows the masses of packages shipped by a company on one particular day. Show the data on a histogram.

Mass in kg, M	Frequency
$0 \leqslant M < 0.5$	76
$0.5 \leqslant M < 1.0$	122
$1.0 \leqslant M < 2.0$	154
$2.0 \leqslant M < 5.0$	276
$5.0 \leqslant M < 10.0$	41

56.5 (a) Construct a histogram for this data.
(b) What is the modal class?
(c) Estimate the mean value of x for this data to 3 sf.
(d) Construct a cumulative frequency diagram for this data.

x	Frequency
$0 \leqslant x < 5$	4
$5 \leqslant x < 10$	5
$10 \leqslant x < 20$	13
$20 \leqslant x < 30$	25
$30 \leqslant x < 35$	6

56.6 The students in a school year group each took two test papers, A and B. The figures in the table are the cumulative percentages of students getting each grade. For example, on paper A 49% of students scored $< 70\%$ and were graded C or below.

Grade	Mark in %, m	Paper A, %	Paper B, %
U	$0 \leqslant m < 40$	5	2
E	$40 \leqslant m < 50$	14	8
D	$50 \leqslant m < 60$	27	21
C	$60 \leqslant m < 70$	49	38
B	$70 \leqslant m < 80$	75	61
A	$80 \leqslant m < 100$	100	100

(a) On the same axes draw a separate cumulative frequency graph for each paper.

(b) Use your diagram to construct box plots for both papers.

(c) Which paper did the students find harder? Give a reason for your answer.

56.7 The histogram below summarises the total annual payments (including expenses) made to employees in a company.

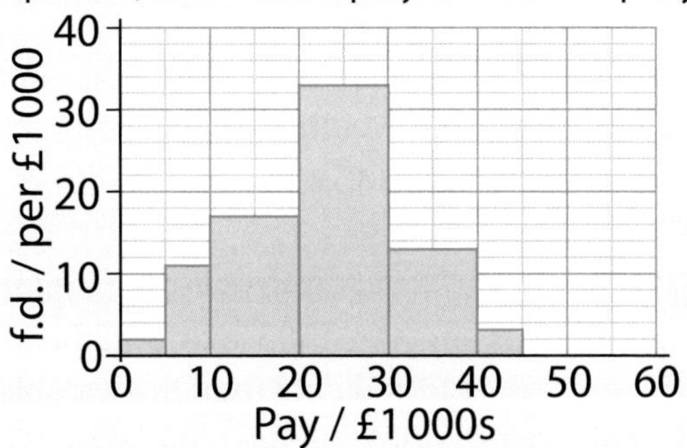

(a) Call the variable for pay p. Make a frequency table for the data in the histogram.

(b) An extra class is added for $45 \leqslant p < 60$. This class has a frequency of 15. What is the frequency density of this class?

(c) Calculate an estimate of the mean amount payed out to an employee, including the extra class from part (b).

56.8 A company conducts plant growth trials of two varieties of chilli pepper, A and B. The graph shows cumulative frequency plots for the heights of both types of pepper after 13 weeks.

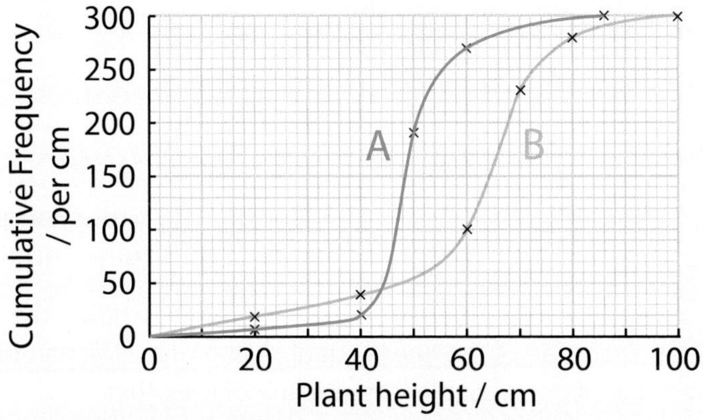

(a) Create box plots for both varieties of pepper.

(b) The company defines failures as plants which do not reach 40 cm in height. Which variety produced fewer failures?

(c) For which plant was the spread of plant heights greater? Explain your answer.

57 Correlation

Real-world data often comes as pairs of values. For example, a biologist studying lambs might record the weight of each lamb and the number of days since it was born. The weight and age of a lamb are both variables. The paired data is bivariate (two-variable).

A bivariate plot or scatter diagram uses the paired data values as coordinates for a graph. One variable is assigned to the x-axis, and the other to the y-axis. If a pattern can be seen in the plotted data then the variables are correlated. When points cluster along a straight line the correlation is linear.

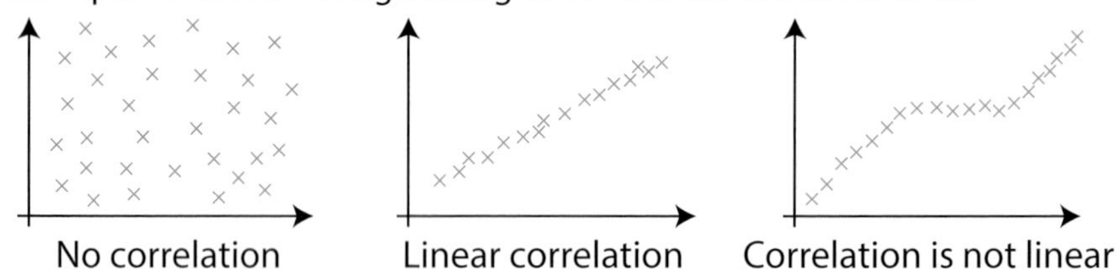

No correlation Linear correlation Correlation is not linear

For data that is linearly correlated, the correlation is positive if the points cluster around a line with positive gradient, and negative if the line has a negative gradient. Correlation is weak if the points are loosely spread out about the line and strong if points cluster tightly about the line.

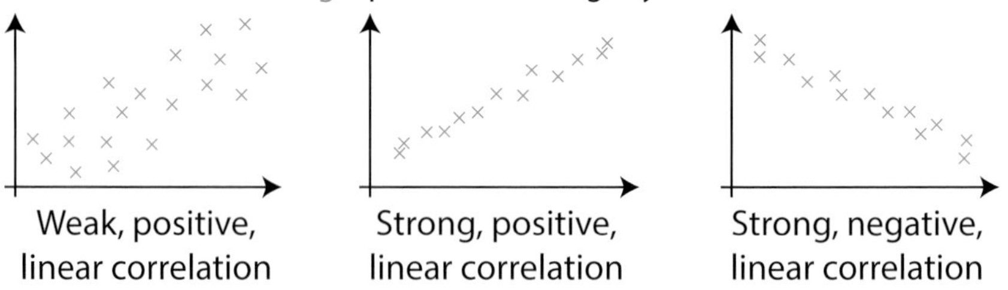

Weak, positive, linear correlation Strong, positive, linear correlation Strong, negative, linear correlation

A straight line of best fit is drawn through the points such that the scatter of the points on each side of the line is equal. A line of best fit can be used to predict the value of one variable from a value of the other.

- Interpolation is where a prediction is made using a variable value that is within the range of the original data.
- Extrapolation is where a prediction is made for a variable value that is outside the range of the original data.

Extrapolation can be unreliable as you do not know whether the pattern you have seen in the data will continue.

Example 1 – In the graph below the lowest value of x in the data is 1.0, and the highest value of x is 4.0.

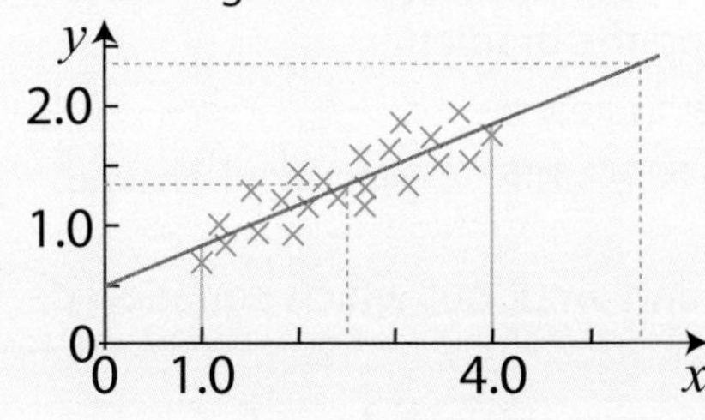

Using the line of best fit to estimate the value of y from a value of x is an interpolation for $1.0 \leqslant x \leqslant 4.0$, and an extrapolation otherwise.

(i) The predicted value of y when $x = 2.5$ is $y = 1.3$ (interpolation).
(ii) The predicted value of y when $x = 5.5$ is $y = 2.3$ (extrapolation).

Note: Correlation between two variables does not imply that one of the variables is responsible for causing a change in the other variable. This may or may not be the case. "Correlation does not imply causation."

57.1 Which of these sketches show linear correlation between x and y?

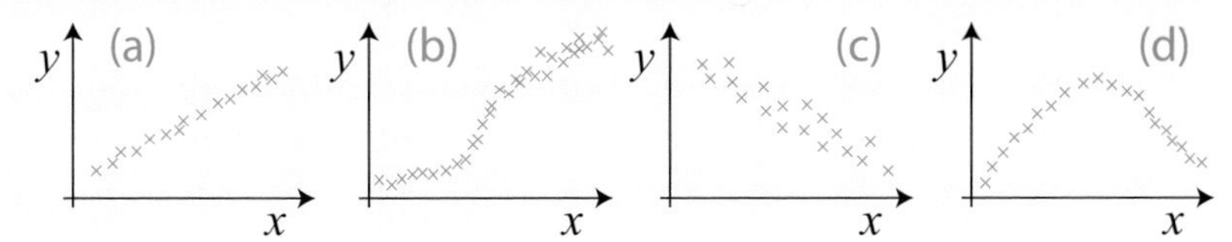

57.2 The graph shows the number of craft hours per week done by a sample group of children.

(a) Find the gradient of the line of best fit.

(b) Estimate the number of craft hours for a child 5.5 years old.

(c) Estimate the age of a child who does 7.0 craft hours per week.

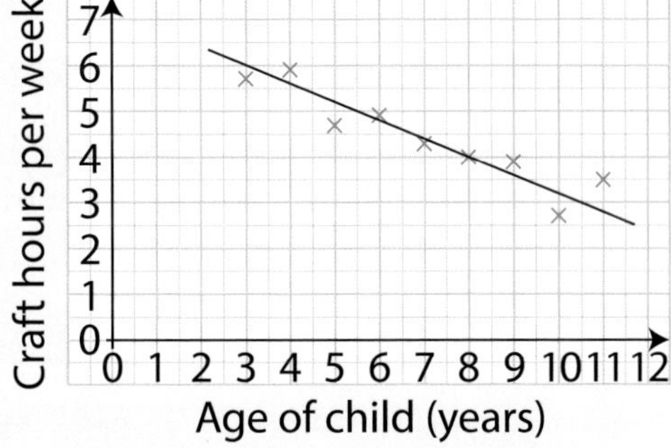

(d) Is your answer to part (c) reliable or unreliable, and why?

57.3 (a) The table on the next page shows how the price of a particular basket of shopping changes from year to year. Draw a scatter plot for this data.

Year	1	2	3	4	5	6	7
Cost (£)	27.00	27.63	27.97	28.38	28.20	29.41	29.75

(b) Draw a line of best fit, and find the gradient.

(c) Predict the cost of the basket in year 8.

(d) Do you think this prediction is reliable? Explain your answer.

57.4 Look at the following sketches and work out which equation describes the line of best fit.

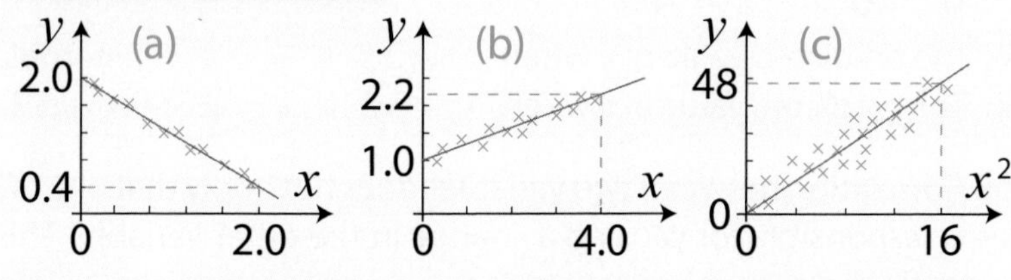

(a)	(b)	(c)
(i) $y = -1.8x + 4.0$	(i) $y = 0.4x - 1.5$	(i) $y = 3.0x^2$
(ii) $y = -0.8x + 2.0$	(ii) $y = 0.4x + 1.5$	(ii) $y = 3.0x$
(iii) $y = 0.8x - 2.0$	(iii) $y = 0.3x + 1.0$	(iii) $y = (3.0x)^2$

57.5 The nuclei of atoms contain protons and neutrons. In this question p is the number of protons and n is the number of neutrons.

(a) Plot a graph with p on the x-axis and n on the y-axis for the following selected light nuclei.

Element	He	Be	C	N	F	Mg	Cl	Ca
p	2	4	6	7	9	12	17	20
n	2	5	6	7	10	12	18	20

(b) What sort of correlation do you see?

(c) What can you conclude from the graph about the value of the ratio $n : p$ for the nuclei given?

(d) Plot a graph with p on the x-axis and n on the y-axis for the following selected heavier nuclei.

Element	Pd	Cs	Pr	Tb	W	Pt	Au	Pb
p	46	55	59	65	74	78	79	82
$p + n$	106	133	141	159	184	195	197	207

(e) What sort of correlation do you see?

(f) Draw a line of best fit on your graph and find the gradient.